Workbook for use with the third edition of
Clinical Procedures for
Medical Assistants

Workbook for use with the third edition of

Clinical Procedures for Medical Assistants

Sharron M. Zakus, RN, BA, MS, CMA

Educator, Health Science Department,
City College of San Francisco, San Francisco, California
Formerly, Director and Instructor, Medical Assistant Program,
College of California Medical Affiliates, San Francisco, California

With 58 illustrations

Mosby Lifeline

St. Louis Baltimore Berlin Boston Carlsbad Chicago London Madrid
Naples New York Philadelphia Sydney Tokyo Toronto

Mosby Lifeline
Dedicated to Publishing Excellence

Publisher: David T. Culverwell
Executive Editor: Richard A. Weimer
Development Editor: Julie Scardiglia
Assistant Editors: Emerson John Probst III and Christine Ambrose
Editorial Assistant: Kay E. Beard
Production Editor: Mary Cusick Drone

SECOND EDITION

Copyright © 1995 by Mosby–Year Book, Inc.

Previous edition copyrighted 1988

Printed in the United States of America

Mosby–Year Book, Inc.
11830 Westline Industrial Drive
St. Louis, Missouri 63146

International Standard Book Number 0-8016-7183-3

LIST OF CREDITS

The following artwork was borrowed from the following books:

Figures 18-1 through 18-19: Gerdin J: *Student workbook for health careers today,* St. Louis, 1991, Mosby.

Un-numbered figures from Chapter 18: Gerdin J: *Instructor's Guide to accompany health careers today,* St. Louis, 1991, Mosby.

Figures 2-1 through 2-4e, 4-2a through 4-2s, 6-1a through 6-1aa, 7-1 through 7-4, 12-1a through 12-le, 16-1 through 16-5, 17-la through 17-lg, 17-5 and un-numbered figures in Chapter 16 and 17: Zakus E, Eggers D: *Workbook for fundamentals of medical assisting administrative and clinical theory and technique,* ed 2, St. Louis, 1990, Mosby.

Figures 4-la through 4-li, 5-1, and 19-l - Zakus S: *Clinical procedures for medical assistants,* ed 3, St Louis, 1994, Mosby.

CONTENTS

Unit 1

Universal Blood and Body Substance Precautions

SUGGESTED ACTIVITIES

1. Discuss the main aspects of Universal Precautions or Body Substance Precautions. (In this book the term *Universal Precautions* is used.) Discuss your feelings about being exposed to infectious agents and diseases through your work.

2. Role-play using the practices of Universal Precautions. Along with a few classmates, act out a work situation that involves one aspect of the Universal Precautions standards. Demonstrate both the *right* and *wrong* way for handling the situation. Be creative. The rest of the class must record the *correct* and the *incorrect* methods used in your play. Follow this role play with a discussion session.

3. Sometimes people take shortcuts that put both themselves and others at an increased risk for contracting or spreading infection. Discuss your feelings toward people that do not follow the prescribed procedures that should be used to prevent the spread of infection. Discuss your feelings about the procedures you use. Discuss how others might feel about the procedures you follow for infection control. Will your procedures prevent or cause the spread of infection?

4. In some medical settings workers are offered the hepatitis B vaccination. Discuss your feelings about accepting or denying this vaccination.

5. Discuss your feelings concerning human immuno-deficiency virus testing (HIV) for medical workers.

STUDY QUESTIONS
Fill-in

In the blanks provided, write the answers that best complete the sentences:

1. According to the concept of Universal Precautions, all human blood and certain human body fluids are treated as _____

   _____.

2. The key to the Universal Precautions is _____

   _____.

3. The regulations covered by the Universal Precautions standard apply to employees of facilities in which a worker could be "reasonably anticipated" to come in contact with_____

   _____

   _____.

4. The federal bloodborne pathogen regulation requires the following procedures:

   a. _____

   _____

   _____

   _____

1

b. _____
   _____
   _____

c. _____
   _____
   _____
   _____
   _____
   _____
   _____
   _____

d. _____
   _____
   _____

e. _____
   _____
   _____

f. _____
   _____

g. _____
   _____

h. _____
   _____

i. _____
   _____

j. _____
   _____

5. Infection control systems are designed to _____
   _____
   _____ .

6. Universal Precautions are designed for use with
   _____ patients, not just those who are identified
   as _____ .

7. Universal Precautions are based on the knowledge
   of _____ .

8. Universal Precautions are based on degree of
   exposure risk to blood and other body substances,
   not on _____ , and precautions should be based
   on _____ .

9. Universal Precautions taken with all patients should
   include routine use of appropriate barrier precautions to prevent _____
   _____
   _____ .

10. Universal Precautions provide protection from not
    only known infected patients but also from _____
    _____ , therefore protecting other patients and
    health care workers alike.

11. _____ is one of the most effective means of
    infection control.

12. Name 12 instances in which handwashing should
    occur.

    a. _____
       _____
       _____

    b. _____
       _____

    c. _____
       _____

    d. _____
       _____

    e. _____
       _____

    f. _____
       _____

    g. _____
       _____

i. _____

j. _____
_____

k. _____
_____

l. _____
_____

m. _____
_____

13. The most important function of handwashing is to
_____.

14. Disposable single-use exam gloves provide additional safety, and they should be worn whenever
_____.

15. _____ , _____ , _____ or other similar alternatives must be readily accessible for employees who are allergic to the disposable single-use exam gloves normally provided.

16. Name seven situations in which disposable single-use exam gloves should be worn.

a. _____
_____

b. _____
_____

c. _____
_____

d. _____
_____

e. _____
_____

f. _____
_____

g. _____
_____

17. If a glove is torn or punctured by a needlestick or other accident, the damaged glove should be
_____.
the hands rewashed, and a _____ glove put on as promptly as patient safety permits.

18. Care providers must _____ gloves between patients and wash hands
_____.

19. Gloves always should be removed when
_____
_____
_____.

20. Masks and protective eyewear should be worn to prevent exposure of the mucous membranes of the care provider's mouth, nose, and eyes during procedures that are likely to _____ and when cleaning _____
_____.

21. A gown or apron or lab coat should be worn to protect the care provider's arms and clothes during all procedures that are _____
_____.

22. The care provider should wear a gown when cleaning _____
_____
_____.

23. Care providers should change a gown or laboratory coat immediately if _____
_____.

24. Most needlesticks occur when _____
_____.

25. Used disposable needles and syringes, scalpel blades, and other sharp items should be placed in
_____
_____.

26. The sharps containers should be located in

    _____

    _____ .

27. One method of disposing of full sharps containers
    is to _____

    _____

    _____

    _____ .

28. Improperly discarded needles should be picked up
    with extreme caution and disposed of in

    _____ .

29. Vacutainer sleeves should be discarded in

    _____ .

30. If outside contamination of the primary container
    used to transport laboratory specimens occurs, the
    primary container must be placed inside

    _____

    during handling, processing, storage, transport, or

    shipping, and must be labeled or _____
    according to the requirements of Occupational
    Safety and Health Act (OSHA) standards.

31. All potentially contaminated materials used in
    laboratory tests should be decontaminated, prefera-

    bly by _____
    before, disposal or reprocessing. All infectious

    laboratory waste should be treated by _____

    _____, _____, or_____before disposal to
    render the waste harmless.

32. When cleaning and decontaminating reusable

    equipment, personnel should wear _____,

    _____ , _____ , and _____ .

33. Blood pressure (BP) equipment, scales, and other
    reusable room equipment should be decontaminat-

    ed with _____
    at the end of each day.

34. Stethoscope earpieces must be cleaned after each

    use with _____ .

35. After each use, goggles, and heavy robber gloves
    used during decontamination procedures must be

    cleaned with _____ .

36. Sharps containers must be closed after they are

    filled and then disposed of as_____
    waste. No additional protective garb is necessary
    when handling these containers.

37. Broken glassware which might be contaminated

    must be cleaned up using _____

    _____

    and then disposed of in _____ .

38. Patient specimens and the containers that hold them

    should be collected and treated as _____
    waste.

39. Cultures and the containers that hold them should

    be collected and treated as _____ waste.

40. For convenience, small items such as contaminated

    cotton balls may be disposed of in the _____
    containers.

41. Other disposable, moist waste generated by clinics
    or offices should be collected in covered foot-

    operated cans that are lined with _____

    _____ .

42. When body fluids are spilled, the visible material

    should be _____

    _____

    _____

    _____ .

    Disposable single-use examine gloves must be
    worn for this process.

43. Materials used for cleanup should be disposed of in

    the _____

    _____ .

44. Uniforms and clothing that are soiled with body secretions should be cleaned with _____ _____.

45. Contaminated laundry should be placed and transported in _____ _____.

46. Regulated waste containers (for example, contaminated sharps containers) must be labeled as a _____ or in a _____ - colored container.

47. Reusable contaminated sharps containers (for example, surgical instruments soaking in at tray) must be labeled as a _____ or be in a _____ -colored container.

48. Containers used for storage, transport, or shipping of blood must be labeled as a _____ or be in a _____ -colored container.

49. Specimens and regulated waste shipped from the primary facility to another facility for service or disposal must be labeled as a _____ or be in a _____-colored container.

50. The "biohazard" labels must be _____ or _____ in color or predominantly so, with lettering or symbols in a contrasting color.

51. Universal Precautions must be observed to prevent contact with _____ _____.

52. When HIV gets into a person's bloodstream, the person is _____. The body will produce antibodies in response to this invasion and then can be referred to as _____.

53. HIV disease attacks several types of cells in a person's immune system, especially the _____ _____.

Name and briefly discuss the three stages of HIV infection.

a. _____
_____
_____

b. _____
_____
_____
_____
_____

c. _____
_____
_____
_____

54. The definition of autoimmune deficiency syndrome (AIDS) includes the following:

a. _____
_____
_____

b. _____
_____
_____

c. _____
_____
_____

55. List five ways through which a person can become infected with HIV.

a. _____
_____
_____

b. _____

_____

_____

c. _____

_____

_____

d. _____

_____

_____

e. _____

_____

_____

56. List 14 signs and symptoms that may be seen in a person who is HIV positive.

a. _____

_____

b. _____

_____

c. _____

_____

d. _____

_____

e. _____

_____

f. _____

_____

g. _____

_____

h. _____

_____

i. _____

_____

j. _____

_____

k. _____

_____

l. _____

_____

m. _____

_____

n. _____

_____

57. A blood test commonly referred to as the _____ is used to determine if a person has been infected with HIV. The technical name for the test is the

_____.

It is used as the screening test. If the test results are positive, the person is said to be

or _____ .

A person who is HIV positive has _____ disease.

58. The _____ can be performed to confirm the results of the test.

59. _____ is an inflammatory process and infection of the liver caused by a virus. There are several forms of this disease since new strains have appeared in as little as the past 10 years.

60. Hepatitis A, the less serious form, is usually transmitted by _____.

The incubation period is_____.

61. Hepatitis B a potentially fatal disease, is transmitted through _____

_____

_____.

It is of particular concern because of its association with the spread of the HIV infection leading to

_____.

The incubation period averages _____ .

62. Signs and symptoms for both hepatitis A and hepatitis B are similar but more severe for hepatitis B. They may include: _____

_____

_____

_____ .

63. Diagnosis of hepatitis is based on _____

_____ .

64. Treatment generally consists of _____ until the disease runs its course.

Multiple Choice

Write the letter of the correct answer in the blank provided. There is only *one* correct answer.

_____ 1. The key element of Universal Precautions is:
A. Handling contaminated body secretions with extra care.
B. Handling contaminated blood and blood-stained items with special care.
C. Handling all blood and body fluids as if known to be infected.
D. Wearing disposable single-use examine gloves when handling contaminated specimens.

_____ 2. Training and education in Universal Precautions must be provided for employees:
A. Every 2 years.
B. Once when the person is hired.
C. Annually.
D. Once within a 5-year period.

_____ 3. Hepatitis B vaccinations must be offered at no cost within _____ days of their hiring date to all employees who will have occupational exposure to blood and other potentially infectious materials.
A. 2
B. 5
C. 10
D. 30 (or 1 month)

_____ 4. Universal Precautions are designed to be used for:
A. Patients known to have an infection.
B. Patients suspected of having an infectious disease.
C. All patients, not just those who are identified as infected.
C. Patients who are recovering from an infectious disease.

_____ 5. The most important function of handwashing is to:
A. Remove infectious microorganisms.
B. Clean the hands.
C. Kill disease-producing agents on the hands.
D. Sterilize the hands before beginning a sterile procedure or before assisting with a sterile procedure.

_____ 6. Disposable single-use exam gloves should be worn when:
A. Taking a patient's blood pressure.
B. Performing a venipuncture.
C. Handling specimens from patients.
D. B and C
E. A, B, and C

_____ 7. After use, a needle must be recapped and broken at the hub so it cannot be used by anyone else.
A. True
B. False

_____ 8. Before discarding a used, disposable syringe and needle, the needle must be removed from the syringe and each must be discarded in separate containers for used equipment.
A. True
B. False

_____ 9. Used, disposable syringes and needles must be disposed of in:
A. A rigid puncture-resistant red container.
B. A strong cardboard box labeled "biohazard."
C. A trash can lined with the red biohazard bag.
D. Any waste container with a lid that closes tightly.

_____ 10. Specimen mailers must have a metal inner container and a rigid outer container to comply with Centers for Disease Control regulations.
A. True
B. False

_____ 11. Bloodstained tourniquets must be:
A. Soaked in a 1:10 solution of 5% sodium hypochlorite for 15 minutes, then rinsed and dried.
B. Soaked in a 1:5 solution of 5% sodium hypochlorite for 15 minutes, and then rinsed in hot water and dried.
C. Washed with soap and water then rinsed and dried.
D. Discarded.

12. Patient specimens and the containers that hold them should be collected and treated

    as _____ waste.
    A. Nonmedical
    B. Contaminated
    C. Moist
    D. Infectious

13. Uniforms and clothing that are soiled with patient body secretions should be cleaned with:
    A. Soap and cool water, then washed following normal laundering procedures.
    B. Soap and hot water, then washed following normal laundering procedures.
    C. Alcohol, then washed in hot water and soap.
    D. Alcohol, then washed in cold water and soap.

14. Contaminated laundry should be placed and transported in bags or containers that are labeled or color coded.
    A. True
    B. False

15. The incubation period for HIV disease is:
    A. 1 to 2 years.
    B. Several months to 10 years.
    C. 2 to 6 months.
    D. 6 to 12 months.

16. The incubation period for hepatitis B is:
    A. 20 to 30 days.
    B. 60 to 90 days.
    C. 3 to 12 months.
    D. 1 to 2 years.

ANSWERS
Fill-In

1. If known to be infectious for HIV, HBV, and other bloodborn pathogens
2. To handle all blood and body fluids as if known to be infected
3. Blood or other potentially infectious materials, including body fluids, saliva, and tissue
4. a. Every healthcare facility must develop a written infection control plan and a policies and procedure manual. These must be updated annually and must be made accessible to employees. This exposure control plan must also describe workplace risks, the workers at risk, and how workers are trained and protected.
   b. Training and education in Universal Precautions must be provided annually for the employees.
   c. Hepatitis B vaccinations must be offered within 10 days of employment to all employees who have occupational exposure at no cost to the employee. If employees decline the vaccination they must sign a form to that effect. The vaccination must be made available to employees at no cost if they decide to receive it at a later date.
   d. Records must be kept for at least 30 days on each employee's training, occupational injuries, and vaccinations.
   e. Personal protective equipment must be provided at no cost to the employee. Examples of protective equipment include disposable single-use exam gloves, masks, and gowns.
   f. Engineering controls, such as puncture-resistant containers for used needles, must be in place.
   g. Work practice controls, such as handwashing, must be enforced.
   h. Biohazard signs must be posted.
   i. Warning labels must be used.
   j. Medical treatment and counseling must be made available to exposed employees.
5. Prevent health care workers from transferring infections to patients and health care workers from acquiring infections themselves
6. All; infected
7. How diseases are transmitted; how disease transmission is prevented
8. Diagnosis; the degree of risk
9. Skin and mucous membrane exposure when contact with the patient's blood or other body substances is anticipated
10. Unrecognized cases
11. Handwashing

12. a. Before eating or preparing food, drinking, smoking, applying cosmetics or lip balm, and before handling contact lenses
    b. Before performing clean or sterile invasive procedures
    c. Before and after performing a clinical procedure
    d. Before and after assisting a physician with a clinical procedure
    e. Before and after touching wounds or other drainage
    f. After coming in contact with blood or body fluids; mucous membranes; secretions; or excretions, such as saliva, urine, and feces
    g. After handling soiled linen or waste
    h. After handling devices or equipment soiled with body substances, for example, urine collection containers
    i. After removing gloves or other personal equipment such as masks, goggles, faceshields, gowns, aprons, and caps
    j. After using the toilet
    k. After blowing your nose or coughing into your hands
    l. Between each patient contact
13. Remove infectious organisms
14. Contact with blood or other body fluids or tissue
15. Hypoallergenic gloves, glove liners, powderless gloves
16. a. When touching blood and body fluids, mucous membranes, or nonintact skin of all patients
    b. When handling items or surfaces moist with blood or body fluids and substances
    c. When performing venipuncture or other vascular access procedures
    d. When working with blood, specimens containing blood, body fluids, excretions, and secretions
    e. When cleaning reusable instruments and equipment, wear heavy rubber gloves over disposable single-use exam gloves, a plastic apron or gown, and safety glasses, goggles, or personal glasses with solid side shields added when involved in decontamination activities of instruments and equipment.
    f. When decontamination areas contaminated with body substances
    g. When cleaning up blood spills and other contaminated areas
17. Removed; new
18. Change; immediately after glove removal
19. Answering the telephone, opening a door or drawer, handling a record book or worksheet, and when performing other clean procedures

10

20. Generate aerosol droplets or splashes of blood or other body fluids; equipment that may have disease-producing microorganisms on it

21. Likely to generate splashes or soiling from blood or body fluids

22. Noncontaiminated equipment, when cleaning and decontaminating reusable instruments and equipment

23. It becomes contaminated with blood or body fluids

24. Used needles are not handled properly

25. A rigid, puncture-resistant disposable container with a lid (needle container) that is easily recognized (for example, a red container) and clearly marked as a biohazard (Figure 1-4). Preferably, the container should be made of rigid plastic and must be leakproof on the sides and bottom.

26. Each treatment room, at each laboratory table, and at any other area where syringes, needles, and slides will be used in the office or clinic

27. Place the full container in a brown cardboard box labeled "infectious waste" and "biohazard" and with the biohazard symbol. The box should be lined with plastic sheeting or a strong red plastic bag marked "biohazardous material."

28. The nearest sharps container

29. The sharps container

30. A second container which prevents leakage; color coded

31. Steam sterilization; steam sterilization, incineration, disinfection

32. Gloves, gown, and face protection

33. A disinfectant solution

34. An alcohol swab

35. Alcohol

36. Infectious/biohazardous

37. Mechanical means, such as a brush and dust pan, tongs, or forceps; a puncture-resistant container that is labeled "biohazardous waste" or color coded to indicate that it is for contaminated sharps

38. Infectious

39. Infectious

40. Sharps

41. Moisture-impervious bags

42. Removed from surfaces followed by decontamination processes with an approved disinfectant such as a 1:10 dilution of sodium hypochlorite (household bleach) or Bytech solution

43. Moist, infectious, waste-covered container

44. Soap and cool water, then washed following normal laundering procedures

45. Bags or containers labeled or color coded

46. Biohazard; red

47. Biohazard; red

48. Biohazard; red

49. Biohazard; red

50. Fluorescent orange or orange-red

51. Blood or other potentially infectious materials

52. Infected with HIV; HIV antibody positive

53. T cells

a. Asymptomatic HIV disease
This is the early stage of infection. The only indication of this stage of HIV infection is a positive HIV antibody blood test. Antibodies to HIV usually can be found in the bloodstream 3 to 6 months from the time the person was infected with HIV. We presume that the person is infected with the virus when antibodies are present. We also assume that the person can pass the virus on to others through the usual routes of transmission. Most people show no signs of illness at this time.

b. Symptomatic HIV disease
This is the middle stage of infection. Many people in this stage experience mild to severe physical symptoms without any other illness to explain the occurrence. Examples include swollen lymph glands at two or more sites in the body, persistent fever, diarrhea, and/or skin problems.

c. AIDS
This is the later stage of the disease when the immune system has been severely damaged by the HIV and can no longer fight some infections. People in this stage may develop one or more opportunistic infections, life-threatening diseases, or other diseases as listed.

54. a. People who are HIV positive, and

b. People who are HIV positive and who have at least one of the 26 reportable opportunistic diseases or other serious diseases

c. All people who are HIV positive with fewer than 200 T cells per cubic millimeter of blood even if they do not have an opportunistic infection

55. a. Having unprotected vaginal, anal, or oral sexual intercourse with a person infected with HIV. The virus can be transmitted through semen or vaginal fluids.

b. Sharing an intravenous drug needle with a person infected with HIV. The virus can be transmitted to the needle user who is injecting infected blood into his/her bloodstream.

c. Mother-to-child transmission. An HIV woman can transmit the virus to the unborn baby through the placenta, to the baby during birth, or after birth through infected breast milk.

d. Transfusions with infected blood or blood products. However, since late spring 1985 all blood donations have been screened for HIV antibodies and donors are also screened for risk factors to ensure that this method of transmission does not occur. NO one can get HIV by donating blood.

e. Accidental contact with blood or body fluids contaminated with HIV by health care workers as discussed in the text. HIV disease is not transmitted through casual contact such as close proximity touching, or sneezing.

56. a. Easy bruising, bleeding gums, or nosebleeds
    b. Fevers greater than 100° F for 10 or more days
    c. Dry cough
    d. Memory, concentration, speech and/or coordination problems
    e. Painful, swollen lymph glands
    f. Persistent diarrhea
    g. Persistent headaches, numbness, or tingling in the feet or hands
    h. Persistent skin problems
    i. Persistent vaginal infections
    j. Recurrent, drenching night sweats
    k. Shortness of breath
    l. Sores or unusual blemishes or patches on the tongue or in the mouth
    m. Unexplained fatigue that interferes with normal activities
    n. Unintentional weight loss greater than 10 pounds

57. HIV or AIDS Antibody Test. ELISA test. HIV positive; HIV antibody positive

58. Western Blot test

59. Hepatitis

60. Fecal contamination of food and water. 3 to 4 weeks

61. Contaminated blood, contaminated needles, and also by other body fluids including semen, saliva, and breast milk. AIDS. 60 to 90 days

62. Fever, chills, headache, generalized aches, loss of appetite, nausea, vomiting, dark-yellow urine which may have a brownish tinge, diarrhea, clay-colored stools, enlarged and tender liver, and jaundice

63. Identifying the virus, the antibodies to the virus, or through liver biopsy

64. Rest and a high-protein diet

Multiple Choice

1. C
2. C
3. C
4. C
5. A
6. E
7. B
8. B
9. A
10. A
11. D
12. D
13. A
14. A
15. B
16. B

Unit 2

Physical Measurements: Vital Signs, Height, and Weight

SUGGESTED ACTIVITIES

1. Purchase a thermometer. At the beginning of each clinical class, take the temperature/pulse/respiration (TPR) and blood pressure (BP) of at least five students.

2. Take and record the height and weight of 10 students in your class. Compare these measurements with Table 2-4 in the textbook to determine if they fall within the suggested desirable values.

3. When doing your work experience, check to see how the thermometers are cleaned and stored for future use; check where and how the BP equipment is kept, and what type of manometer is used.

STUDY QUESTIONS
Fill-in

In the blanks provided, write the answers that best complete the sentences:

1. List the four vital signs of body function.

   a. _____

   b. _____

   c. _____

   d. _____

2. List three body locations that may be used to take a patient's temperature. State one reason why these body sites are used.

   a. _____

   b. _____

   c. _____

   d. _____

3. What time of day does the lowest body temperature occur? _____

4. What time of day does the highest body temperature occur? _____

5. List three conditions in which the body temperature decreases.

   a. _____

   b. _____

   c. _____

6. List three conditions in which the body temperature increases.

   a. _____

   b. _____

   c. _____

7. Fever is present when the oral temperature is _____ degrees or higher.

8. List the normal average readings for the following:

   a. Oral temperature in adults: _____

   b. Rectal temperature in adults: _____

   c. Axillary temperature in adults: _____

9. The _____ temperature is considered to be the most reliable and accurate reading.

10. To take an oral temperature, the thermometer should be placed _____ .

11. List four situations for which an oral temperature should not be taken.

    a. _____

    b. _____

    c. _____

    d. _____

12. List two types of patients on whom an axillary temperature should not be taken.

    a. _____

    b. _____

13. Define pulse.

    _____

    _____

    _____

14. List the equipment needed to take a pulse rate.

    a. _____

    b. _____

15. The most frequently used site for taking a pulse rate in adults is the _____ artery located _____ .

16. List the common causes of increased pulse rate.

    a. _____

    b. _____

    c. _____

    d. _____

    e. _____

    f. _____

    g. _____

17. List the common causes of decreased pulse rate.

    a. _____

    b. _____

c. _____

d. _____

e. _____

f. _____

18. The *rhythm* of the pulse pertains to:

    _____

    _____

    _____ .

19. Name the three important characteristics of note when taking the respiratory rate of a patient.

    a. _____

    b. _____

    c. _____

20. During respiration, the body takes in _____ and gives off _____ .

21. List five situations that increase a person's respiratory rate.

    a. _____

    b. _____

    c. _____

    d. _____

    e. _____

22. Labored or difficult breathing is known medically as _____ .

23. Hyperventilation is _____

    _____

    _____ .

24. Blood pressure is _____

    _____ .

    The pressure results from _____

    _____ .

25. In the systolic BP phase, the heart is in a state of _____ , forcing blood _____

26. In the diastolic BP phase, the heart _____

    _____.

27. Give five factors that determine arterial BP.

    a. _____

    b. _____

    c. _____

    d. _____

    e. _____

28. Two pieces of equipment used to obtain a BP

    reading are a _____ and an

    _____.

29. Two common types of sphygmomanometers for

    general use are the _____

    manometer and the _____ .

30. List five common causes of increased BP.

    a. _____

    b. _____

    c. _____

    d. _____

    e. _____

31. List five common causes of decreased BP.

    a. _____

    b. _____

    c. _____

    d. _____

    e. _____

32. Medically speaking, high BP is referred to as

    _____.

33. When taking a BP, the manometer reading at
    which the first distinct sound is heard is referred

    to as the _____ pressure.

34. BP is most commonly measured in the antecubital

    space on the _____

    over the _____ artery.

35. List three things the medical assistant should do
    when retaking a questionable temperature.

    a. _____

    b. _____

    c. _____

36. Clear plastic disposable covers called

    _____ are available to fit over
    the stem and bulb of all glass thermometers (Figure
    2-3). These can be used when taking the tempera-
    ture by any method.

37. Give the advantages that electronic and tympanic
    thermometers have over the glass thermometers.

    _____

    _____

    _____

38. Clinical studies show that the eardrum is an accu-
    rate indicator of true core body temperature be-

    cause _____

    _____.

39. It is easy to read the temperature from a tympanic
    thermometer because it is displayed as a

    _____.
    This eliminates the need for visual interpretation of
    a mercury column.

40. Cerumen (ear wax) does not effect the tympanic
    membrane thermometer readings because

    _____

    _____.

41. Infrared tympanic thermometers eliminate potential

    risks such as _____

    _____ , _____ , and

    _____

42. The length of time that tympanic thermometers
    take to display temperatures on an easy-to-read

    display is _____ . Since infrared waves
    travel at the speed of light, readings can be taken
    almost instanteously.

43. When the pulse feels normal and is regular, count the number of pulsations for 30 seconds. This number can be multiplied by _____ to obtain the pulse rate for 1 minutes.

44. Regular respirations may be counted for 30 seconds. This number can be multiplied by _____ to obtain the rate per minute.

45. Definite hypertension is systolic pressure consistently over _____ mm Hg or diastolic pressure over _____ mm Hg. If BP consistently above this level is not treated it could damage the heart, eyes, kidneys, and even the arteries.

46. Treatment of any form of high BP markedly reduces the risk of _____,
_____, _____,
_____, and _____ .

47. The major myth about high BP is that
_____
_____
_____ .

48. When measuring BP the series of sounds that are listened for are called _____ sounds. These sounds are produced by the blood as it flows through the _____ .

Multiple Choice

Write the letter of the correct answer in the blank provided. There is only *one* correct answer.

_____ 1. The normal oral temperature is:
    A.   96.8° F.
    B.   98.6° F.
    C.   97.6° F.
    D.   38° C.
    E.   36° C.

_____ 2. The normal pulse rate in adults is:
    A.   130 to 160 beats per minute.
    B.   110 to 130 beats per minute.
    C.   80 to 120 beats per minute.
    D.   80 to 90 beats per minute.
    E.   60 to 80 beats per minute.

_____ 3. The normal respiratory rate for adults is:
    A.   30 to 60 respirations per minute.
    B.   30 to 38 respirations per minute.
    C.   20 to 26 respirations per minute.
    D.   14 to 20 respirations per minute.
    E.   10 to 16 respirations per minute.

_____ 4. The pulse rate is:
    A.   Usually higher in adults than in children (1 to 8 years of age).
    B.   Usually higher in children than in adults.
    C.   Approximately the same for adults and children.
    D.   Lower in children than in adults.
    E.   Higher in adults than in infants (0 to 1 year of age).

_____ 5. A patient's vital signs are:
    A.   Temperature.
    B.   TPR.
    C.   BP.
    D.   Both B and C
    E.   Both A and C

_____ 6. On an initial examination for new patients, it is advisable to take the BP on:
    A.   The right arm on right-handed patients.
    B.   The left arm on left-handed patients.
    C.   Both arms.
    D.   The right arm for all patients.
    E.   The left arm for all patients.

_____ 7. The pulse rate is:
    A.   Usually higher in adults than in children.
    B.   Usually higher in children than in adults.
    C.   Approximately the same for both.
    D.   Lower at birth than at 1 year of age.
    E.   Higher in adults over 60 years of age than in a 7-year-old child.

_____ 8. The pulse rate is increased by:
   A. Physical activity, fever.
   B. Fear, certain drugs, shock.
   C. Hypothyroidism.
   D. Both A and B.
   E. A, B, and C.

_____ 9. The pulse rate is decreased by:
   A. Sleep.
   B. Brain injury that causes pressure.
   C. Certain drugs, such as digitalis.
   D. Both A and C.
   E. A, B, and C.

_____ 10. Accurate rectal temperature registers approximately _____ higher than accurate oral temperature.
   A. 1° F
   B. 2° F
   C. 3° F
   D. 2° C
   E. 1° C

_____ 11. A high fever occurs when the body temperature is:
   A. 99° to 101° F (37.2° to 38.3° C).
   B. 101° to 103° F (38.3° to 39.5° C).
   C. 103° to 105° F (39.5° to 40.6° C).

_____ 12. The slender bulb thermometer is considered more effective for taking a(n) _____ temperature.
   A. Oral
   B. Axillary
   C. Rectal

_____ 13. The carotid artery, which may be used to determine pulse rate, is located:
   A. At the right and left sides of the neck, at the anterior edge of the sternocleidomastoid muscle.
   B. Over the inner aspect at the bend of the elbow.
   C. At the back of the knee.
   D. On the upper surface of the foot between the ankle and toes.
   E. At the temple, on the side of the forehead.

_____ 14. The pulse pressure is:
   A. When the apical pulse is greater than the radial pulse rate.
   B. A pulse when occasional pulse beats are missed.
   C. The difference between the systolic and the diastolic blood pressure.
   D. Apparent absence of the radial pulse.
   E. Alternating weak and strong pulsations.

_____ 15. When taking a patient's pulse rate, the medical assistant's _____ should be placed on the patient's wristbone just over the radial artery.
   A. Thumb
   B. First two fingers
   C. Index finger
   D. Index finger and thumb
   E. First three fingers

_____ 16. In a BP reading of 124/72, the systolic pressure is:
   A. 124.
   B. 72.

_____ 17. A patient who weighs 150 pounds also weighs _____ kg.
   A. 63.5
   B. 52.12
   C. 68.18
   D. 88.45
   E. 58.91

_____ 18. A patient who weights 45 kilograms would also weigh _____ pounds.
   A. 45
   B. 99
   C. 150
   D. 145
   E. 105

_____ 19. A patient's whose height measures 65 inches is:
   A. 6 feet.
   B. 5 feet 3 inches.
   C. 6 feet 2 inches.
   D. 5 feet 5 inches.
   E. 5 feet 6 inches.

_____ 20. A patient whose height measures 72 inches
is:
A. 6 feet 2 inches.
B. 5 feet 2 inches.
C. 5 feet 7 inches.
D. 6 feet 4 inches.
E. 6 feet.

_____ 21. When taking a rectal temperature the ther-
mometer should be inserted into the rectum
approximately:
A. 1 inch.
B. 1½ inches.
C. 2 inches.
D. 2½ inches.
E. 3 inches.

_____ 22. A rectal thermometer must be held in place
for:
A. 1 minute.
B. 2 minutes.
C. 3 to 4 minutes.
D. 3 to 5 minutes.
E. 5 to 6 minutes.

_____ 23. When taking an oral temperature, the ther-
mometer must be left in place for a period
of:
A. 1 minute.
B. 2 minutes.
C. 3 minutes.
D. 4 minutes.
E. 5 minutes.

_____ 24. When taking an axillary temperature, the
thermometer must be left in place for a
period of:
A. 1 minute.
B. 10 minutes.
C. 3 minutes.
D. 4 to 5 minutes.
E. 2 minutes.

_____ 25. An oral temperature of 98.6° F, would
probably register as _____ on a rectal
thermometer.
A. 97.6° F
B. 100.6° F
C. 98.6° F
D. 101.6° F
E. 99.6° F

18

Labeling

1. Label the parts indicated on the following:
   a. Sphygmomanometer (Figure 2-1)

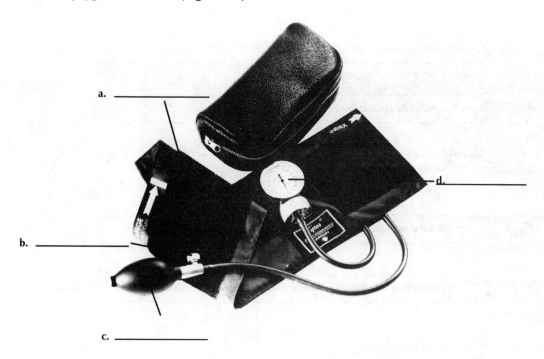

a. _____

b. _____

c. _____

d. _____

   b. Stethoscope (Figure 2-2)

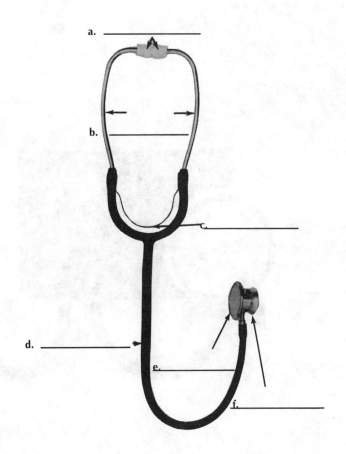

a. _____

b. _____

c. _____

d. _____

e. _____

f. _____

2. Determine the temperatures recorded on the
    following thermometers (Figure 2-3)

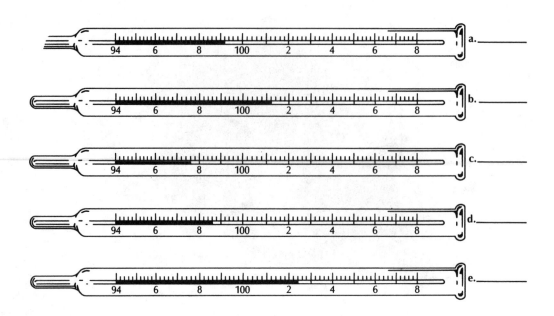

3. Read and record the following BP measurements
    (Figure 2-4).

Figure 2-4 (continued)

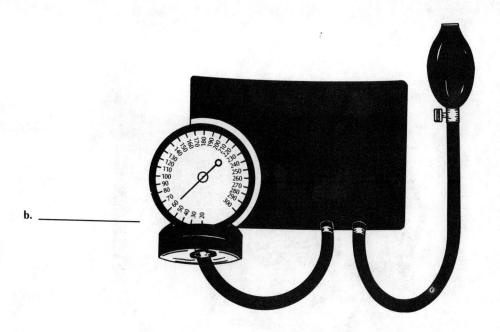

b. _____

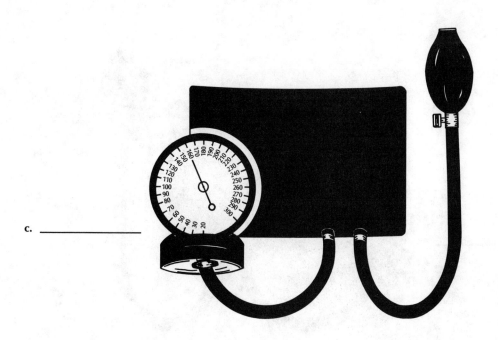

c. _____

Figure 2-4 (continued)

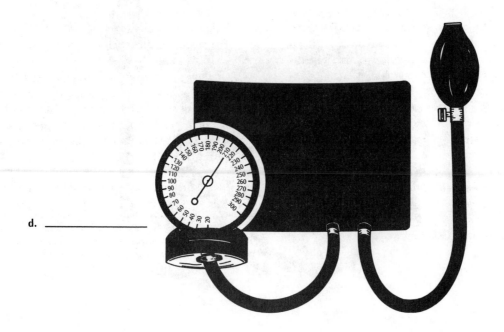

d. _____

e. _____

PERFORMANCE TEST

In a skills laboratory, a simulation of a joblike environment, the medical assistant student is to demonstrate knowledge and skill in performing the following procedures without reference to source materials. For these activities the student will need a watch with a sweep second hand, rectal, oral, and ear thermometers, a stethoscope, a sphygmomanometer, alcohol sponges, containers for used thermometers, scale with height measuring bar, various individuals to play the role of a patient, and a patient chart. Time limits and the number of patients to be tested for each procedure are to be assigned by the instructor.

Given an ambulatory patient and the appropriate equipment and supplies, obtain and record accurately:*

Oral temperatures

Axillary temperatures

Rectal temperatures (a model may be used for this
    procedure)

Ear temperature

Pulse rates

Respiratory rates

BPs taken on the brachial artery

BPs taken on the popliteal artery

Apical heartbeat

Orthostatic BP

Heights and weights

The student is expected to perform these skills with
    100% accuracy (9 out of 10 times).

Grading systems are flexible in order to meet each instructor's preference. The instructor may wish to use satisfactory/unsatisfactory grading system, or a pass/fail system, or a point-value system for each step on the checklist. It is recommended that each procedure be assigned a time limit by the instructor.

*Results obtained for the pulse rates and the respiratory rates are acceptable if within two beats or respirations as determined and recorded by the instructor. Results for BP readings are acceptable if within 2 to 4 mm Hg, as determined and recorded by the instructor. The student is expected to attain proficiency in these procedures before progressing to other procedures in this book.

PERFORMANCE CHECKLIST: Taking a temperature

DIRECTIONS: Evaluate student performance of each procedure using the following checklist. When you evaluate "not applicable," "unsatisfactory," or "not observed," please comment.

Checklist	S or NA*	U	NO	Comment
1. Identified and evaluated patient.				
2. Washed hands. **Use appropriate Personal Protective Equipment (PPE) as dictated by facility.**				
3. Obtained appropriate clean equipment.				
4. Positioned patient correctly and explained the procedure.				
5. Prepared equipment:				
a. Rinsed thermometer with cold water and wiped with a tissue				
b. Shook thermometer down to 96° F or 35.5° C.				
c. Donned disposable single-use exam gloves, then lubricated bulb of thermometer for a rectal temperature.				
6. Placed thermometer correctly in patient's				
a. Mouth, under tongue, lips closed.				
b. Axilla, with patient's arm crossed over chest.				
c. Rectum: inserted approximately 1 inch, held thermometer in place, and instructed patient to remain still.				
7. Left thermometer in position for required time:				
a. Oral—3 minutes				
b. Axillary—10 minutes				
c. Rectal—3 to 5 minutes				
8. Removed thermometer from patient, and wiped it from stem toward bulb.				
9. Read thermometer for temperature registered.				
10. Recorded date and time, temperature, route used, and signature on the patient's chart:				
11. Shook thermometer down to 96° F or below.				
12. Placed thermometer in appropriate container for used thermometers.				
13. Repeated procedure if temperature registered was questionable.				
14. Removed gloves.				
15. Washed hands.				
16. Completed each procedure within the time limit assigned by instructor.				

Total Satisfactory Points _____

Comments

Student's signature: _____ Instructor's signature: _____

Date: _____

*S or NA, Satisfactory or not applicable; U, unsatisfactory; NO, not observed.

PERFORMANCE CHECKLIST: Taking a temperature in the ear

DIRECTIONS: Evaluate student performance of each procedure using the following checklist. When you evaluate "not applicable," "unsatisfactory," or "not observed," please comment.

Checklist	S or NA*	U	NO	Comment
1. Washed hands. **Use appropriate Personal Protective Equipment (PPE) as dictated by facility.**				
2. Assembled equipment.				
3. Identified and evaluated patient.				
4. Positioned patient correctly and explained the procedure.				
5. Prepared equipment: a. Applied disposable cover to the probe tip b. Selected oral or rectal equivalent and pressed ON				
6. For *adults* gently pulled the ear up and back. For *children* gently pulled the ear back.				
7. Gently inserted the probe tip into the patient's ear until the tip fully "sealed off" the year canal. *Did not* apply pressure.				
8. Depressed and held the activation button for 1 second.				
9. Removed thermometer from the ear.				
10. Read and recorded temperature accurately.				
11. Discarded disposable probe cover in designated waste container				
12. Returned equipment to designated area.				
13. Washed hands.				
14. Attended to the patient as needed.				

Total Satisfactory Points _____

Comments

Student's signature: _____ Instructor's signature: _____
Date: _____

*S or NA, Satisfactory or not applicable; U, unsatisfactory; NO, not observed.
PERFORMANCE CHECKLIST: Taking a pulse

DIRECTIONS: Evaluate student performance of each procedure using the following checklist. When you evaluate "not applicable," "unsatisfactory," or "not observed," please comment.

Checklist	S or NA*	U	NO	Comment
1. Identified patient and explained procedure.				
2. Obtained appropriate equipment.				
3. Washed hands.				
Use appropriate Personal Protective Equipment (PPE) as dictated by facility.				
4. Positioned patient correctly.				
5. Located arterial pulses with first three fingers:				
a. Radial				
b. Facial				
c. Right and left carotid				
d. Brachial				
e. Temoral				
f. Femoral				
g. Popliteal				
h. Dorsalis pedis				
6. Counted pulse rate correctly for 1 minute (plus or minus two beats differential acceptable).				
7. Recorded on the patient's chart: date and time; pulse rate, rhythm, volume, and any abnormality if present; and signature.				
8. Repeated procedure if any doubt of accuracy.				
9. Completed procedure in the time limit assigned by instructor.				

Total Satisfactory Points _____

Comments

Student's signature:_____ Instructor's signature: _____
Date: _____

*S or NA, Satisfactory or not applicable; U, unsatisfactory; NO, not observed.

26

PERFORMANCE CHECKLIST: Taking a respiratory rate

DIRECTIONS: Evaluate student performance of each procedure using the following checklist. When you evaluate "not applicable," "unsatisfactory," or "not observed," please comment.

Checklist	S or NA*	U	NO	Comment
1. Washed hands. **Use appropriate Personal Protective Equipment (PPE) as dictated by facility.**				
2. Obtained appropriate equipment.				
3. Identified patient; *did not* explain procedure.				
4. Placed first three fingers on patient's wrist as if taking pulse.				
5. Counted number of respirations correctly for 1 minute (plus or minus two respirations differential acceptable).				
6. Recorded on the patient's chart: date and time; respiratory rate, rhythm, and depth; any noticeable abnormality, such as dyspnea, rates over 22 or under 12; any pain associated with breathing; and signature.				
7. Repeated procedure if any doubt of accuracy.				
8. Completed procedure in time limit assigned by instructor.				

Total Satisfactory Points _____

Comments

Student's signature: _____ Instructor's signature: _____
Date: _____
*S or NA, Satisfactory or not applicable; U, unsatisfactory; NO, not observed.

PERFORMANCE CHECKLIST: Taking a blood pressure

DIRECTIONS: Evaluate student performance of each procedure using the following checklist. When you evaluate "not applicable," "unsatisfactory," or "not observed," please comment.

Checklist	S or NA*	U	NO	Comment
1. Washed hands. **Use appropriate Personal Protective Equipment (PPE) as dictated by facility.**				
2. Obtained appropriate equipment.				
3. Identified patient and explained procedure.				
4. Positioned patient carefully.				
5. Applied cuff properly 1 to 2 inches above the antecubital space.				
6. Located brachial artery, adjusted earpieces of stethoscope in ears, and placed bell or diaphragm of stethoscope over brachial artery.				
7. Correctly inflated cuff to about 20 to 30 mm Hg above palpated or previously measured systolic pressure.				
8. Deflated cuff slowly.				
9. Correctly read mercury column or aneroid gauge for: a. systolic pressure b. diastolic pressure (Plus or minus 2 to 4 mm Hg differential with instructors reading acceptable)				
10. Deflated cuff completely.				
11. Removed equipment from the patient's arm.				
12. Recorded on the patient's chart: date and time; systolic pressure over diastolic (as a mathematical fraction); which arm was used; and signature.				
13. Cleaned earpieces and diaphragm of stethoscope.				
14. Prepared equipment for storage according to type of apparatus used.				
15. If there was any doubt of an accurate reading, waited 15 seconds, the repeated the procedure.				
16. Completed the procedure in the time limit assigned by instructor.				

Total Satisfactory Points   _____

Comments

Student's signature: _____   Instructor's signature: _____
Date: _____
*S or NA, Satisfactory or not applicable; U, unsatisfactory; NO, not observed.

PERFORMANCE CHECKLIST: Measuring adult height and weight

DIRECTIONS: Evaluate student performance of each procedure using the following checklist. When you evaluate "not applicable," "unsatisfactory," or "not observed," please comment.

Checklist	S or NA*	U	NO	Comment
1. Washed hands. **Use appropriate Personal Protective Equipment (PPE) as dictated by facility.**				
2. Identified patient and explained procedure.				
3. Placed a clean paper towel on scale foot stand.				
4. Balanced scale.				
5. Had patient remove shoes and heavy outer clothing.				
6. Directed/assisted patient onto scale.				
7. Varying with preferred technique: raised the height bar above patient's estimated height and extended he hinged arm and then directed or assisted the patient onto scale.				
8. Asked patient usual weight.				
9. Moved 50-pound weight; and secured in the correct weight indicator groove.				
10. Moved upper weight across individual pound register until the arm balanced.				
11. Read the weight correctly.				
12. Returned weight to zero.				
13. Recorded weight.				
14. Instructed patient to remain on scale, stand erect, and look straight ahead.				
15. If height bar was not raised previously (see step 7), raised height bar over patient's head, and extended the hinged arm.				
16. Carefully lowered the bar until it touched the top of the patient's head lightly.				
17. Read the height measurement.				
18. Assisted the patient off scale when necessary.				
19. Returned height bar to resting position.				
20. Recorded the date, time, weight, height, and signature on the patient's chart.				
21. Completed the procedures in the time limit assigned by instructor.				

Total Satisfactory Points   _____

Comments

Student's signature: _____   Instructor's signature: _____

Date: _____

*S or NA, Satisfactory or not applicable; U, unsatisfactory; NO, not observed.

Evaluation of student's technique   Name: _____   Date: _____

Satisfactory*   Unsatisfactory**

	Very Good	Good	Fair	Poor	Score		
• Temperature	☐	☐	☐	☐	_____	Very good	= Perfect
• Pulse rate	☐	☐	☐	☐	_____	Good	= Sufficient
• Respiratory rate	☐	☐	☐	☐	_____	Fair	= Not acceptable requires more practice
• Blood pressure	☐	☐	☐	☐	_____	Poor	= Totally unacceptable
• Height	☐	☐	☐	☐	_____	Pass*	= Satisfactory
• Weight	☐	☐	☐	☐	_____	Fail**	= Unsatisfactory

Comments:

1. a. Temperature
    b. Pulse
    c. Respiration
    d. Blood pressure
2. a. Under the tongue in the mouth
    b. In the rectum
    c. In the axilla
    d. Large blood vessels are near the surface at these body sites.
3. In the early morning (2 a.m. to 6 a.m.)
4. In the evening (5 p.m. to 8 p.m.)
5. a. In some illnesses
    b. If a patient faints, collapses, or hemorrhages
    c. If the patient is in a fasting state, is dehydrated, or has sustained a central nervous system (CNS) injury. Subnormal temperatures, below 96° F (35.6° C), may occur in cases of collapse.
6. a. With infection
    b. Following a chill. The muscular activity that occurs as a result of of shivering (chills) is one way the body increases heat production; this activity releases heat.
    c. The increases in body temperature are also produced by the following:
    • Activity
    • Emotions
    • Environmental changes
    • Age (the elderly and infants show 1° F higher)
    • Reactions to certain drugs
    • The amount and type of food eaten (An increase in metabolic rate increases heat production in the body.)
7. 100° F (38.8° C)
8. a. 98.6° F or 37° C
    b. 99.6° F or 37.6° C
    c. 97.6° F or 36.4° C
9. Rectal (or infrared tympanic if available)
10. Under the tongue in the mouth
11. a. Children who are not old enough to know how to hold the thermometer in the mouth (4 years of age and under)
    b. Patients with nasal obstruction, dyspnea, coughing, weakness, a sore mouth, mouth diseases, or oral surgery
    c. Patients receiving oxygen
    d. Uncooperative, delirious, unconscious, or intoxicated patients
12. a. On thin patients who cannot make the hollow under the arm airtight
    b. On perspiring patients whose axilla cannot be kept dry for the required 5 to 10 minutes
13. The pulse is the beat of the heart as felt through the walls of the arteries. It is the palpable distention or pulsation of the arteries produced by the wave of blood that travels along the arteries with each contraction of the left ventricle of the heart.

    The pulse can also be described as a throbbing caused by the alternate expansion and recoil of an artery.
14. a. A watch with a sweep second hand
    b. Pen and paper or graphic sheet to record the pulse
15. Radial; over the inner aspect of the wrist area, on the thumb side.
16. a. Fear or excitement
    b. Physical activity, exercise
    c. Fever
    d. Certain types of heart disease
    e. Hyperthyroidism
    f. Shock
    g. Pain
    h. Certain drugs
    i. Many infections
17. a. Mental depression
    b. Certain types of heart disease
    c. Chronic illness
    d. Hypothyroidism
    e. Certain brain injuries that cause pressure
    f. Certain drugs, such as digitalis
18. The time interval between each pulse. Normal rhythm is described as regular; that is, the intervals between pulsations are of equal length. Abnormal rhythm may be described as irregular, arrhythmic, bigeminal, skipping beats, or intermittent.
19. a. Rate
    b. Rhythm
    c. Depth
20. Oxygen; carbon dioxide
21. a. Excitement
    b. Nervousness
    c. Any strong emotion
    d. Increased muscular activity, such as running or exercising
    e. Certain drugs, such as ephedrine
    f. Diseases of the lungs
    g. Diseases of the circulatory system
    h. Fever
    i. Pain
    j. Shock
    k. Hemorrhage
    l. Gas poisoning

m. High altitudes

n. Obstruction of the air passages

o. An increase in the carbon dioxide levels in arterial blood, which in turn stimulates the respiratory center.

22. Dyspnea

23. Increase of air in the lungs above the normal amount—abnormally prolonged rapid and deep breathing, usually associated with acute anxiety or emotional tensions

24. The pressure of the blood against the walls of the blood vessels. The pumping action of the heart muscle. This pressure inside the arteries varies with the contracting and the relaxing phases of the heartbeat cycle.

25. Contraction; through the arteries

26. Relaxes between contractions

27. a. The pumping action of the heart and cardiac output

b. The volume of blood within the blood vessels

c. The peripheral resistance of blood vessels to the flow of blood

d. The elasticity of the walls of the main arteries

e. The blood's viscosity, or thickness

28. Sphygmomanometer and stethoscope

29. Mercury; aneroid

30. a. Exercise

b. Stress, anxiety, excitement

c. Increased arterial blood volume

d. Conditions in which blood vessels become more rigid and lose some of their elasticity, as occurs in advanced age

e. Increased peripheral resistance, resulting form vasoconstriction or narrowing of peripheral blood vessels

f. Endocrine disorders, such as hyperthyroidism and acromegaly

g. Increased weight

h. Renal disease and diseases of the liver and heart

i. In the right arm, it is about 3 to 4 mm Hg higher than in the left arm

j. Certain drug therapy

k. Increased intracranial pressure

31. a. Cardiac failure

b. Massive heart attack

c. Decreased arterial blood volume (such as in hemorrhage)

d. Shock and collapse

e. Dehydration

f. Adrenal insufficiency

g. Drug treatment

h. Disorders of the nervous system

i. Hypothyroidism

j. Sleep

k. Infections, fevers

l. Cancer

m. Anemia

n. Neurasthenia

o. Approaching death

32. Hypertension

33. Systolic

34. Arm opposite the elbow; brachial

35. a. Check that the thermometer is shaken down to 96° F (35.5° C) or below, *or*

b. Use another thermometer, *or*

c. Use another method, either rectal or axillary

36. Thermometer sheaths

37. The former register body temperature more quickly than glass, and they provide protection from infection and the possibility of breakage and mercury spillage.

38. It shares blood supply and is in close proximity with the hypothalamus, the body's "thermostat."

39. Clear digital readout

40. Cerumen is transparent to infrared energy

41. Bowel perforation, breakage of glass thermometers, mercury ingestion or contamination

42. 1 second

43. Two

44. Two

45. 160; 90

46. Stroke, heart attack, heart failure, kidney failure, blindness

47. People know when their blood pressure is elevated

48. Korotkoff artery

Multiple Choice

1. B
2. E
3. D
4. B
5. D
6. C
7. B
8. D
9. E
10. A
11. C
12. A
13. A
14. C
15. E
16. A
17. C
18. B

19. D
20. E
21. A
22. D
23. C
24. B
25. E

Labeling

1. A. a. Cuff
      b. Pressure control valve
      c. Inflation bulb
      d. Aneroid gauge pressure indicator
   B. a. Earpieces
      b. Binaurals
      c. External spring
      d. Tapered tubing
      e. Diaphragm
      f. Chestpiece
2. A. 99.2° F
   B. 101.2° F
   C. 97.6° F
   D. 98.6° F
   E. 102.4° F
3. A. 120
   B. 60
   C. 160
   D. 210
   E. 90

Unit 3

Health History and Physical Examinations

SUGGESTED ACTIVITIES

1. Using copies of the forms presented in Figure 3-1 in the textbook, practice recording another person's identifying information and patient history.

2. Review medical charts at the facility where you do your work experience and observe the ways in which different doctors record the patient history and physical examinations.

3. Obtain a patient chart containing blank forms from the facility where you are doing your work experience. Explain the chart and the purpose of each form. Compare your chart and the organization of it with charts that other students have obtained. Discuss which chart you believe is the most efficient and the reason(s) for your choice.

4. Learn how the facility where you do your work experience stores medical records for both current and past patients. Compare your findings with those of the other students in the class.

STUDY QUESTIONS
Fill-in

In the blanks provided, write the answers that best complete the sentences:

1. List the six major components of every diagnostic workup.

    a. _____

    b. _____

    c. _____

    d. _____

    e. _____

    f. _____

2. Information gathered from a history and general or special physical examination can be used by the physician to determine the following:

    a. _____

    b. _____

    c. _____

    d. _____

    e. _____

    f. _____

    g. _____

    h. _____

3. List six parts of a patient's medical history.

    a. _____

    b. _____

    c. _____

    d. _____

    e. _____

    f. _____

4. Give three examples of subjective symptoms.

    a. _____

    b. _____

    c. _____

5. Give three examples of a physical sign.

    a. _____

    b. _____

c. _____

6. Name seven diseases among relatives that are thought to have a hereditary or familial tendency or cases in which contact may play a role.

   a. _____

   b. _____

   c. _____

   d. _____

   e. _____

   f. _____

   g. _____

7. The patient's dietary habits, and use of tobacco and alcohol would be recorded under the

   _____ history.

8. A patient's prior illnesses, childhood diseases, and injuries would be recorded under the _____ history.

9. List six methods of physical examination used by the physician to learn about a patient's condition.

   a. _____

   b. _____

   c. _____

   d. _____

   e. _____

   f. _____

10. The method of physical examination in which the physician would tap the body lightly but sharply with the fingers is called _____ .

11. The method of physical examination in some of the body cavities as the organs perform their functions is referred to as _____ .

12. Mensuration is the process of _____ .

13. Other tests that a physician may have performed as part of the physical examination include:

    a. _____ .

    b. _____ .

c. _____ .

d. _____ .

14. Give three reasons why diagnostic studies are important for patient care.

    a. _____

    b. _____

    c. _____

15. A statement that indicates the cause of the patient's current, most important problem/condition is called

    the _____ diagnosis.

16. A statement based on comparison of signs and symptoms of two or more similar diseases to determine from which the patient is suffering is

    referred to as the _____ diagnosis.

17. List the four basic parts of the problem-oriented medical record (POMR).

    a. _____

    b. _____

    c. _____

    d. _____

18. Define health.

    _____

19. Spell out the following medical abbreviations:

    a. CVS_____

    b. NS_____

    c. CC_____

    d. a&w_____

    e. BP_____

    f. WNL_____

    g. R/O_____

    h. TPR_____

    i. TM_____

    j. SOB_____

    k. ASHD_____

    l. MI_____

m. LMP _____

n. CVA _____

o. CBC _____

p. FBS _____

q. D&C _____

r. D/C _____

s. PRN _____

t. FUO _____

u. CPR _____

v. PVC _____

20. Explain as many of the abbreviations as possible in this history and physical examination.

CC: ASHD c̄ possible MI

_____

HPI: See note from LMD

_____

PH: Pt. had MI 5 years PTA. UCHD.

_____

FH: No TB, ASHD, Ca.

_____

SH: N/A

_____

ROS: WNL. LMP 10-28-94

_____

PE: This is a wd wn white female in no acute distress. HEENT: PERLA. EOMs normal. TMs clear. No AV nicking. NECK: No LOM. CR: Clear to IPPA. No PND. NSR. Occasional PVCs. Grade II systolic murmur. The PMI is in the 5th ICS 5 cm's from the MCL. No cva tenderness. GI: LKS WNL. GU: BUS negative. MS: DTRs are 2+ and equal.

_____

R/O: MI

_____

21. The medical record is a legal document belonging

to _____

_____.

22. Explain the steps that should be taken if a charting error is discovered on the patient's medical record.

a. _____

b. _____

c. _____

d. _____

e. _____

23. Inactive medical records may be stored in _____

_____.

Multiple Choice

Write the letter of the correct answer in the blank provided. There is only *one* correct answer.

_____ 1. A statement made by the physician indicating the probable or anticipated outcome of a disease process in a patient is called the:
A. Prodrome.
B. Syndrome.
C. Prognosis.
D. Positive findings.

_____ 2. The purpose of the _____ is to reveal *subjective* symptoms that either the patient forgot to discuss or, at the time, seemed relatively unimportant to the patient.
A. Past history
B. Review of systems
C. Physical examination
D. Family history

_____ 3. During a physical examination, percussion is most commonly used when examining the:
A. Eyes and ears.
B. Breast.
C. Mouth and throat.
D. Chest and back.

4. The physician uses a stethoscope to listen to body sounds during the method of examinations called:
   A. Auscultation.
   B. Percussion.
   C. Inspection.
   D. Palpation.

5. _____ is performed by applying the tips of the fingers, the whole hand, or both hands to the body part.
   A. Inspection
   B. Palpation
   C. Percussion
   D. Auscultation

6. A patient's job, education, and marital status have some bearing on the diagnosis and treatment program given.
   A. True
   B. False

7. A person's reactions to stress, defense mechanisms used, and resources for support and assistance would be recorded in the patient history under the:
   A. Past history.
   B. History of present illness.
   C. Social and occupational history.
   D. Chief complaint.

8. Additional tests that a physician may perform as part of the general physical examination include a(n):
   A. BUN.
   B. EEG.
   C. IVP.
   D. CBC.

9. Statements made by the patient, how the patient feels, and other information from the patient's family is recorded under the _____ in the POMR.
   A. Subjective findings
   B. Objective findings
   C. Assessment
   D. Suggested plan

10. A statement that indicates a problem/condition that is less important or urgent than a patient's primary diagnosis is called a:
    A. Tentative diagnosis.
    B. Provisional diagnosis.
    C. Differential diagnosis.
    D. Secondary diagnosis.

11. A change in the physical or mental state of the body that is perceptible or apparent *only* to the individual experiencing the change is referred to as a:
    A. Sign.
    B. Subjective symptom.
    C. Objective symptom.
    D. Physical sign.

PERFORMANCE TEST

In a skills laboratory, a simulation of a joblike environment, the medical assistant student is to demonstrate knowledge and skill in obtaining identifying information and the medical history from a patient. The student may use a preprinted history form or make a list of questions that should be asked of the patient from the information presented in this unit. For these activities the student will need a person to play the role of the patient and the necessary supplies. Time limits for the performance of this procedure are to be assigned by the instructor.

ANSWERS
Fill-in

1. a. History
   b. Physical examination
   c. Summary of positive findings
   d. Interpretation of completed diagnostic studies
   e. Examiner's impression based on all the information gathered
   f. Care plans including suggested further study
2. a. The individual's level of health
   b. The body's level of physiological functioning
   c. A tentative diagnosis of a condition or disease
   d. A confirmed diagnosis of a condition or disease
   e. The need for additional special examinations or testing
   f. The type of treatment to be prescribed
   g. An evaluation of the effectiveness of the prescribed treatment
   h. Preventive measures to be used

3. a. Chief complaint
   b. History of present illness
   c. Past history
   d. Family history
   e. Social and occupational history
   f. Review of systems
4. a. Anorexia
   b. Nausea
   c. Headache
   d. Pain
   e. Itching
   f. Dizziness
5. a. Swollen ankles
   b. Distended rigid abdomen
   c. Elevated blood pressure
   d. Decreased sensation
6. a. Cardiovascular diseases
   b. Renal diseases
   c. Endocrine diseases
   d. Metabolic diseases
   e. Mental diseases
   f. Infectious diseases
   g. Neoplasma or carcinoma
   h. Allergies
7. Social and occupational
8. Past
9. a. Inspection
   b. Palpation
   c. Percussion
   d. Auscultation
   e. Mensuration
   f. Smell
10. Percussion
11. Auscultation
12. Measuring
13. a. A routine urinalysis (UA)
    b. A complete blood count (CBC)
    c. A chest x-ray film
    d. An electrocardiogram (EKG)
14. a. To determine (diagnose) the condition from which the patient is suffering so that treatment may be initiated if feasible
    b. To discover disease in its early stage before the patient experiences any signs or symptoms. This is called screening
    c. To evaluate past or ongoing treatment received by the patient
15. Primary diagnosis
16. Differential
17. a. Data base
    b. Problem list
    c. Plans
    d. Progress notes

18. The state of mental, physical, and social well-being of an individual.
19. a. Cardiovascular system
    b. Nervous system
    c. Chief complaint
    d. Alive and well
    e. Blood pressure
    f. Within normal limits
    g. Rule out
    h. Temperature, pulse, respiration
    i. Tympanic membrane(s)
    j. Shortness of breath
    k. Arteriosclerotic heart disease
    l. Myocardial infarction
    m. Last menstrual period
    n. Cerebral vascular accident
    o. Complete blood count
    p. Fasting blood sugar
    q. Dilatation and curettage
    r. Discontinue
    s. Whenever necessary
    t. Fever of unknown origin
    u. Cardiopulmonary resuscitation
    v. Premature ventricular contraction

20. *Chief complaint*: Arteriosclerotic heart disease with possible myocardial infarction.
    History of present illness: See note from local medical doctor.
    Past history: Patient had myocardial infarction 5 years prior to admission. Usual childhood diseases.
    Family history: No tuberculosis, arteriosclerotic heart disease, cancer.
    Social history: Not applicable.
    Review of systems: Within normal limits. Last menstrual period 10-28-94.
    Physical examination: This is a well-developed well-nourished white female in no acute distress.
    Head, ears, eyes, nose, and throat: pupils equal and reacting to light and accommodation. Extraocular movements normal. Tympanic membranes clear. No arteriovenous nicking. *Neck*: No loss of movement. *Cardiorespiratory*: Clear to inspection, percussion, palpation, and auscultation. No paroxysmal nocturnal dyspnea. Normal sinus rhythm. Occasional premature ventricular contractions. Grade II systolic murmur. The point of maximal intensity is in the 5th intercostal space 5 cm from the midclavicular line. No costovertebral angle tenderness. *Gastrointestinal*: Liver, kidney, spleen within normal limits. *Genitourinary*: Bartholin, urethral, and Skene glands negative. *Musculoskeletal*: Deep tendon reflexes are 2+ and equal.
    Rule out: Myocardial infarction.

21. The physician or clinical agency.
22. a. Strike a single line through the error
    b. Date and initial the strikeout.
    c. If the problem is incorrect data, enter the correct information directly below the strike-out. Date and initial the entry.
    d. If the entry is made in the wrong chart, follow Step 1 and note "Recorded in chart by error. Information transferred to chart of John C. Adams."
    e. Date and sign the strikeout and explanation.
23. Specifically designed file storage boxes in a storage area on the office premises, with a professional storage company, or on microfilm.

Multiple Choice

1. C
2. B
3. D
4. A
5. B
6. A
7. C
8. D
9. A
10. D
11. B

Unit 4

Preparing for and Assisting with Routine and Specialty Physical Examinations

SUGGESTED ACTIVITIES

1. Identify and arrange the equipment and materials needed for the following examinations:
   a. A complete physical examination
   b. Pelvis examination and a Papanicolaou (Pap) smear
   c. Rectal examination
   d. Sigmoidoscopy
   e. Neurologic examination
   f. Hearing examination
   g. Eye examination

2. Practice positioning other students in the following positions. State the examination(s) that would be performed when a patient assumes these positions.
   a. Dorsal-recumbent
   b. Lithotomy
   c. Knee-chest
   d. Sim's
   e. Trendelenburg
   f. Supine
   g. Prone
   h. Fowler's
   i. Semi-Fowler's

3. Practice checking the following equipment to ensure that it is in good working condition.
   a. Otoscope
   b. Ophthalmoscope
   c. Sigmoidoscope
   d. Flashlight

4. When doing your work experience, make a list of the equipment that is kept in the examination room. Describe the purpose of each piece of equipment.

STUDY QUESTIONS
Fill-In

In the blanks provided, write the answers that best complete the sentences:

1. State the purposes of positioning a patient for a physical examination.

   a. _____
   _____

   b. _____
   _____

2. State the purposes for draping a patient for a physical examination.

   a. _____
   _____

   b. _____
   _____

   c. _____
   _____

3. In the _____ position the patient is lying on the back with the feet placed in stirrups that are raised approximately 12 inches from table level.

4. In the _____ position the patient is lying on the back with the knees bent and the feet placed flat at the end of the examining table.

5. In the _____ position the patient lies on the abdomen with both head and legs lowered, so that the buttocks are elevated. Arms are placed along the side of the head.

6. In the _____ position the patient rests on the knees and chest, with the head turned to one side. Arms may be placed _____ to help support the patient. Buttocks extend up in the air, and the back is straight.

7. In the _____ position the patient lies on the left side and chest, with the left leg slightly flexed and the right leg sharply flexed on the abdomen.

8. In the _____ position the patient lies on the back with the head lower than the rest of the body.

9. In the _____ position the patient lies flat on the back, arms placed at the side, and head elevated slightly on a pillow.

10. In the _____ position the patient lies flat on the abdomen, arms flexed under the head, which is turned to one side.

11. In the _____ position the patient sits up.

12. In the _____ position the patient lies in a supine position, with the head of the examining table or bed raised 18 to 20 inches above the level of the feet.

13. List the common instruments and supplies that would be needed during a physical examination.

a. _____
b. _____
c. _____
d. _____
e. _____
f. _____
g. _____
h. _____
i. _____
j. _____
k. _____

l. _____
m. _____
n. _____
o. _____
p. _____
q. _____
r. _____
s. _____
t. _____
u. _____
v. _____
w. _____
x. _____
y. _____
z. _____

14. A speculum or endoscope inserted into the anal canal for direct visual examination is a(n)

_____.

15. A slender rod of wood with a pledget of cotton on one end used to apply medicine or to take a culture from the body is a(n) _____.

16. Two-pronged instruments of varying sizes and shapes used to remove tissue from the body for examination are called _____.

17. An endoscope designed specifically for passage through the trachea to allow visual examination of the interior of the tracheobronchial tree is a(n)

_____.

18. A hollow metal tube instrument (endoscope) designed specifically for passing through the urethra into the urinary bladder to permit internal inspection is a(n) _____

19. A specifically designed instrument made of metal or rubber that is used for direct visual examination of hollow organs or body cavities is a(n)

_____.

20. An instrument, device, or bag used for blowing air, powder, or gas into a cavity is a(n)

_____ .

21. An instrument used to view the pharynx and larynx consisting of a small rounded mirror attached to the end of a slender (metal or chrome plate) handle is a(n) _____ .

22. An endoscope used to examine the larynx is a(n)

_____ .

23. A short funnel-like instrument used to examine the nasal cavity is a(n) _____ .

24. An instrument used for examining the interior parts of the eye is the _____ .

25. An instrument used to examine the external ear canal and eardrum is the _____ .

26. A small hammer with a triangular-shaped rubber head used for percussion is the _____ .

27. A specifically designed tubular endoscope that is passed through the anus to permit internal inspection of the lower part of the large intestine is the

_____ .

28. A tubular endoscope used to examine the interior of the sigmoid colon is the _____ .

29. An instrument used for distending or opening a body cavity or orifice to allow visual inspection of

a(n) _____ .

30. A form of bivalve speculum used in the examination of the vagina and cervix is the

_____ .

31. An instrument used in auscultation to amplify the sounds produced by the lungs, heart, intestines, and other internal organs; also used when taking a BP reading is the _____ .

32. A _____ is a flat, thin, smooth piece of wood or metal with rounded ends approximately 6 inches long. It is used for pressing tissue down to permit a better view when examining the mouth and throat. In addition, it may be used for application of ointments to the skin.

33. A steel, two-pronged, forklike instrument used for testing hearing is the _____ .

34. The _____ is used for measuring intra-ocular pressure and tension of the eyeball.

35. The patient should be in the _____ position when the physician examines the head, ears, eyes, nose, and throat.

36. The patient should be in the _____ position when the physician palpates the abdomen and breasts.

37. Mrs. Jones should assume the _____ position when she is having a pelvic examination.

38. Explain the steps a pelvic examination includes.

_____

_____ .

39. The purpose of the Pap smear is: _____

_____

_____ .

40. The vaginal speculum (should *or* should not)

_____ be lubricated when the physician inserts it into the vagina before obtaining a Pap smear.

41. Explain the purpose of a rectal examination.

_____ .

42. The special patient preparation required before a sigmoidoscopy is performed includes:

a. _____

b. _____

c. _____

43. When a sigmoidoscopy is performed the patient should be positioned in the _____ or _____ position.

44. Pins and cotton to test the senses of touch, sensation, and pain on the external surfaces of the body are used during a _____ examination.

45. The _____ eye chart is used to measure distance visual acuity.

46. Tonometry is an important test used to determine the presence of an eye condition termed _____, in which the pressure within the eyeball is increased.

47. When the letters on the row marked 20/50 on the Snellen chart are read, this means that the person can read _____.

48. When measuring distance visual acuity using the Snellen eye chart you usually test only one eye at a time because _____ _____.

49. List the seven warning signals for cancer.

    a. _____
    b. _____
    c. _____
    d. _____
    e. _____
    f. _____
    g. _____

50. When sending slides to the laboratory for cytological examination, the following information should be entered on the laboratory requisition.

    a. _____
    b. _____
    c. _____
    d. _____
    e. _____

51. _____ is the branch of medicine that deals with maintaining the health of the female reproductive tract, and the diseases and conditions that affect this body system. The medical specialist in this branch of medicine is called a _____.

52. Explain the procedures that a gynecologic examination generally includes when performed by itself.

    a. _____
    b. _____
    c. _____
    d. _____

53. The _____ is a gland just below the bladder in the male genital tract. It has the second highest incidence of cancer in men _____ years of age and older.

54. Recommendations for prostate cancer screening for men over 50 years of age include _____ and _____.

55. The American Cancer Society recommends that after the age of _____ an annual health checkup for everyone include a digital rectal examination. A more extensive examination of the interior surfaces of the rectum is done by a _____.

56. A malignant tumor is _____ (is or is not) cancer.

57. A benign tumor _____ (is or is not) cancer.

58. Cancer cells may metastasize. This means that the cells _____. This occurs either by direct extension of growth or by cells becoming detached and carried through the _____ or _____ systems to other parts of the body.

59. For testing distance visual acuity in preschoolers or for non-English-speaking or illiterate people the _____ eye chart can be used.

60. The tests for near vision are used to determine if the patient can read average-sized type at a normal reading distance of _____ inches.

61. Color vision should be tested when _____ or _____.

62. Commonly used color plates for color vision screening are the _____ plates.

63. Color vision is regarded as normal if _____ (what number) of the Ishihara plates are read normally.

64. During pregnancy, tests that are commonly used for detecting genetic defects are _____ and _____ . These tests are currently recommended for certain pregnant women:

    a. _____

    b. _____

    c. _____

65. A patient who had a cesarean section should return for a checkup _____ weeks after delivery and the _____ to _____ weeks after delivery.

66. _____ is the branch of medicine that deals with the care and development of neonates (the first 28 days of life), infants, children, and adolescents, and with the diseases and treatment affecting them. The physician specialist for this branch of medicine is called a _____ .

67. Two broad classifications of pediatric patient physician office visits are the _____ visit and the _____ visit.

68. Assessing a child's growth and development is best accomplished by _____ _____.

69. Today's well-child checkups are designed to _____ , _____ and _____ health problems early.

70. The approach to any pediatric physical examination is based on the _____ , _____ , and _____ .

71. The average length of a newborn is _____ to _____ inches. The average weight of a newborn ranges from _____ to _____ pounds. Male infants on average are usually longer and heavier than the female infant.

72. State the measurements that are routinely taken and plotted on a standardized chart for infants.

    a. _____

    b. _____

    c. _____

    d. _____

73. The type of scale used to weigh children up to 14 months of age is a _____ scale or _____ scale.

74. The length of a child up to 24 to 36 months is measured from the _____ .

75. List six common vaccines available and given to children.

    a. _____

    b. _____

    c. _____

    d. _____

    e. _____

    f. _____

76. The National Childhood Vaccine Injury Act of 1988 requires the following information to be recorded in a child's permanent medical record for all childhood mandated vaccinations.

    a. _____

    b. _____

    c. _____

    State the other types of information that should be recorded.

    a. _____

    b. _____

Multiple Choice

Write the letter of the correct answer in the blank provided. There is only *one* correct answer.

_____ 1. The most extensive examination from the following is the:
A. Rectal examination.
B. Proctoscopy.
C. Sigmoidoscopy.
D. Endoscopy.

_____ 2. A Pap smear is performed to help in the early diagnosis of unusual cell growth:
A. On the cervix.
B. On the rectum.
C. In the sigmoid.
D. In the urinary bladder.

_____ 3. Visual acuity means:
A. Pressure in the eyeball.
B. Clearness or acuteness of vision.
C. Nearsightedness.
D. Farsightedness.

_____ 4. Patients should be instructed not to put any creams or foams in the vagina, not to douche, and not to have sexual intercourse for _____ hours before having a Pap smear taken.
A. 8 to 12
B. 12 to 18
C. 18 to 22
D. 24 to 48

_____ 5. A Pap smear must not be taken during the patient's menstrual period because:
A. The hormone levels change at that time.
B. The cervix is much too tender at that time.
C. The red blood cells interfere with obtaining accurate findings.
D. The cervix is secreting too much mucus at that time.

_____ 6. Abnormal Pap smear results do not mean that the patient has cancer unless the findings are in:
A. Class II.
B. Class III.
C. Class IV.
D. Class V.

_____ 7. When spraying the slides after obtaining a Pap smear, the nozzle of the fan should be held at least _____ inches away from the slide and the slide sprayed lightly from left to right and then from right to left.
A. 2 to 3
B. 4 to 5
C. 5 to 6
D. 6 to 7

_____ 8. The purpose of a proctoscopy is to examine the:
A. Rectum.
B. Sigmoid colon.
C. Prostate gland.
D. Uterus.

_____ 9. The American Cancer Society recommends that individuals have an annual stool test for occult blood after the age of _____.
A. 20.
B. 30
C. 40
D. 50

_____ 10. When measuring distance visual acuity using the Snellen eye chart, the person taking the test must be standing or sitting _____ feet away from the chart.
A. 50
B. 20
C. 40
D. 10

_____ 11. The patient assuming the Sim's position is lying on the:
A. Right side with left leg flexed.
B. Left side and chest with right leg flexed.
C. Right side with right leg flexed.
D. Left side with left leg flexed.

_____ 12. A patient lying on the back with the feet placed in stirrups that are raised approximately 12 feet from table level, is in the _____ position.
A. Lithotomy
B. Knee-chest
C. Trendelenburg
D. Jackknife

13. A patient lying flat on the abdomen is said to be in the _____ position.
    A. Recumbent
    B. Dorsal
    C. Supine
    D. Prone

14. The patient should assume the _____ position for a sigmoidoscopy.
    A. Lithotomy
    B. Sim's or left lateral
    C. Supine
    D. Trendelenburg

15. Another position that a patient may assume for a sigmoidoscopy is the _____ position.
    A. Knee-chest
    B. Prone
    C. Dorsal-recumbent
    D. Semi-Fowler's

16. During a physical examination, the patient should assume the _____ position when the physician is examining the head, ears, mouth, and throat.
    A. Supine
    B. Prone
    C. Sitting
    D. Standing

17. The physician palpates the patient's breasts, liver, spleen, and other abdominal organs when the patient assumes the _____ position.
    A. Supine
    B. Prone
    C. Sitting
    D. Dorsal-recumbent

18. The patient should assume the _____ position when having a Pap smear taken.
    A. Sim's
    B. Semi-Fowler's
    C. Dorsal-recumbent
    D. Proctologic

19. The physician uses an otoscope to examine the patient's:
    A. Eyes.
    B. Ears.
    C. Throat.
    D. Rectum.

20. The physician uses the _____ to test the patient's hearing.
    A. Ophthalmoscope
    B. Percussion hammer
    C. Tonometer
    D. Tuning fork

21. The audiometer is used to test:
    A. Vision.
    B. Pupil reactions and equality.
    C. Hearing.
    D. Deep tendon reflexes.

22. If a patient's vision is recorded as OD 20/30, it would mean that the patient can read with the:
    A. Right eye at 20 feet what the normal eye can read at 30 feet.
    B. Right eye at 30 feet what the normal eye can read at 20 feet.
    C. Left eye at 20 feet what the normal eye can read at 30 feet.
    D. Left eye at 30 feet what the normal eye can read at 20 feet.

23. During an obstetric examination, the urine is routinely checked for the presence of:
    A. Glucose and acetone.
    B. Sugar and albumin.
    C. Protein and Ketone bodies.
    D. Glucose and blood.

24. Routine blood test performed on pregnant women at the time of the initial obstetrical examination include a:
    A. CBC and blood glucose.
    B. CBC, blood glucose, and blood typing.
    C. CBC, the Rh factor and blood typing of the ABO blood groups, a VDRL, and a rubella titer.
    D. CBC, VDRL, blood glucose, and blood chemistries.

25. The best time to do a breast self-examination for women who are still menstruating is about:
    A. 2 weeks after her period.
    B. 1 week before her period.
    C. 2 weeks before her period.
    D. 1 week after her period.

Labeling

1. Identify by name the positions illustrated in Figure 4-1.

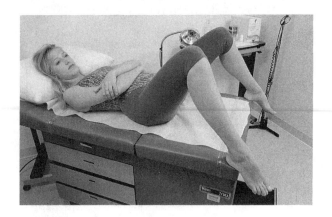

a. _____

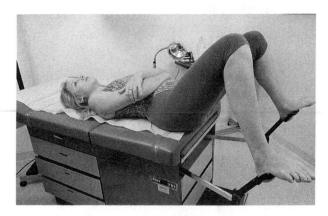

b. _____

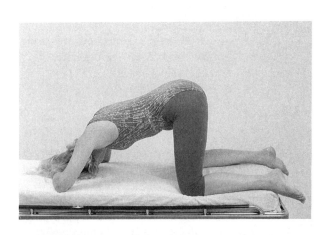

c. _____

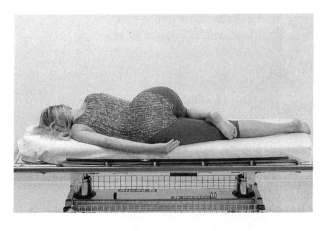

d. _____

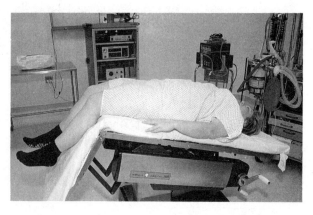

e. _____

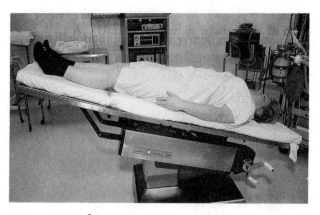

f. _____

Figure 4-1 (continued)

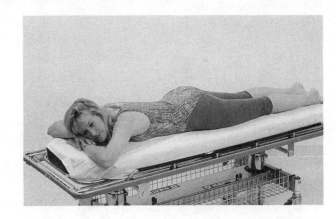

g. _____

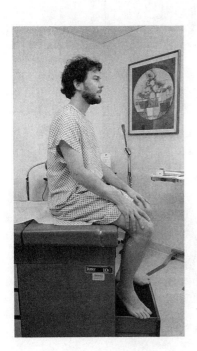

h. _____

i. _____

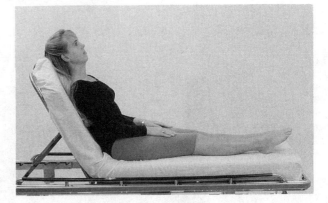

2. Identify by name the instruments illustrated in Figure 4-2.

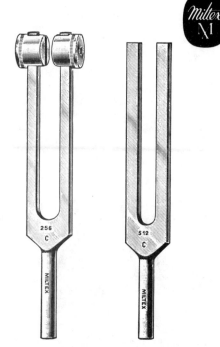

a. _____

b. _____

c. _____

d. _____

e. _____

Figure 4-2 (continued)

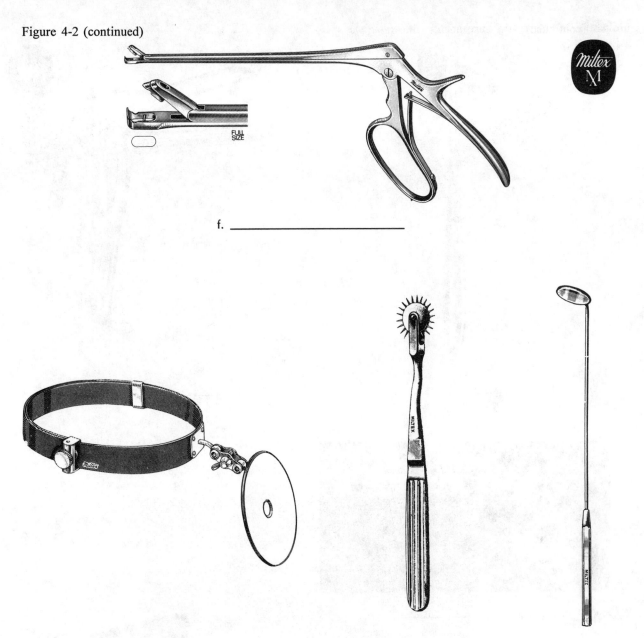

f. _____

g. _____

h. _____

i. _____

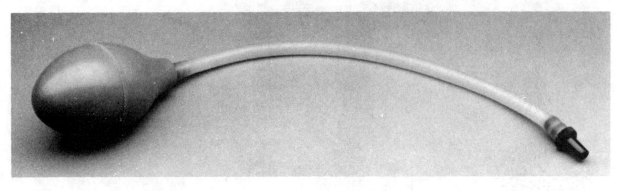

j. _____

Figure 4-2 (continued)

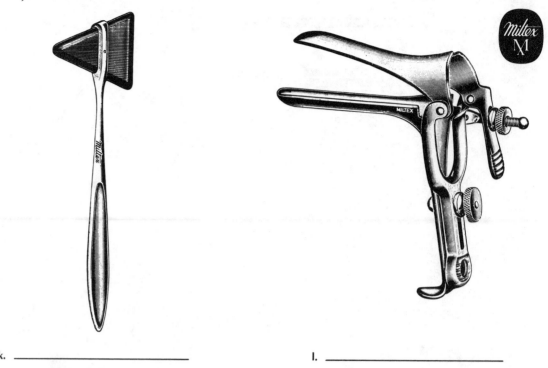

k. _____

l. _____

m. _____

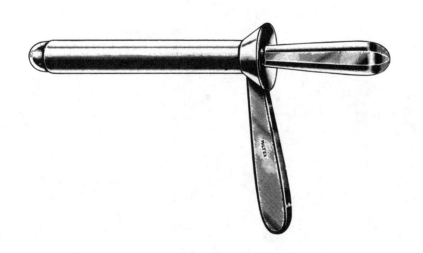

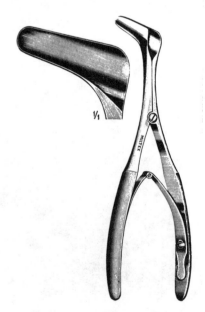

n. _____

o. _____

Figure 4-2 (continued)

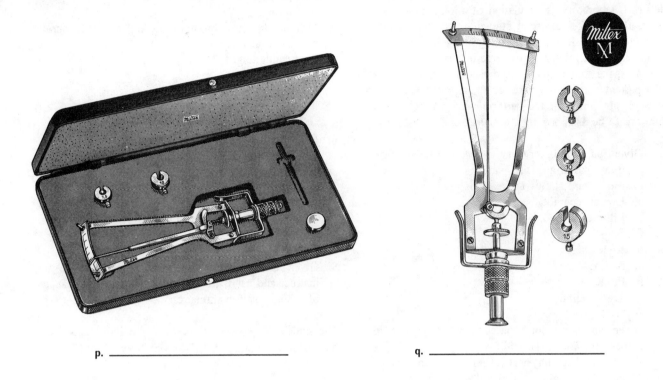

p. _____

q. _____

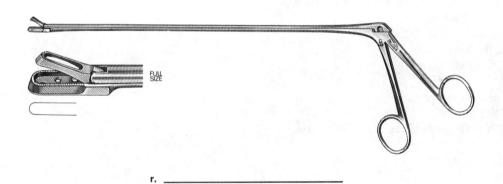

FULL
SIZE

r. _____

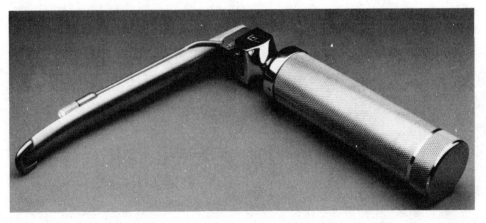

s. _____

PERFORMANCE TEST

In a skill laboratory, a simulation of a joblike environment, the medical assistant student is to demonstrate knowledge and skill in performing the following procedures without reference to source materials. For these activities, the student will need a person to play the role of a patient and all the necessary equipment and supplies. Time limits for the performance of each procedure are to be assigned by the instructor.

1. Given an ambulatory patient, the student is to position and drape the patient in the following positions, and state when each is used:
    a. Dorsal-recumbent
    b. Lithotomy
    C. Sims
    d. Knee-chest
    e. Supine
    f. Prone
    g. Trendelenburg

2. Given an ambulatory patient, the student is to prepare for and assist with:
    a. A complete physical examination that is to include a vaginal and rectal examination
    b. A proctosigmoidoscope, including a description of the patient preparation that is to be completed before the examination
    c. A pelvic examination and a Pap smear.
    d. An obstetric examination.
    e. A pediatric examination

3. Given an ambulatory patient, the student is to prepare for and measure:
    a. Distance visual acuity using the Snellen eye chart
    b. Near visual acuity
    c. Color vision

4. Demonstrate how to carry an infant in the cradle, upright, and football positions.

5. Demonstrate how to obtain the following measurements on an infant.
    a. Length/height
    b. Weight
    c. Head circumference
    d. Chest circumference

6. Demonstrate the procedures used for performing a urine test to screen an infant for phenylketonuria (PKU).

7. Demonstrate the method used to obtain a blood specimen from an infant to perform a test to screen for PKU.

8. Given an ambulatory patient, the student is to instruct and assist the patient with the performance of a breast self-examination.

The student is expected to perform the above activities with 100% accuracy 90% of the time (9 out of 10 times).

PERFORMANCE CHECKLIST: Preparing for and assisting with a complete physical examination, including a vaginal and rectal examination

DIRECTIONS: Evaluate student performance of each procedure using the following checklist. When you evaluate "not applicable," "unsatisfactory," or "not observed," please comment.

Checklist	S or NA*	U	NO	Comment
1. Washed hands. **Use appropriate Personal Protective Equipment (PPE) as dictated by facility.**				
2. Assembled and prepared the equipment and supplies needed, and was able to identify each instrument by name.				
3. Identified the patient, and explained the procedure.				
4. Recorded on the patient's chart: TPR, BP, and weight and height.				
5. Prepared the patient for the examination:				
• Had the patient void; saved specimen if needed				
• Had the patient disrobe completely and put on patient gown				
• Positioned the patient on the examining table in a sitting or supine position				
• Draped the patient				
6. Assisted the physician as required during the examination (supplied or handed supplies and equipment to the physician as needed).				
7. Assisted the patient during the examination, giving reassurance and support; observed the patient for any unusual reactions.				
8. Assisted the patient in changing positions to the Sims for the rectal examination, draped the patient, and had the required equipment read for the physician.				
9. Helped the patient change positions to the lithotomy for the vaginal examination, draped the patient, and had the required equipment ready for the physician.				
10. Provided for the patient's comfort at the conclusion of the examination by removing drapes, answering any questions the patient may have had, informing the patient of special or future instructions, and helping the patient.				
11. Carried out the physician's order for additional examinations or tests. If specimens were obtained, donned disposable single-use exam gloves and prepared them properly to be sent to be sent to the laboratory.				
12. Wearing gloves collected, disposed of, cleaned, returned, and replaced all used equipment as needed.				
13. Removed gloves and washed hands.				
14. Recorded on the patient's chart: date, hour, procedure, results (where applicable) and signature.				

PERFORMANCE CHECKLIST: Preparing for and assisting with a complete physical examination, including a vaginal and rectal examination (continued)

Checklist	S or NA*	U	NO	Comment
15. Completed the procedure in the time limit assigned by the instructor.				

Total Satisfactory Points _____

Comments

Student's signature: _____ Instructor's signature: _____

Date: _____

*S or NA, Satisfactory or not applicable; U, unsatisfactory; NO, not observed.

NOTE: Wear disposable single-use exam gloves when you handle any specimen and when cleaning used supplies and the work area.

PERFORMANCE CHECKLIST: Preparing for and assisting with a proctosigmoidoscopy

DIRECTIONS: Evaluate student performance of each procedure using the following checklist. When you evaluate "not applicable," "unsatisfactory," or "not observed," please comment.

Checklist	S or NA*	U	NO	Comment
1. Described the preparation of the patient for the examination as follows: • A laxative the evening before • Only liquids for breakfast • Tap water or saline enemas until clear, 1 hour before the examination				
2. Washed hands. **Use appropriate Personal Protective Equipment (PPE) as dictated by facility.**				
3. Assembled and prepared the supplies and equipment needed, and was able to identify all equipment by name. Tested suction apparatus and the light on the scopes.				
4. Identified the patient and explained the procedure.				
5. Prepared the patient for the examination: • Had the patient void; saved a specimen if needed. • Had patient disrobe and put on patient gown. • Positioned patient in the knee-chest position or Sim's position, as requested. • Draped the patient.				
6. Assisted the physician as required during the examination (supplied or handed supplies and equipment to the physician as needed).				
7. Assisted the patient during the examination, giving reassurance and support; observed the patient for any unusual reaction.				
8. Provided for the patient's comfort at the conclusion of the examination by assisting to a supine position, removing drapes, answering questions, providing any further instructions, and helping the patient dress.				
9. Carried out the physician's order for additional examinations or tests. If specimens were obtained, donned disposable single-use exam gloves and prepared them properly to be sent to the laboratory.				
10. Wearing gloves collected, disposed of, cleaned, returned, and replaced all used equipment and supplies.				
11. Removed gloves and washed hands.				
12. Recorded on the patient's chart: date, hour, procedure, source and disposal of specimens (when obtained), results (where applicable), condition and of the patient (when pertinent) and signature.				

Checklist	S or NA*	U	NO	Comment
13. Completed the procedure in the time limit assigned by the instructor.				

Total Satisfactory Points _____

Comments

Student's signature:_____ Instructor's signature: _____

Date: _____

*S or NA, Satisfactory or not applicable; U, unsatisfactory; NO, not observed.

PERFORMANCE CHECKLIST: Preparing for and assisting with a pelvic exam and a Papanicolaou smear

DIRECTIONS: Evaluate student performance of each procedure using the following checklist. When you evaluate "not applicable," "unsatisfactory," or "not observed," please comment.

Checklist	S or NA*	U	NO	Comment
1. Washed hands. **Use appropriate Personal Protective Equipment (PPE) as dictated by facility.**				
2. Assembled and prepared the necessary equipment and instruments needed, and prepared the room. Identified the instruments by name.				
3. Identified the patient and explained the procedure. Reassured the patient.				
4. Prepared the patient for the examination:				
a. Had the patient void; saved the specimen if needed				
b. Took vital signs if required				
c. Had patient remove clothing from waist down; left shoes on				
d. Positioned the patient on the examining table in a dorsal-recumbent or lithotomy position				
e. Draped the patient				
5. Called the physician.				
6. Assisted the physician as required (supplied or handed supplies and equipment to the physician as needed; received *or* assisted in the preparation of the slides. Wore disposable single-use exam gloves if handling slides.				
7. Assisted the patient as required during and after the examination.				
8. Wearing gloves collected, disposed of, cleaned, returned, and replaced all used equipment as needed.				
9. Prepared specimens properly to be sent to the laboratory.				
10. Removed gloves and washed hands.				
11. Did any recording required completely and accurately.				
12. Completed the procedure in the time limit assigned by the instructor.				

Total Satisfactory Points _____

Comments

Student's signature:_____ Instructor's signature: _____
Date: _____
*S or NA, Satisfactory or not applicable; U, unsatisfactory; NO, not observed.

PERFORMANCE CHECKLIST: Measuring distance visual acuity with the Snellen eye chart

DIRECTIONS: Evaluate student performance of each procedure using the following checklist. When you evaluate "not applicable," "unsatisfactory," or "not observed," please comment.

Checklist	S or NA*	U	NO	Comment
1. Washed hands. **Use appropriate Personal Protective Equipment (PPE) as dictated by facility.**				
2. Prepared room; determined distance of 20 feet from the chart where patient is to be positioned.				
3. Assembled supplies and equipment.				
4. Identified the patient and explained the procedure.				
5. Positioned patient comfortably (sitting or standing) 20 feet from the eye chart.				
6. Positioned the center of the Snellen eye chart at the patient's eye level.				
7. Instructed the patient to cover the left eye with opaque card or eye cover, and to keep the left eye open.				
8. Instructed the patient to use the right eye and to orally identify one row at a time on the chart as the student pointed to each row, starting at row 20/70 (or several lines above row 20/20).				
9. Proceeded down the chart if the patient identified the 20/70 row, or proceeded up the chart if the patient was unable to identify the 20/70 row.				
10. Continued testing until the smallest row of letters that the patient could read was reached.				
11. Provided instructions to the patient during the test, and observed for any unusual reaction(s).				
12. Recorded the results of visual acuity on a piece of paper.				
13. Instructed the patient to cover the right eye and to keep it open.				
14. Measured visual acuity of the left eye using steps 8 through 12.				
15. Gave further instructions to the patient as required.				
16. Returned equipment and left room neat and clean.				
17. Recorded the date, procedure, results, and signature on the patient's chart.				
18. Completed the procedure in the time limit assigned by the instructor, such as 10 minutes.				

Total Satisfactory Points _____

Comments

Student's signature:_____ Instructor's signature: _____

Date: _____

*S or NA, Satisfactory or not applicable; U, unsatisfactory; NO, not observed.

PERFORMANCE CHECKLIST: Determining color vision using the Ishihara plates

DIRECTIONS: Evaluate student performance of each procedure using the following checklist. When you evaluate "not applicable," "unsatisfactory," or "not observed," please comment.

Checklist	S or NA*	U	NO	Comment
1. Washed hands. **Use appropriate Personal Protective Equipment (PPE) as dictated by facility.**				
2. Assembled and prepared equipment.				
3. Identified the patient and explained the procedure.				
4. Positioned the patient sitting comfortably in a room well lit by natural daylight.				
5. Held the first plate 30 inches away from the patient and at a right angle to the patient. Had the patient identify the number on the plate and recorded the results.				
6. Had the patient continue to identify the numbers on all of the plates that student displayed.				
7. Recorded the patient's answer after each plate was shown. The plate number and the patient's answer must be recorded together. For example: Plate 5:21. When the patient could not identify a number on the plate, recorded the result as "X." For example: Plate 2:X.				
8. Assisted the patient as needed when the test was completed.				
9. Returned the color plates to a storage area designated for the plates. Kept the book of plates closed when not in use.				
10. Completed the procedure in the time limit assigned by the instructor.				

Total Satisfactory Points _____

Comments

Student's signature: _____ Instructor's signature: _____

Date: _____

*S or NA, Satisfactory or not applicable; U, unsatisfactory; NO, not observed.

PERFORMANCE CHECKLIST: Measuring the weight of an infant

DIRECTIONS: Evaluate student performance of each procedure using the following checklist. When you evaluate "not applicable," "unsatisfactory," or "not observed," please comment.

Checklist	S or NA*	U	NO	Comment
1. Washed hands. **Use appropriate Personal Protective Equipment (PPE) as dictated by facility.**				
2. Identified the infant.				
3. Explained the procedure to the parent/caregiver.				
4. Placed a clean impervious paper on the scale basket.				
5. Balanced the scale.				
6. Undressed the infant (or had the parent undress the infant).				
7. Gently laid or sat the infant in the basket of the scale.				
8. Protected the infant from falling. Placed hand over the infant if lying down.				
9. Adjusted the pound weight, then the ounce weight on the scale.				
10. Read the weight in pounds and ounces.				
11. Returned the weights to zero.				
12. Removed the infant from the scale.				
13. Recorded the infant's weight, time, date, infant's age, and your signature on the patient's chart.				
14. Removed and discarded paper covering the scale.				
15. Washed hands.				
16. Completed the procedure in the time limit assigned by the instructor.				

Total Satisfactory Points _____

Comments

Student's signature: _____ Instructor's signature: _____
Date: _____
*S or NA, Satisfactory or not applicable; U, unsatisfactory; NO, not observed.

PERFORMANCE CHECKLIST: Measuring the length of an infant

DIRECTIONS: Evaluate student performance of each procedure using the following checklist. When you evaluate "not applicable," "unsatisfactory," or "not observed," please comment.

Checklist	S or NA*	U	NO	Comment
1. Washed hands. **Use appropriate Personal Protective Equipment (PPE) as dictated by facility.**				
2. Identified the infant.				
3. Explained the procedure to the parent/caregiver.				
4. If needed, solicit the parent's help in supporting the infant.				
5. Placed the infant on a clean disposable drape on the examining table. The infant should be on the back.				
6. Placed the vertex (top) of the infant's head at the beginning of the measuring tape.				
7. Grasped the knees and gently pushed them toward the table so that the infant's legs were fully extended.				
8. Took the measurements from the heels of the feet with the toes pointing upward.				
9. Provided for the infant's support and safety.				
10. Recorded the infant's length, date, time, infant's age, and your signature in the patient's chart.				
11. Recorded the infant's length on the growth chart when required.				
12. Completed the procedure in the time limit assigned by the instructor.				

Total Satisfactory Points _____

Comments

Student's signature:_____ Instructor's signature: _____

Date: _____

*S or NA, Satisfactory or not applicable; U, unsatisfactory; NO, not observed.

PERFORMANCE CHECKLIST: Guthrie Test—a blood test to screen infants for PKU

DIRECTIONS: Evaluate student performance of each procedure using the following checklist. When you evaluate "not applicable," "unsatisfactory," or "not observed," please comment.

Checklist	S or NA*	U	NO	Comment
1. Washed hands. **Use appropriate Personal Protective Equipment (PPE) as dictated by facility.**				
2. Assembled and prepared equipment and test card, and prepared room.				
3. Identified the infant and explained the procedure and purpose of the test to the parent/caregiver.				
4. Donned disposable single-use exam gloves.				
5. Placed the infant prone on a flat surface. Made the heel accessible.				
6. Grasped infant's heel; cleansed with an alcohol sponge.				
7. Maintained hold of the infant's heel and took a sterile lancet to puncture the side of the heel at a right angle.				
8. Wiped away the first drop of blood.				
9. Collected the next drops of blood in the circles on the special test filter paper. Filled each of the circles on the test card with blood.				
10. Applied pressure with cotton ball to the puncture site.				
11. Observed infant and attended to the infant's needs as necessary.				
12. Removed gloves and washed hands.				
13. Allowed test card to dry on nonabsorbent surface.				
14. Recorded the date, time, procedure, and any observations made, and signature on the patient's chart.				
15. Placed the *dry* test care in the protective envelope and sent it to the laboratory within 48 hours.				
16. Completed the procedure in the time limit assigned by the instructor.				

Total Satisfactory Points ———

Comments

Student's signature: ——————————— Instructor's signature: ———————————
Date: ———————————
*S or NA, Satisfactory or not applicable; U, unsatisfactory; NO, not observed.

Evaluation of student's technique   Name: _____   Date: _____

	Satisfactory*		Unsatisfactory**		
	Very Good	Good	Fair	Poor	Score
• Positioning and draping	☐	☐	☐	☐	_____
• Complete physical examination including a vaginal and rectal examination	☐	☐	☐	☐	_____
• Proctosigmoido-scopy	☐	☐	☐	☐	_____
• Snellen eye chart	☐	☐	☐	☐	_____
• Pelvic examination and Pap smear					
• Color vision examination	☐	☐	☐	☐	_____
• Weight of an infant	☐	☐	☐	☐	_____
• Length of an infant	☐	☐	☐	☐	_____
• Guthrie test—blood test to screen infants for PKU	☐	☐	☐	☐	_____

Very good = Perfect
Good   = Sufficient
Fair   = Not acceptable requires more practice
Poor   = Totally unacceptable
Pass*   = Satisfactory
Fail** = Unsatisfactory

Comments:

ANSWERS
Fill-in

1. a. To allow for better visibility and accessibility for the physician during the examination of the patient.
    b. To provide support for the patient when being examined.
2. a. To avoid unnecessary exposure of the patient's body during an examination, thereby protecting the patient's modesty
    b. To contribute to the patient's feeling of being cared for, which helps the patient relax
    c. To provide some comfort and warmth and avoid chilling
3. Lithotomy
4. Dorsal-recumbent
5. Jackknife or proctological
6. Knee-chest; along the side of the head
7. Sim's or left lateral
8. Trendelenburg
9. Supine
10. Prone
11. Fowler's
12. Semi-Fowler's
13. a. Examination table covered with a clean sheet
    b. Patient gown, either cloth or paper
    c. Draping material, drape sheet, small towel
    d. Watch with a sweep second hand
    e. Stethoscope
    f. Thermometer
    g. Sphygmomanometer
    h. Scale with height measure rod
    i. Tape measure
    j. Tuning fork
    k. Percussion or reflex hammer
    l. Tongue blades
    m. Laryngeal mirror
    n. Head mirror
    o. Flashlight and/or gooseneck lamp
    p. Otoscope
    q. Ophthalmoscope
    r. Nasal speculum
    s. Safety pin
    t. Tissues
    u. Cotton balls
    v. Alcohol or prepackaged alcohol swabs
    w. Urine specimen bottle
    x. Laboratory request form
    y. X-ray request form
    z. Emesis basin or waste container used for soiled equipment and/or waste
14. Anoscope
15. Applicator
16. Biopsy forceps
17. Bronchoscope
18. Cystoscope
19. Endoscope
20. Insufflator
21. Laryngeal mirror
22. Laryngoscope
23. Nasal speculum
24. Ophthalmoscope
25. Otoscope
26. Percussion hammer
27. Proctoscope
28. sigmoidoscope
29. speculum
30. Sim's vaginal speculum
31. Stethoscope
32. Tongue blade
33. Tuning fork
34. Tonometer
35. Sitting
36. Supine
37. Lithotomy
38. Inspection of the vulva, vagina, and cervix for any abnormalities, and a bimanual palpation of the uterus, fallopian tubes, and ovaries. The physician notes the size, shape, position, and consistency of the uterus and if any masses are present in the uterus, fallopian tubes, or ovaries.
39. To detect precancerous conditions or any unusual cell growth, and to detect cancer of the cervix or uterus. The value of the test is that it can detect potential problems early so that they can be treated.
40. Should not
41. To detect polyps, early cancer, lesions, inflammatory conditions, and hemorrhoids. In addition, examination of the rectum can show how far the uterus is displaced and if there are any masses in the rectum or pelvic region in a female and the size, any enlargement, and texture of the prostate gland in a male.
42. a. A laxative the evening before (type and amount as prescribed by the physician)
    b. Only liquids for breakfast
    c. Tap water or saline enemas until the return is clear, usually 1 hour before the examination *NOTE*: Enemas are usually avoided for patients who have colitis or bleeding from the rectum or have Crohn's disease.
43. Knee-chest *or* Sim's *or* left lateral
44. Neurologic
45. Snellen
46. Glaucoma

47. At only 20 feet what the normal eye can read at 50 feet.
48. The stronger eye usually compensates for the weaker eye.
49. a. Change in bowel or bladder habits
    b. A sore that does not heal
    c. Unusual bleeding or discharge
    d. Thickening or lump in breast or elsewhere
    e. Indigestion or difficulty in swallowing
    f. Obvious change in wart or mole
    g. Nagging cough or hoarseness
       IF YOU HAVE A WARNING SIGNAL, SEE YOUR DOCTOR
50. a. Date
    b. Physician's name and address
    c. Patient's name and age
    d. Source of specimen
    e. Test(s) requested
51. Gynecology, gynecologist
52. a. A breast examination performed by the physician and instructions to the patient on how to perform a breast self-examination (BSE)
    b. A pelvic examination
    c. A Pap smear
    d. Individual cultures and smears for suspected vaginal infections.
53. Prostate; 55
54. A digital rectal examination; a blood test, the prostate specific antigen (PSA)
55. 40, proctoscopy
56. Is
57. Is not
58. Invade distant or neighboring organs or tissues, lymph, blood
59. Snellen Big E
60. 14
61. A defect is suspected; when employment requires a person to be able to differentiate colors such as is required in certain vehicle operation and industrial jobs
62. Ishihara
63. 13 or more
64. Chorionic villi sampling (CVS); amniocentesis
    a. women age 35 years or older
    b. women who have previously borne a child with chromosomal abnormalities
    c. women who are likely to bear a child with other genetic abnormalities, as they are known carriers of a detectable genetic disorder including sickle cell anemia, Tay Sachs disease, and Thalassemia.
65. 2; four-; six-
66. Pediatrics, pediatrician
67. well-child; sick-child
68. Monitoring and comparing each child's growth and development with that of other children within the same age group using established norms and expectations
69. prevent, detect, stop
70. age, development, level of wellness or illness, past experience of the child with the health care system
71. 18, 20, 7, 7½
72. a. length or height
    b. weight
    c. head circumference
    d. chest circumference
73. baby, pediatric
74. top of the head to the heels of the feet when the child is lying flat and straight and toes pointing upward
75. a. Diphtheria and tetanus toxoid combined with tetanus vaccine (DPT). This is given intramuscularly.
    b. Diphtheria, tetanus toxoid. This is given intramuscularly.
    c. Trivalent oral polio vaccine. This is given by mouth.
    d. Measles (rubeola), mumps (parotitis) and rubella (German measles). This is given subcutaneously.
    e. Haemophilus b polysaccharide vaccine (also called hemophilus influenza type b vaccine). This is given intramuscularly.
    f. Hepatitis B vaccine (in late 1992 specialists started to recommend hepatitis B vaccine for all children under 6 years of age). This is given intramuscularly.
76. a. Type, manufacturer, and lot number of the vaccine
    b. Date of administration
    c. Name, address, and title of the person administering the vaccine
       Other information:
    a. The site and route of administration
    b. The expiration date of the vaccine

Multiple Choice

1. C
2. A
3. B
4. D
5. C
6. D
7. C
8. A
9. D

10. B
11. B
12. A
13. D
14. B
15. A
16. C
17. A
18. C
19. B
20. D
21. C
22. A
23. B
24. C
25. D

Labeling

1. a. Dorsal-recumbent
   b. Lithotomy
   c. Knee-chest
   d. Sim's or left lateral
   e. Trendelenburg
   f. Prone
   g. Fowler's
   h. Semi-Fowler's
2. a. Hirschman anoscope
   b. Tuning forks
   c. Otoscope
   d. Ear specula to be used with an otoscope
   e. Tape measure
   f. Tischler cervical biopsy punch forceps
   g. Headband and mirror set
   h. Neurological pin wheel
   i. Laryngeal mirror
   j. Insufflator
   k. Percussion hammer
   l. Graves vaginal speculum
   m. Ophthalmoscope
   n. Kellyproctoscope
   o. Nasal speculum
   p. Schiotz tonometers
   q. Schiotz tonometers
   r. Yeoman biopsy forceps
   s. Laryngoscope

Unit 5

Infection Control: Practices of Medical Asepsis and Sterilization

SUGGESTED ACTIVITIES

1. Practice wrapping different items for sterilization using the different equipment that you have at your school.
2. Note the infection control techniques used at the facility where you do your work experience. Compare your findings with that of others in a class discussion.

STUDY QUESTIONS
Fill-In

In the blanks provided, write the answers that best complete the sentences:

1. A condition caused by the multiplication of pathogenic microorganisms that have invaded the body of a susceptible host is called a(n) _____ _____.

2. The interval of time between the invasion of a pathogen into the body and the appearance of the first symptoms of disease is called the _____ period.

3. When an item is free from all microorganisms or contamination, it is said to be _____ .

4. _____ is the degree of ability of a pathogen to produce disease.

5. The term _____ implies the study of pathogens and involves identification and development of effective methods of control or elimination.

6. The classifications or divisions of microscopic life include _____ , _____ , _____ , _____ , and _____ .

7. State the goals of infection control.

   a. _____

   b. _____

   c. _____

8. Name six factors essential for the development of the infectious process.

   a. _____

   b. _____

   c. _____

   d. _____

   e. _____

   f. _____

9. Five diseases that are caused by viruses are _____ , _____ , _____ , _____ , and _____ .

10. Name five types of bacteria and cite examples of some diseases they cause.

   a. _____

   b. _____

c. _____

d. _____

e. _____

11. Two diseases that are caused by fungi are

_____ and _____ .

12. Two diseases that are caused by protozoa are

_____ and _____ .

13. _____ is term given to an animal disease that is transmissible to humans.

14. Explain the routes pathogens commonly take to exit their reservoirs.

a. _____

b. _____

c. _____

d. _____

e. _____

f. _____

g. _____

15. Two means of transmission of a pathogen from the

reservoir to a new host include _____

and _____ transmission.

16. The body's resistance level to pathogens is influenced by the general health status of the individual and other related circumstances, such as the following:

a. _____

b. _____

c. _____

d. _____

e. _____

f. _____

g. _____

17. _____ , the resistance of the body to pathogenic microorganisms and their toxins, occurs as a result of the antigen-antibody reaction.

18. List four types of immunity:

a. _____

b. _____

c. _____

d. _____

19. Name five classical local signs and symptoms of infection.

a. _____

b. _____

c. _____

d. _____

e. _____

20. Name four systemic signs and symptoms of infection.

a. _____

b. _____

c. _____

d. _____

21. Describe twelve medical aseptic practices to follow when working with patients.

a. _____

b. _____

c. _____

d. _____

e. _____

f. _____

g. _____

h. _____

i. _____

j. _____

k. _____

l. _____

22. When working in a medical setting, the time involved to wash the hands, wrists, and forearms well should be _____ minutes; _____ minutes if the hands are highly contaminated.

23. _____ refers to the destruction of microorganisms after they leave the body, and includes those practices that help reduce the number and transfer of pathogens.

24. _____ refers to the destruction of all microorganisms before they enter the body. The goal of _____ is to prevent infection or the introduction of microorganisms into the body.

25. _____, the first step that must always be done before items can be reliably disinfected or sterilized, is a process of cleansing and scrubbing items with agents such as water and soap, detergents, or chemicals.

26. _____ involves methods that destroy *most* infectious microorganisms. Agents employed include various types of chemical germicides and boiling water or flowing steam.

27. _____ is the complete destruction of all forms of microscopic life.

28. Name five sterilization methods.
    a. _____
    b. _____
    c. _____
    d. _____
    e. _____

29. The _____ is the most commonly used sterilizing method in a physician's office.

30. The _____ _____ attained is the sterilizing influence that destroys the microorganisms in the autoclave.

31. Wrapped surgical instruments must be autoclaved for _____ minutes at 250° F for all microorganisms to be killed.

32. Unwrapped instruments must be autoclaved for _____ minutes once the temperature has reached 250° F.

33. Sterilization indicators are used to _____ _____ and _____.

34. List three items that may be disinfected with a chemical solution.
    a. _____
    b. _____
    c. _____

35. When disinfecting instruments with boiling water, the hinges or clamps must be left (open *or* closed) _____.

36. The purpose of sterilization is to _____ _____.

37. Steam sterilization may be adequately accomplished at any temperature above _____, provided the related time period of exposure is used.

38. Articles placed in an autoclave for sterilization should be placed as (tightly *or* loosely) _____ as possible inside the chamber.

39. Linen and dressing packs must be placed in a _____ position for sterilization in an autoclave.

40. Cite five causes of inefficient sterilization in an autoclave.
    a. _____
    b. _____
    c. _____
    d. _____
    e. _____

Multiple Choice

Write the letter of the correct answer in the blank provided. There is only *one* correct answer.

_____ 1. A substance capable of inhibiting the growth or action of microorganisms without necessarily killing them, and is generally safe for use on body tissues is called a(n):
   A. Disinfectant.
   B. Antiseptic.
   C. Antibiotic.
   D. Germicide.

_____ 2. An infection that is of rapid onset with severe symptoms, and that usually subsides within a relatively short period of time is referred to as a(n) _____ infection.
   A. acute
   b. chronic
   c. latent
   d. localized

_____ 3. The interval of time between the invasion of a pathogen into the body and the appearance of the first symptom of disease is the _____ period.
   A. Incubation
   B. Prodromal
   C. Acute
   D. Recovery

_____ 4. The most common temperature and pressure used to sterilize equipment in the autoclave is:
   A. Temperature 121° F; pressure 15 pounds per square inch.
   B. Temperature 150° F; pressure 15 pounds per square inch.
   C. Temperature 225° F; pressure 15 pounds per square inch.
   D. Temperature 250° F; pressure is 15 pounds per square inch.

_____ 5. Sterile items wrapped in cloth or paper can safely be stored and considered to remain sterile for a period up to:
   A. 7 to 14 days.
   B. 14 to 21 days.
   C. 21 to 30 days.
   D. 28 to 35 days.

_____ 6. Articles sterilized in the dry heat oven must be sterilized for at least:
   A. 30 minutes at 250° F.
   B. 60 minutes at 320° F.
   C. 45 minutes at 160° F.
   D. 50 minutes at 212° F.

_____ 7. Articles disinfected with boiling water must be exposed to *boiling* water for:
   A. 30 to 40 minutes.
   B. 30 minutes.
   C. 15 to 20 minutes.
   D. 5 minutes.

_____ 8. Wrapped surgical instruments and wrapped syringes and needles must be autoclaved at the correct temperature for _____ for sterilization to occur.
   A. 10 minutes
   B. 15 minutes
   C. 20 minutes
   D. 30 minutes

_____ 9. Unwrapped instruments must be autoclaved at the correct temperature for _____ for sterilization to occur.
   A. 10 minutes.
   B. 15 minutes
   C. 20 minutes
   D. 30 minutes

_____ 10. _____ is the complete destruction of all forms of microscopic life on objects.
   A. Sterilization
   B. Disinfection
   C. Sanitation
   D. Medical asepsis

_____ 11. Chemical solutions are generally used for sterilizing only the following:
   A. Rubber goods
   B. Forceps
   C. Glass items
   D. Heat sensitive items, such as delicate cutting instruments

12. When you are disinfecting an instrument by the boiling method, you should start timing the exposure period:
   A. As soon as you lower the instrument into the water.
   B. Once the water is boiling vigorously.
   C. 1 minute after you turn on the boiler.
   D. As soon as you close the lid of the boiler.

13. When removing a dry pack from the autoclave, you observe that the sterilization indicator has not changed color. Your next step would be to:
   A. Replace the pack in the autoclave and resterilize it.
   B. Unwrap, then rewrap the pack, place a new sterilization indicator on the pack, and place it in the autoclave to sterilize it.
   C. Place a new sterilization indicator on the pack and sterilize it.
   D. Replace the pack in the autoclave, but place it in a different position.

14. Unused unwrapped sterile items must be reprocessed and resterilized _____ before being used.
   A. Once a week
   B. Once a month
   C. Every 2 weeks
   D. Every 2 months

15. The process of cleaning and scrubbing items with agents such as soap and water or other detergents before you autoclave the items is referred to as:
   A. Sanitization.
   B. Disinfection.
   C. Sterilization.
   D. Antisepsis.

16. _____ immunity develops when antigens are introduced into the body.
   A. Active
   B. Passive
   C. Natural
   D. Congenital

17. _____ immunity develops when ready-made antibodies are introduced into the body.
   A. Active
   B. Passive
   C. Natural
   D. Congenital

18. _____ immunity results from being a carrier, recovering from or having a disease, or having an atypical or subclinical case of the disease.
   A. Artificial passive
   B. Artificial active
   C. Natural active
   D. Inherited active

19. _____ immunity is obtained by injecting various products, which are usually prepared commercially to produce a high level of antibodies immediately.
   A. Active
   B. Passive
   C. Artificial active
   D. Artificial passive

20. _____ immunity is acquired through vaccinations with inactivated or attenuated organisms.
   A. Artificial passive
   B. Natural active
   C. Passive
   D. Artificial active

21. Name the equipment that should be worn when cleaning contaminated instruments.
   A. Rubber gloves
   B. Masks and protective eyewear
   C. Plastic apron
   D. A and C
   E. A, B, and C

22. Waste containers should be cleaned _____ with a disinfectant solution.
   A. Once a day
   B. Once a week
   C. Once a month
   D. Every 2 months
   E. Every 6 months

PERFORMANCE TEST

In a skills laboratory, a simulation of a joblike environment, the medical assistant student is to demonstrate skill in performing the following activities without reference to source materials. Time limits for the performance of each procedure are to be assigned by the instructor.

1. Given soap, perform a medical aseptic handwash.
2. Given reusable syringes, and needles, and instruments, sanitize these items and then wrap them for sterilization.
3. Given wrapped supplies for sterilization, position these correctly in the chamber of the sterilizer.
4. Given various types of sterilizers and the manufacturer's instructions, sterilize wrapped and unwrapped items, correctly remove them from the sterilizer on completion of the sterilizing cycle, and determine if sterilization has been effective.
5. Given thermometers, a percussion hammer, and a variety of blunt instruments, correctly disinfect these items using chemicals; disinfect blunt instruments using boiling water.

The student is expected to perform these skills with 100% accuracy 90% of the time (9 out of 10 times).

PERFORMANCE CHECKLIST: Handwashing technique

DIRECTIONS: Evaluate student performance of each procedure using the following checklist. When you evaluate "not applicable," "unsatisfactory," or "not observed," please comment.

Checklist	S or NA*	U	NO	Comment
1. Removed jewelry except plain wedding band. Removed watch or moved it up.				
2. Stood in front of, but not touching, the sink.				
3. Adjusted the water flow and temperature.				
4. Wetted hands, and applied soap.				
5. Washed hands well and rinsed; kept hands and forearms at elbow level or below and hands pointed down.				
6. Washed wrists and forearms.				
7. If used, rinsed soap bar, and dropped on a rack, into the dish without touching the dish.				
8. Rinsed hands, wrists, and forearms under running water.				
9. Cleaned fingernails (at least once a day), and rinsed well.				
10. Repeated the wash if hands were highly contaminated.				
11. Dried hands, wrists, and forearms well.				
12. Turned off water faucet using a paper towel.				

Total Satisfactory Points _____

Comments

Student's signature:_____ Instructor's signature: _____

Date: _____

*S or NA, Satisfactory or not applicable; U, unsatisfactory; NO, not observed.

PERFORMANCE CHECKLIST: Sanitizing, wrapping, and positioning instruments for sterilization

DIRECTIONS: Evaluate student performance of each procedure using the following checklist. When you evaluate "not applicable," "unsatisfactory," or "not observed," please comment.

Checklist	S or NA*	U	NO	Comment
1. Donned disposable single-use exam gloves and removed the instruments to work area.				
2. Put on a plastic apron or gown and face shield or eye protection and bulk rinsed in a solution of water and a blood solvent, low-sudsing detergent, or germicide.				
3. Rinsed in fresh water.				
4. Scrubbed each instrument thoroughly with a brush and warm detergent solution.				
5. Rinsed completely with hot water.				
6. Removed gloves and washed hands.				
7. Dried the instruments, and checked for working condition.				
8. Placed all instruments to be used together on a diagonal in the center of a square of muslin or special sterilization disposable paper.				
9. Folded the material up from the bottom, doubling back a small corner.				
10. Folded the right, then the left edges over, leaving the corners doubled back.				
11. Folded the pack up from the bottom and secured envelope style.				
12. Wrapped pack in a second wrapper following steps 7 through 11 except now secured with pressure-sensitive tape or special sterilizing masking tape (Figure 5-1).				
13. Dated and labeled the pack according to contents.				
14. Placed the pack in the sterilizer chamber correctly so that steam could flow between and penetrate the packs (placed jars or similar containers on their sides, hard packs on the bottom).				

Total Satisfactory Points _____

Comments

Student's signature:_____   Instructor's signature: _____

Date: _____

*S or NA, Satisfactory or not applicable; U, unsatisfactory; NO, not observed.

Figure 5-1

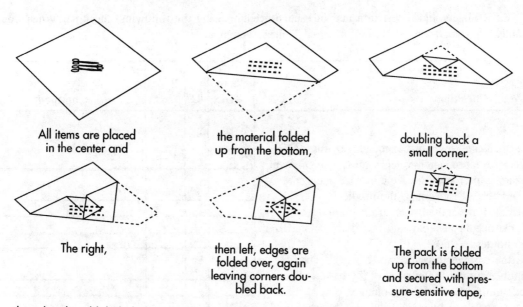

All items are placed
in the center and

the material folded
up from the bottom,

doubling back a
small corner.

The right,

then left, edges are
folded over, again
leaving corners dou-
bled back.

The pack is folded
up from the bottom
and secured with pres-
sure-sensitive tape,

then dated and labeled according to its contents. The pack should be firm enough for handling, but loose enough to permit proper circulation of steam. The materials included in each pack can be varied to suit the needs of each office, but the same wrapping pattern should be followed for all packs.

PERFORMANCE CHECKLIST: Sanitizing, wrapping, and positioning syringes and needles in the sterilizer

DIRECTIONS: Evaluate student performance of each procedure using the following checklist. When you evaluate "not applicable," "unsatisfactory," or "not observed," please comment.

Checklist	S or NA*	U	NO	Comment
1. Wore disposable single-use exam gloves, plastic apron, and eye protection when sanitizing equipment.				
2. Immediately after use, filled the syringe with cool water and flushed it through the needle.				
3. Disassembled the unit.				
4. Placed the needle in a tray and then into the sterilizer for 30 minutes at 250° F (121° C).				
5. Soaked the syringe in water and detergent, and thoroughly brushed the interior of the barrel.				
6. Cleaned the inside tip and the plunger.				
7. Flushed the syringe twice with tap water, once with distilled water.				
8. After 30 minutes exposure time, removed the needles from the sterilizer.				
9. Cleaned inside the needle hub.				
10. Passed a stylet through the interior of the needle several times.				
11. Checked the needle point for sharpness and/or snags.				
12. Cleaned the exterior of the needle.				
13. Rinsed the hub and the needle exterior well under running water.				
14. With a syringe, flushed tap water through the needle interior.				
15. Rinsed the exterior and interior of the needle with distilled water.				
16. Labeled a disposable sterilization paper bag with the date and the size of the syringe.				
17. Placed matching separated and wrapped plunger and syringe barrel inside the bag.				
18. Folded the top of the bag, and sealed securely.				
19. When the needle was to be sterilized with the syringe:				
a. Placed the needle in a disposable paper form.				
b. Labeled the bag with the size of syringe, needle, and the date.				
c. Placed the needle in the bag with the syringe.				
d. Folded the top of the bag, and sealed it securely.				

PERFORMANCE CHECKLIST: Sanitizing, wrapping, and positioning syringes and needles in the sterilizer (continued)

Checklist	S or NA*	U	NO	Comment
20. When the needle was to be sterilized individually, placed it in a glass tube with constricted sides, or a test tube with gauze or cotton padding in the bottom, and topped with a gauze cotton, or autoclave tape.				
21. Placed a disposable bag with contents horizontally on the tray of the sterilizer; placed a constriction tube with a needle horizontally on the sterilizer tray for the sterilization cycle.				

Total Satisfactory Points _____

Comments

Student's signature:_____ Instructor's signature: _____

Date: _____

*S or NA, Satisfactory or not applicable; U, unsatisfactory; NO, not observed.

PERFORMANCE CHECKLIST: Disinfecting/sterilizing with chemical solution

DIRECTIONS: Evaluate student performance of each procedure using the following checklist. When you evaluate "not applicable," "unsatisfactory," or "not observed," please comment.

Checklist	S or NA*	U	NO	Comment
1. Sanitized items as for sterilization by autoclave.				
2. Poured chemical solution into designated container with an airtight lid; diluted chemical if necessary, according to manufacturer's instructions.				
3. Completely immersed item(s) in solution, and closed cover of container.				
4. Left for required time (time will vary from 20 minutes to 3 hours or longer depending on the solution used).				
5. Removed the tray from the container, and rinsed items in a pan of sterile distilled water before using.				
6. Removed items for use from the tray using sterile transfer forceps.				
7. Changed the solution in the container every 7 to 14 days or as recommended by the manufacturer.				
8. Items such as percussion hammers and stethoscopes were disinfected by wiping these instruments off with a germicide or antiseptic solution.				

Total Satisfactory Points _____

Comments

Student's signature: _____ Instructor's signature: _____

Date: _____

*S or NA, Satisfactory or not applicable; U, unsatisfactory; NO, not observed.

PERFORMANCE CHECKLIST: Disinfection with boiling water

DIRECTIONS: Evaluate student performance of each procedure using the following checklist. When you evaluate "not applicable," "unsatisfactory," or "not observed," please comment.

Checklist	S or NA*	U	NO	Comment
1. Filled the boiler half full with water.				
2. Cleaned items thoroughly.				
3. Positioned items on a tray in the boiler, hinges or clamps open, jars and so forth on their sides.				
4. Lowered the tray to completely immerse items in the water.				
5. Closed the lid, and turned the power switch on.				
6. When the water was boiling, started timing the exposure period for 15 to 20 minutes.				
7. When the cycle was completed, stood back or to the side, and opened the lid of the boiler.				
8. Allowed the items to cool.				
9. Removed and dried the items.				
10. Stored the items in a designated place, or used immediately.				
11. When the boiler was used for disinfecting items because of the absence of an autoclave or other sterilizer, removed items from the boiler with a sterile transfer forceps, dried with a sterile towel, and transferred to a sterile field for immediate use.				

Total Satisfactory Points _____

Comments

Student's signature:_____ Instructor's signature: _____
Date: _____
*S or NA, Satisfactory or not applicable; U, unsatisfactory; NO, not observed.

Evaluation of student's technique   Name: _____   Date: _____

	Satisfactory*	Unsatisfactory**			
	Very Good	Good	Fair	Poor	Score

- Handwashing ☐ ☐ ☐ ☐ _____   Very good = Perfect
- Preparing instru-   Good   = Sufficient
  ments for sterili-   Fair   = Not acceptable requires more practice
  zation ☐ ☐ ☐ ☐ _____   Poor   = Totally unacceptable
- Preparing syringes   Pass* = Satisfactory
  and needles for   Fail** = Unsatisfactory
  sterilization ☐ ☐ ☐ ☐ _____
- Disinfecting/
  sterilization with
  chemicals ☐ ☐ ☐ ☐ _____
- Disinfecting with
  boiling water ☐ ☐ ☐ ☐ _____

Comments:

ANSWERS
Fill-in

1. Infection
2. Incubation
3. Sterile
4. Virulence
5. Medical microbiology
6. Viruses, rickettsiae, bacteria, fungi, parasites
7. a. To prevent the spread of pathogenic microorganisms
   b. To attain a state of asepsis (absence of pathogens)
   c. To educate the public in ways that they too can help
8. a. A cause or an etiologic agent (pathogen)
   b. A source or a reservoir of the etiological agent
   c. A means of escape (portal of exit) of the etiological agent from the reservoir
   d. A means of transmission of the etiological agent from the reservoir to the new host
   e. A means of entry (portal of entry) of the etiologic agent into the new susceptible host
   f. A susceptible host
9. flu, poliomyelitis, colds, mumps, measles, rabies, smallpox, chickenpox, as well as hepatitis A, hepatitis B, and herpes simplex I and herpes simplex II
10. a. Staphylococci are readily found in pimples, boils, suture abscesses, and osteomyelitis.
    b. Streptococci are the cause of strep throat, rheumatic heart disease (RHD), scarlet fever, and septicemia.
    c. Diplococci cause gonorrhea, pneumonia, and meningitis.
    d. Bacilli cause tuberculosis (TB), typhoid and paratyphoid fever, tetanus (lockjaw), gas gangrene, bacillary dysentery, and diphtheria.
    e. Spirilla cause cholera, syphilis, and relapsing fever.
11. Some infections of the skin, such as athlete's foot and ringworm, thrush (an infection of the mouth and throat), and also some vaginal infections.
12. malaria, amebic dysentery, and trichomonas infections of the vagina
13. Zoonosis
14. a. Respiratory tract in secretions from the nose, nasal sinuses, nasopharynx, larynx, trachea, bronchial tree, and lungs
    b. Intestinal tract through discharge with the feces
    c. Urinary tract through discharge or in the urine
    d. Open lesions or discharges on the surface of the body, or skin or mucous membranes

e. Reproductive tract through discharges
    f. Blood
    g. Across the placenta
15. Direct and indirect
16. a. Amount of rest, sufficient or insufficient
    b. Dietary intake of nutritional foods, adequate or inadequate
    c. How the individual copes with stress
    d. Age of the individual (The young and aged are most susceptible to infection because of the immaturity of the immune system in the young and the decline in this system in the aged.)
    e. Presence of other disease processes in the body
    f. Condition of the external environment (such as poor living conditions)
    g. Influence of genetic traits (For example, people with diabetes mellitus and sickle cell anemia are more prone to some infections than other individuals.)
17. Immunity
18. a. Active
    b. Passive
    c. Natural
    d. Acquired or induced
19. a. Redness
    b. Heat
    c. Swelling
    d. Pain
    e. Limitation of function in the area
20. a. Leukocytosis (increased number of white blood cells in the blood)
    b. Fever
    c. Increased pulse rate
    d. Increased respiration rate
21. a. Wash your hands before and after handling supplies and equipment and before and after assisting with each patient.
    b. Handle all specimens as though they contain pathogens.
    c. Use disposable equipment when available, and dispose of it properly according to office policy. All equipment is considered contaminated after patient use.
    d. Clean nondisposable equipment before and after patient use.
    e. Use disposable single-use exam gloves when handling highly contaminated articles to protect yourself.
    f. Use clean or sterile equipment and supplies for each patient.
    g. Avoid contaminating uniform with used supplies to prevent the transfer of pathogens to yourself and to other patients.

h. Place damp or wet dressings, bandages, and cottonballs in a waterproof bag when discarding them to prevent the possible spread of infection to the individuals who handle the garbage.

i. Cover any break in your skin as a protective measure against self-infection.

j. Discard items that fall on the floor or clean them before using, because all floors are contaminated.

k. Use damp cloths for dusting or cleaning to avoid raising dust, which carries airborne microorganisms.

l. If you are unsure whether supplies are clean or sterile, do not use them until they have been cleaned or sterilized.

22. 1 to 2; 2 to 4
23. Medical asepsis
24. Surgical asepsis; surgical asepsis
25. Sanitation
26. Disinfection
27. Sterilization
28. a. Dry heat
    b. Moderately heated chemical gas mixtures
    c. Chemical agents
    d. Steam under pressure (autoclaves)
    e. Unsaturated chemical vapor (Chemiclaves)
29. Autoclave
30. High temperature
31. 30
32. 20
33. Indicate the effectiveness of the sterilization process; give assurance that the parameters of the sterilization process were met.
34. a. Thermometers
    b. Percussion hammers
    c. Laryngeal mirrors
35. Open
36. Completely destroy all living microorganisms
37. 212° F (100° C)
38. Loosely
39. Vertical
40. a. Faulty preparation of materials
    b. Improper loading of the sterilizer
    c. Faulty sterilizer
    d. Air in the sterilizer
    e. Wet steam

5. C
6. B
7. C
8. E
9. C
10. A
11. D
12. B
13. B
14. B
15. A
16. A
17. B
18. C
19. D
20. D
21. E
22. B

Multiple Choice

1. B
2. A
3. A
4. D

SANITIZING SYRINGES AND NEEDLES

Disposable syringes and needles have largely replaced the reusable units. However, if you are still using reusable units, special care must be taken before sterilizing the syringes and needles, because they are a common means of transmitting hepatitis B. **Remember to wear heavy rubber gloves over disposable gloves, a plastic apron or gown, and protective eyewear when cleaning all instruments.**

Procedure

1. Rinse immediately by filling the syringe with cool tap water and flushing it through the needle.
2. Disassemble the unit.
3. Place the needle in a separate tray; then put into the sterilizer for 30 minutes at 250° F.
4. Put syringe in water containing a low-sudsing, nonetching detergent, and thoroughly brush the interior of the syringe barrel.
5. Clean the inside of the tip and the plunger.
6. Flush the syringe twice with tap water and once with distilled water.
7. The syringe is now ready to be wrapped and sterilized.
8. Remove needles from sterilizer after the 30 minutes of exposure.
9. Clean the inside of the hub with a cotton-tipped applicator that is soaked with water and blood solvent or detergent solution.
10. Pass a stylet in and out of the inter (lumen) of the needle several times.
11. Check the point of the needle.

12. Thoroughly clean the exterior of the needle.
13. Rinse the hub and exterior of the needle well under running tap water.
14. Using a syringe, flush tap water through the interior of the needle twice.
15. Rinse both the exterior and the interior with distilled water

16. The needle is now ready to be wrapped and sterilized.

Rationale

Rinsing immediately prevents coagulation of materials in the syringe and needle.

Needles must first be decontaminated so they can be handled safely when cleaned.
All parts of the syringe must be cleaned to remove any foreign matter and contamination.

The needles are now decontaminated.

This removes any foreign matter or tissue left in the needle.
If it is damaged or dull, it must be resharpened and recleaned before sterilizing. Use a special whetstone or smooth oil stone (Arkansas stone) for sharpening. Directions for using these are provided by the manufacturer.

Both the exterior and the interior of the needle must be rinsed.
Rinsing is repeated with distilled water to ensure that all detergent is removed. Contaminants have been eliminated in distilled water.

SANITIZING RUBBER GOODS

All rubber goods must also be cleaned and some must be sterilized. Such items as hot water bottles, ice caps, and rubber sheets should be covered with a towel or sheet before being used in patient care. Because they normally do not come in direct contact with the patient, these items are not usually sterilized, but must be thoroughly washed, rinsed, and dried after each usage. Other rubber goods, such as gloves, catheters, and tubing require special care and sterilization. Immediately after use they should be washed in cold water, then washed in warm water and a low-sudsing detergent, rinsed thoroughly, dried, and wrapped for sterilization. **Always wear heavy rubber gloves over disposable gloves, a plastic apron or gown, and protective eyewear when cleaning equipment.**

Procedure

1. Immediately after use, wash in cold water.
2. Wash thoroughly in warm water with a low-sudsing detergent, and rinse.
3. Turn gloves inside out to wash and rinse again with fresh tape water.
4. Fill gloves with water or air and inspect for punctures and unremoved soil.
5. Dry the gloves; pat with a towel to remove excess moisture, then allow to air dry. When exposed side is dry, turn to expose the inner surface for drying.
6. The gloves are now ready to be wrapped for sterilization.

Rationale

Cold water will remove blood and other soiling.

Thorough rinsing is necessary to remove all detergent.

Water or air will leak out if any puncture hole is present.

WRAPPING REUSABLE SYRINGES AND NEEDLES

Syringes are best wrapped in special disposable paper bags or peel pouches that are available for sterilization.

Unit 6

Surgical Asepsis and Minor Surgery

SUGGESTED ACTIVITIES

1. Practice opening sterile packs of instruments and materials needed for minor surgery, and arranging this equipment for use.
2. Practice donning and removing disposable single-use exam gloves.
3. Practice pouring sterile solutions into a container on a sterile field.
4. Work with a partner and practice changing a dressing and taking a wound culture.
5. Work with a partner and practice applying different types of bandages. Note if the bandage appeared smooth and if it felt comfortable once it was applied.
6. Have you ever had minor surgery performed in a physician's office or clinic? What feelings do you have about that experience? How can you use that experience to give better care to patients that you encounter?

STUDY QUESTIONS
Fill-In

In the blanks provided, write the answers that best complete the sentences:

1. Surgical asepsis, more commonly referred to as

   _____ or _____ , is the practice used when an area and supplies in that area are to be made and kept sterile.

2. When in doubt about the sterility of an object, consider it _____.

3. Cite five basic rules to keep in mind when assisting with or performing a sterile procedure.

   a. _____

   b. _____

   c. _____

d. _____

e. _____

4. If a glove is punctured by a needle or instrument during a sterile procedure you should _____

   _____ .

5. The outer wrappings and edges of packs that contain sterile items (are *or* are not) _____ sterile.

6. What should be done with a sterile pack that had been opened but then not used? _____

   _____ .

7. When pouring sterile solutions the bottle should be held so that the label is facing _____ .

8. During certain procedures disposable single-use exam gloves are worn to _____

   _____ .

9. Give examples of minor surgical procedures that may be performed in the physician's office or clinic.

   a. _____

   b. _____

   c. _____

   d. _____

   e. _____

10. Local anesthesia refers to _____

    _____ .

11. Local anesthetics can be administered by

    or _____ by _____ .

12. The purpose of sutures is to _____

    _____ .

13. Absorbable sutures do not have to be removed
    from the body when used because they

    _____

    _____ .

14. An example of an absorbable suture material is

    _____ .

15. List five examples of nonabsorbable suture materi-
    als.

    a. _____

    b. _____

    c. _____

    d. _____

    e. _____

16. The thinnest type of suture material should be

    labeled as _____ .

17. The size and type of a suture material used in a

    procedure is determined by _____

    _____ .

18. Describe the responsibilities of the medical assis-
    tant during minor surgery.

    a. _____

    b. _____

    c. _____

19. When a biopsy is performed during minor surgery
    the specimen must be placed immediately into

    _____ .

20. During minor surgery, soiled dressings and spong-

    es should be placed in _____

    _____ .

21. List the materials needed for preparing the skin
    area for minor surgery.

    a. _____

    b. _____

    c. _____

    d. _____

    e. _____

    f. _____

22. List the materials needed for administering a local
    anesthetic.

    a. _____

    b. _____

    c. _____

    d. _____

    e. _____

    f. _____

    g. _____

23. List the materials needed for suturing lacerations.

    a. _____

    b. _____

    c. _____

    d. _____

    e. _____

    f. _____

    g. _____

    h. _____

    i. _____

    j. _____

    k. _____

24. List the materials needed for removing sutures.

    a. _____

    b. _____

    c. _____

    d. _____

    e. _____

25. Define a wound. _____
_____
_____.

26. An _____ wound is one in which the skin and mucous membranes are broken; in a _____ wound, the skin is not broken, but there is a contusion or a hematoma.

27. Name the types of open wounds.

a. _____
b. _____
c. _____
d. _____
e. _____

28. Give the signs and symptoms that indicate the presence of an infection.

a. _____
b. _____
c. _____
d. _____
e. _____
f. _____
g. _____

29. An indication that an infection is spreading from a wound caused by needle pricks, splinters, or small cuts is the presence of _____ _____.

30. Wounds that are most susceptible to infection are those in which there is:

a. _____
b. _____
c. _____

31. Name the common pathogenic organisms causing a wound infection.

a. _____
b. _____
c. _____

d. _____
e. _____

32. Explain the goals of wound care.

a. _____
b. _____

33. Describe eight basic purposes of dressings.

a. _____
b. _____
c. _____
d. _____
e. _____
f. _____
g. _____
h. _____

34. A wound culture is taken to _____ _____.

35. When changing a dressing on a patient you find that the tape does not pull away easily. You should then do the following to remove the tape.

_____

36. After removing a dressing from a patient's wound, you should inspect it for _____ .

37. When cleansing a wound you should start at the _____ and work toward the _____ .

38. State four basic purposes of bandages.

a. _____
b. _____
c. _____
d. _____

39. Triangular bandages are used most frequently for

_____.

40. When applying a bandage, the bony prominences and joints over which the bandage is placed must be padded in order to:

    a. _____

    b. _____

    c. _____

41. A colposcopy is an examination of _____ done with a colposcope.

42. A colposcopy is performed to _____
_____ .

43. Depending on the findings from a colposcopy and to further examine for precancerous conditions the physician may perform _____ . In an endocervical curettage (ECC) cells are scraped from inside the _____ .

44. Explain the reasons an endometrical biopsy is performed:

    a. _____

    b. _____

    c. _____

    e. _____

    f. _____

45. The _____ and _____ determine when suture materials can be removed.

46. Explain why casts are used.

    a. _____

    b. _____

    c. _____

47. The healing time for a fracture depends on

    _____ , _____ , and

    _____ .

48. The patient who has a cast should contact the physician immediately if any of the following is observed:

    a. _____

    b. _____

    c. _____

    d. _____

    e. _____

    f. _____

    g. _____

    h. _____

    i. _____

    j. _____

Multiple Choice

Write the letter of the correct answer in the blank provided. There is only *one* correct answer.

_____ 1. The type of local anesthesia in which the anesthetic solution is injected under the skin to anesthetize the nerve endings and nerve fibers at the site to be worked on is called:
A. Infiltration.
B. Nerve block anesthesia.
C. Topical anesthesia.
D. Surface anesthesia.

_____ 2. The type of local anesthesia in which the anesthetic solution is injected into or adjacent to accessible main nerves, thus desensitizing all the adjacent tissue is called:
A. Infiltration.
B. Nerve block anesthesia.
C. Topical anesthesia.
D. Surface anesthesia.

_____ 3. The thickest type of suture material from the following list is:
A. 0.
B. 00.
C. 000.
D. 4 to 0.

_____ 4. When opening a sterile pack, you should unfold the top flap:
A. Toward your body.
B. Toward the right side.
C. Away from your body.
D. Toward the left side.

5. To remove transfer forceps from the container the prongs must be kept:
   A. Separated and facing upwards.
   B. Separated and facing downwards.
   C. Together and facing upwards.
   D. Together and facing downwards.

6. When pouring a moderate amount of a sterile solution into a container the bottle should be held with the label in the palm of the hand and about _____ inches above the container.
   A. 4
   B. 5
   C. 6
   D. 7

7. _____ are instruments of varied sizes and shapes used for grasping, compressing, or holding tissue or objects.
   A. Probes
   B. Scalpels
   C. Forceps
   D. Sponge forceps

8. Povidone-iodine (Betadine) is used for:
   A. Disinfecting instruments for a medical procedure.
   B. Handwashing before a medical procedure.
   C. Disinfecting a sterile setup.
   D. Disinfecting the skin.

9. A number _____ blade is usually used for fine and small incisions when the physician is performing an I&D of an abscess.
   A. 10
   B. 11
   C. 12
   D. 15

10. Incision into and removal of part of a lesion from the body is called a(n) _____ biopsy.
    A. Aspiration
    B. Incisional
    C. Excisional
    D. Needle

11. A scrape on the surface of the skin or on a mucous membrane is called a(n):
    A. Avulsion.
    B. Abrasion.
    C. Laceration.
    D. Incision.

12. The type of open wound in which a piece of soft tissue is torn loose or left hanging as a flap is called a(n):
    A. Avulsion
    B. Abrasion.
    C. Laceration.
    D. Incision.

13. Wounds that are most susceptible to infection are _____ wounds.
    A. Avulsion
    B. Puncture
    C. Abrasion
    D. Laceration

14. When the edges of wounds can be brought together, as in sutured surgical incisions, or when there is a minimal amount of tissue loss or damage, they heal by:
    A. First intention.
    B. Second intention.
    C. Granulation healing.
    D. Indirect healing.

15. During the _____ phase of the healing process blood serum and cells form a fibrin network in the wound and a clot is formed.
    A. Lag
    B. Fibroplasia
    C. Contraction
    D. Keloid

16. Drainage from a wound that consists of blood is called _____ drainage.
    A. Serous
    B. Serosanguineous
    C. Purulent
    D. Sanguineous

17. Drainage from a wound that consists of or contains pus is called_____ drainage.
    A. Serous
    B. Serosanguineous
    C. Purulent
    D. Sanguineous

_____ 18. If a dressing is hard to remove, _____
may be applied to help loosen it.
- A. Alcohol peroxide
- B. Hydrogen peroxide
- C. Sterile saline
- D. Povidone-iodine (Betadine)

_____ 19. A physician usually inserts an IUD:
- A. 3 days before the patient's menstrual period.
- B. On the third day of the patient's menstrual period.
- C. 3 days after the patient's menstrual period is over.
- D. 3 days before ovulation is anticipated.

_____ 20. When the physician is performing a needle biopsy of the breast, a No. _____ needle is used for the aspiration.
- A. 25
- B. 22
- C. 21
- D. 18

_____ 21. A _____turn is the type of bandage turn that is used to anchor a bandage.
- A. Circular
- B. Spiral
- C. Spiral-reverse
- D. Recurrent

_____ 22. A _____ bandage is used to make a sling.
- A. Roller
- B. Triangular
- C. Tubegauz
- D. Cravat

_____ 23. An example of a topical spray anesthetic is:
- A. Lidocaine 1%.
- B. Lidocaine 2%.
- C. Procaine hydrochloride 1%.
- D. Ethyl chloride.

Labeling

1. Label each of the following instruments illustrated in Figure 6-1 in the space provided.

Figure 6-1

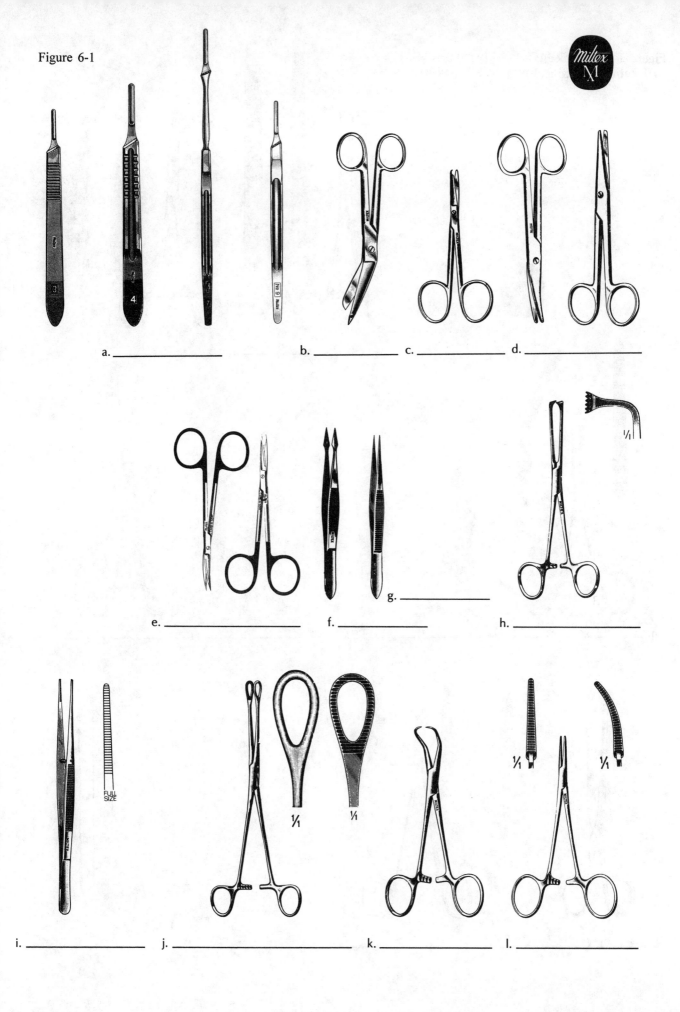

a. _____

b. _____

c. _____

d. _____

e. _____

f. _____

g. _____

h. _____

i. _____

j. _____

k. _____

l. _____

Figure 6-1 (continued)
III Labeling—cont'd

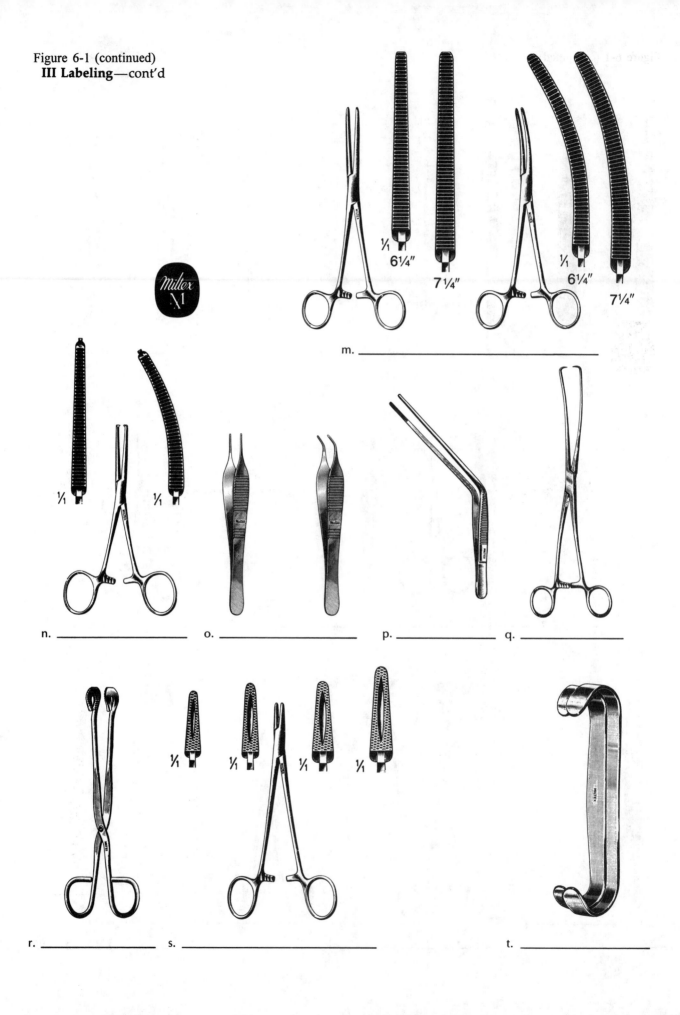

m. _____

n. _____ o. _____ p. _____ q. _____

r. _____ s. _____ t. _____

Figure 6-1 (continued)

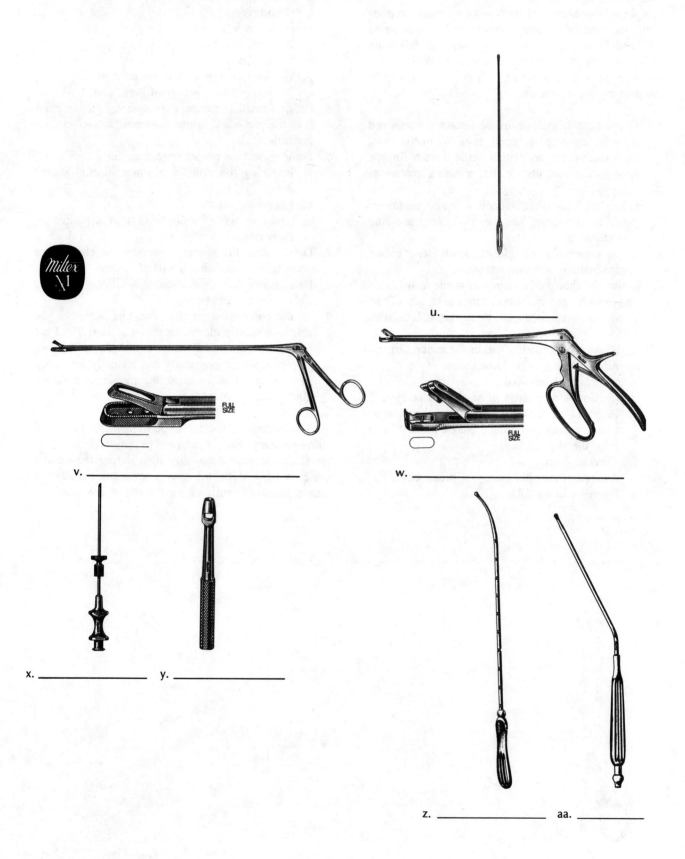

u. _____

v. _____

w. _____

x. _____   y. _____

z. _____   aa. _____

PERFORMANCE TEST

In a skills laboratory, a simulation of a joblike environment, the medical assistant student is to demonstrate skill and knowledge when performing the following activities without reference to source materials. Time limits for the performance of each procedure are to be assigned by the instructor.

1. Given a sterile syringe in a peel-down package and a sterile envelope-wrapped pack of instruments, open these packs and with a sterile transfer forceps arrange the contents for use, avoiding contamination.
2. Given a sterile solution and a sterile container, pour the solution into the container, avoiding contamination.
3. Given a pair of sterile gloves, don these, avoiding contamination, and then remove.
4. Given the choice of a variety of sterile instruments and prepackaged instrument sets, select, identify by name, and prepare for use those that will be used for:
    a. Preparing the patient's skin for minor surgery.
    b. Administering a local anesthetic.
    c. Suturing a laceration.
    d. Incision and drainage of an abscess or cyst.
    e. Removal of a foreign body in subcutaneous tissue, a wart and a mole, and a tissue biopsy from the skin surface.
    f. Cervical biopsy.
    g. Aspiration (needle) biopsy of breast tissue.
    h. Insertion of an IUD.
    i. Vulvar biopsy.
    j. Endocervical curettage.
    l. Cryosurgery.
    m. Colposcopy.
    n. A 6 mm skin biopsy.
    o. Suture removal.
    p. Dressing change with a wound culture.
    q. Application of a plaster-of-Paris cast.
5. Given a sterile hemostat while wearing gloves, hand it to the physician in the way most convenient for immediate use.
6. Demonstrate the proper procedure for:
    a. Preparing the skin for a minor surgical procedure.
    b. Removing sutures.
    c. Assisting with the application of a plaster-of-Paris cast.
7. Demonstrate the proper procedure for changing a dressing and obtaining a wound culture.
8. Demonstrate the application of a roller, triangular, and Tubegauz bandage.
9. At the completion of the preceding activities, be able to discuss with the instructor at least 10 of the principles of surgical aseptic technique, how to prepare a patient physically and mentally for minor surgery, and how to assist the physician during a minor surgical procedure.

The student is expected to perform these skills with 100% accuracy 90% of the time (9 out of 10 times). If the student contaminates any item during the performance of these skills, the correct actions to remedy the contaminated site must be used 100% of the time.

PERFORMANCE CHECKLIST: Opening a sterile peel-down package

DIRECTIONS: Evaluate student performance of each procedure using the following checklist. When you evaluate "not applicable," "unsatisfactory," or "not observed," please comment.

Checklist	S or NA*	U	NO	Comment
1. Washed hands. **Use appropriate Personal Protective Equipment (PPE) as dictated by facility.**				
2. Obtained sterile package.				
3. Using both hands, grasped the extended edges on the package, and pulled evenly along the sealed edges.				
4. Placed opened package on a flat surface, ready for use; or, using sterile forceps, removed contents from wrapper and transferred to sterile field, avoiding contamination; or, holding bottom of the package with the edges folded back, allowed someone with sterile gloves on to take the item; or, when the item is a syringe to be used by the student, grasped the plunger end of the syringe, and removed from the package.				

Total Satisfactory Points _____

Comments

Student's signature: _____   Instructor's signature: _____
Date: _____
*S or NA, Satisfactory or not applicable; U, unsatisfactory; NO, not observed.

PERFORMANCE CHECKLIST: Opening an envelope-wrapped package

DIRECTIONS: Evaluate student performance of each procedure using the following checklist. When you evaluate "not applicable," "unsatisfactory," or "not observed," please comment.

Checklist	S or NA*	U	NO	Comment
1. Washed hands. **Use appropriate Personal Protective Equipment (PPE) as dictated by facility.**				
2. Obtained sterile package, and placed on a flat surface.				
3. Removed tape or string fastener, and discarded.				
4. Opened top (distal) flap away from himself/ herself.				
5. Opened the second layer of folded corners to the sides of the package.				
6. Opened fourth (last) flap toward himself/ herself.				
7. Did not at any time reach across the sterile field; did not touch the inside of the wrapper; handled only the outside of the wrapper				
8. Using sterile transfer forceps with prongs facing downward, or a gloves hand, arranged the items for use.				
9. Used the same technique to open small packages to be opened while holding in one hand; then carefully placed the contents on a sterile field, avoiding contamination, or allowed a person with sterile gloves to pick the item off the wrapper, or removed the item from the pack with sterile transfer forceps.				

Total Satisfactory Points   _____

Comments

Student's signature:_____   Instructor's signature: _____
Date: _____
*S or NA, Satisfactory or not applicable; U, unsatisfactory; NO, not observed.

98

PERFORMANCE CHECKLIST: Handling transfer forceps

DIRECTIONS: Evaluate student performance of each procedure using the following checklist. When you evaluate "not applicable," "unsatisfactory," or "not observed," please comment.

Checklist	S or NA*	U	NO	Comment
1. Kept one forceps per container.				
2. Washed hands.				
3. Grasped forceps by handle, lifted vertically, prongs together and facing downward.				
4. Did not touch the container above the solution line; gently tapped prongs together to remove excess solution.				
5. Used to transfer or assemble sterile supplies, avoiding contact of the prongs with the sterile field. Kept prongs facing downward at all times.				
6. Replaced the forceps in container, avoiding contamination.				

Total Satisfactory Points _____

Comments

Student's signature: _____ Instructor's signature: _____
Date: _____

*S or NA, Satisfactory or not applicable; U, unsatisfactory; NO, not observed.

PERFORMANCE CHECKLIST: Pouring sterile solutions

DIRECTIONS: Evaluate student performance of each procedure using the following checklist. When you evaluate "not applicable," "unsatisfactory," or "not observed," please comment.

Checklist	S or NA*	U	NO	Comment
1. Washed hands. **Use appropriate Personal Protective Equipment (PPE) as dictated by facility.**				
2. Obtained solution, and checked label.				
3. Obtained sterile container for solution, and unwrapped correctly.				
4. Removed bottle cap and placed on a level surface, upside down.				
5. Checked the label again. Held bottle with label facing the palm of the hand; poured small amount of solution into a waste container; and then, holding the bottle 6 inches above the sterile container, poured the solution for use. Did not splash.				
6. To pour solution onto a sponge, held the sponge in forceps, poured solution over sponge, and allowed excess solution to drip into a waste basin.				
7. Replaced cap on the bottle without contaminating.				
8. Checked label, and returned to storage area.				

Total Satisfactory Points _____

Comments

Student's signature: _____ Instructor's signature: _____

Date: _____

*S or NA, Satisfactory or not applicable; U, unsatisfactory; NO, not observed.

PERFORMANCE CHECKLIST: Donning and removing disposable single-use exam gloves.

DIRECTIONS: Evaluate student performance of each procedure using the following checklist. When you evaluate "not applicable," "unsatisfactory," or "not observed," please comment.

Checklist	S or NA*	U	NO	Comment
1. Washed hands. **Use appropriate Personal Protective Equipment (PPE) as dictated by facility.**				
2. Placed wrapped gloves on a clean, dry, flat surface, with cuff end toward body.				
3. Opened the outside and inside wrapper, handling outside of the packages only.				
4. With left hand, grasped cuff of right-hand glove; lifted up and away from wrapper.				
5. Pulled glove on.				
6. Placed glove right fingers under cuff of left glove, and lifted up and away from the wrapper.				
7. Pulled left glove over hand and wrist.				
8. With left gloved hand, placed fingers under right cuff and pulled up over wrist.				
9. Adjusted fingers of both gloves as necessary.				
10. To remove gloves, grasped cuff of one glove with opposite hand; pulled glove down, turning inside out and discarded.				
11. Repeated to remove remaining glove.				

Total Satisfactory Points   ————

Comments

Student's signature:————————————— Instructor's signature: —————————————
Date: —————————————
*S or NA, Satisfactory or not applicable; U, unsatisfactory; NO, not observed.

PERFORMANCE CHECKLIST: Dressing change with a wound culture

DIRECTIONS: Evaluate student performance of each procedure using the following checklist. When you evaluate "not applicable," "unsatisfactory," or "not observed," please comment.

Checklist	S or NA*	U	NO	Comment
1. Washed hands. **Use appropriate Personal Protective Equipment (PPE) as dictated by facility.**				
2. Assembled equipment.				
3. Identified the patient, and explained the procedure.				
4. Prepared the patient; that is, gowned, positioned, and draped as necessary.				
5. Prepared supplies for use.				
6. Donned disposable single-use exam gloves.				
7. Loosened tape on the dressing.				
8. Removed soiled dressing with a forceps or with a gloved hand, or grasped dressing with hand covered with a plastic bag.				
9. Inspected dressing for type and amount of drainage; discarded soiled dressing in the plastic bag.				
10. Observed the wound for type and amount of drainage; degree of healing, presence of pus, necrosis, or a putrid odor. When sutures were present, noted if they were intact.				
11. Removed the sterile applicator from the tube, and swabbed the drainage area once to obtain a specimen.				
12. Placed applicator in the culture tube.				
13. Removed disposable single-use exam gloves.				
14. Donned another pair of disposable single-use exam gloves.				
15. Cleansed the wound using aseptic technique.				
16. Applied fresh sterile dressing, and secured correctly with tape.				
17. Attended to the patient's comfort; gave further instructions when indicated.				
18. Labeled culture tube, completed laboratory requisition, and sent together to the laboratory.				
19. Assembled used supplies and disposed of according to office or agency policy.				
20. Washed hands.				

PERFORMANCE CHECKLIST: Dressing change with a wound culture

Checklist	S or NA*	U	NO	Comment
21. Replaced supplies as needed, leaving the room neat and tidy.				
22. Recorded the date, procedure, observations, and signature on the patient's chart.				
Total Satisfactory Points	_____			

Comments

Student's signature: _____ Instructor's signature: _____

Date: _____

*S or NA, Satisfactory or not applicable; U, unsatisfactory; NO, not observed.

Evaluation of student's technique   **Name:** _____ **Date:** _____

	Satisfactory*		Unsatisfactory**		
	Very Good	Good	Fair	Poor	Score
• Opening peel-down	☐	☐	☐	☐	_____
• Opening envelope wrapped package	☐	☐	☐	☐	_____
• Handling transfer forceps	☐	☐	☐	☐	_____
• Pouring sterile solutions	☐	☐	☐	☐	_____
• Donning disposable single-use exam gloves	☐	☐	☐	☐	_____
• Dressing change with wound culture	☐	☐	☐	☐	_____

Very good = Perfect
Good   = Sufficient
Fair   = Not acceptable requires more practice
Poor   = Totally unacceptable
Pass* = Satisfactory
Fail** = Unsatisfactory

Comments:

1. Sterile technique; aseptic technique
2. Nonsterile
3. a. Know what is sterile.
   b. Know what is not sterile.
   c. Keep sterile items separate from nonsterile items.
   d. Prevent contamination.
   e. Remedy a contaminated situation immediately.
4. Remove the damaged glove, wash your hands, and put on a new glove as promptly as patient safety permits. Remove the needle or instrument from the sterile field.
5. Are not
6. Replace any fabric items, sponges, and dressing materials then rewrap and resterilize pack.
7. The palm of the hand
8. Protect the patient from infection caused by microorganisms that may be on your hands and provide a means of safely handling sterile supplies and equipment without contaminating these items
9. a. Suturing a laceration
   b. The incision and drainage of an abscess or cyst
   c. Incision and removal of foreign bodies in subcutaneous tissues
   d. Removal of small growths such as warts, moles, and skin tags
   e. Various types of biopsies
   f. Cauterization of tissue (such as cauterization of the uterine cervix, or of a wart, mole, or skin tag)
   g. Insertion of an intrauterine device
10. The absence of feeling or sensation and pain in a limited area of the body without the loss of consciousness
11. Injection; topical application
12. Hold the edges of tissues together until healing occurs.
13. Are absorbed or digested by the body fluids and tissues during and after the healing process
14. Surgical gut (catgut)
15. a. Cotton
    b. Silk
    c. Nylon
    d. Stainless steel wire
    e. Metal skin clips or staples
16. 10-0
17. The areas and the purpose for which it will be used and the physician's preference

18. a. Preparing the room and supplies
    b. Preparing the patient, both physically and mentally
    c. Assisting the physician as needed
19. The designated jar containing a preservative solution
20. a. Plastic bag
21. a. Surgical detergent for washing the skin
    b. Sterile sponges (cotton balls and gauze—2 x 2 inch and 4 x 4 inch)
    c. Sterile forceps
    d. Antiseptic solution such as povidone-iodine (Betadine) for disinfecting the skin
    e. Razor and blade (if skin is to be shaved)
    f. Draping materials
22. a. Sterile antiseptic in sterile container, such as povidone-iodine solution.
    b. Applicators or cotton balls and a forceps to use when painting the skin. Prepackaged sterile povidone-iodine applicators are available and may be used instead.
    c. Sterile syringe (3 ml or 5 ml)
    d. Sterile needles: 25-gauge, ½-inch, and 23- or 24-gauge, 1½-inch (Size and gauge will vary with site to be infiltrated.)
    e. Local anesthetic: ampules or vials of lidocaine 1% to 2% or procaine hydrochloride 1% to 2%. For a topical spray anesthetic, ethyl chloride may be used.
    f. Alcohol sponge to cleanse the vial top
    g. Disposable single-use exam gloves (depending on physician's preference and procedure to be performed). This setup may be prepared individually or added to the sterile setup used for the procedure.
23. a. Materials for preparing the skin
    b. Local anesthetic setup
    c. Sterile gloves
    d. Toothed tissue forceps
    e. Hemostat
    f. Needle holder
    g. Suture scissors
    h. Suture material with suture needle
    i. Sterile gauze 2 x 2 inch and 4 x 4 inch (for sponging and dressing wound; larger dressings are needed for lacerations larger than 3 inches)
    j. Adhesive or preferably hypoallergenic tape and bandage scissors to cut it
    k. Container for used instruments and sponges. If the wound is infected or abscesses are to be incised, suture material is not needed because infected wounds are usually not sutured.

24. a. Disposable single-use exam gloves
    b. Suture removal kit that includes suture scissors, plain-tipped tissue forceps, sterile gauze 4 x 4 inch
    c. Antiseptic solution in container (or disposable povidone-iodine applicators)
    d. Sterile applicators or gauze or cotton balls
    e. Container for removed sutures, used instruments, and sponges
25. A break in the continuity of external or internal soft body parts, caused by physical trauma to the tissues
26. Open; closed
27. a. Abrasion
    b. Avulsion
    c. Incision
    d. Laceration
    e. Puncture
28. a. Redness
    b. Heat
    c. Pain
    d. Swelling
    e. At times the presence of pus and a throbbing sensation at the wound site
    f. Fever often accompanies infection
    g. As the temperature rises, pulse and respiration rates also rise
29. a. A red streak running up the extremity from the wound site
30. a. Not a free flow of blood
    b. A crushing of the tissues
    c. A break in the skin that closes or falls back in place, thus preventing entrance of air, as seen in puncture wounds
31. a. Staphylococci
    b. Streptococci
    c. Colon bacillus (*Escherichia coli* or *E. coli*)
    d. Gas bacillus (*Clostridium perfringens*)
    e. Tetanus bacillus (*Clostridium tetani*)
32. a. Promote healing
    b. Prevent additional injury
33. a. To protect wounds from additional trauma
    b. To help prevent contamination of the wound
    c. To absorb drainage
    d. To provide pressure for controlling hemorrhage, promoting drainage, and reducing edema
    e. To immobilize and support the wound site
    f. To ease pain
    g. To provide a means for applying and keeping medications on the wound
    h. To provide psychologic benefits for the patient by concealing, protecting, and giving support to the wound

34. Determine the presence and type of microscopic organism that is causing the infection
35. Moisten the tape with a sponge soaked with acetone, benzine, baby oil, or a commercial tape remover.
36. The amount and type of drainage on the dressing
37. Center; end
38. a. To hold dressings or splints in place
    b. To immobilize or support body parts
    c. To protect an injured body part
    d. To apply pressure over an area
39. Slings on an injured arm
40. a. Prevent skin irritation
    b. Provide comfort
    c. Maintain equal pressure on body parts
41. The vagina and cervix
42. Assess patients with cervical lesions that were observed during a pelvic examination, to assess the cervical cells and tissues when the results of a Pap smear fall within abnormal ranges, to visualize abnormalities, to assess patients who were exposed to diethylstilbestrol in utero, and to obtain a biopsy specimen and at times to substitute for a cone biopsy when the physician is evaluating the cause of abnormal cervical cytologic findings.
43. ECC and/or cryosurgery. cervical canal
44. a. To detect endometrial carcinoma and precancerous conditions
    b. To monitor the effects of hormonal therapy on the uterine endometrium. This could include the effects of estrogen in patients with suspected ovarian dysfunction or to determine adequate levels of circulating progesterone.
    c. Routine screening of selected patients for early detection of endometrial carcinoma. The American Cancer Society recommends that women at high risk have this done at menopause. A woman is considered to be at high risk if she has a history of infertility, obesity, failure to ovulate, abnormal bleeding or estrogen therapy.
    d. To determine if ovulation has occurred
    e. To detect inflammatory conditions or polyps
    f. To assess abnormal uterine bleeding
45. condition of the suture line, the progress of healing
46. a. Immobilize broken bones, injuries, joint disorders, or congenital disorders, such as a dislocated hip or club foot
    b. Protect the affected area
    c. Reduce pain
47. The type of fracture, the kind of bone affected, the age of the person

48.
   a. Broken, cracked, soft or loose places on the cast
   b. Skin irritation due to the cast rubbing the skin
   c. A bad odor coming from the cast
   d. Raw or red skin under the edges of the cast
   e. The cast feeling too tight
   f. Prolonged swelling
   g. Fingers or toes below the cast become numb, difficult to move, discolored, or cold. Casts are applied snugly but are fit to allow adequate circulation necessary for proper healing.
   h. General discomfort changing to constant or severe pain
   i. A burning sensation especially over a bony prominence
   j. Bleeding or a red-pink discoloration on the cast

Multiple

1. A
2. B
3. A
4. C
5. D
6. C
7. C
8. D
9. D
10. B
11. B
12. A
13. B
14. A
15. A
16. D
17. C
18. C
19. B
20. D
21. A
22. B
23. D

Labeling

a. Knife handles
b. Lister bandage scissors
c. Spencer stitch scissors
d. Mayo dissecting scissors
e. Iris scissors
f. Carmalt splinter forceps
g. Plain splinter forceps
h. Allis tissue forceps
i. Potts-Smith dressing forceps
j. Foerster sponge forceps
k. Backhaus towel clamp
l. Halsted mosquito forceps
m. Rochester pean forceps
n. Kocher forceps
o. Adson dressing forceps
p. Wilde nasal dressing forceps
q. Duplay uterine tenaculum forceps
r. Utility-sterilizer forceps
s. Mayo-Hegar needle holder
t. Parker retractors
u. Probe with eye
v. Yeoman biopsy forceps
w. Menghini biopsy needle
y. Keyes dermal punch
z. Sims uterine sound
aa. Authony suction tube

Unit 7

Principles of Pharmacology and Drug Administration

SUGGESTED ACTIVITIES

1. Make a list of drugs frequently used or prescribed at the facility where you do your work experience. Then using the Physician's Desk Reference (PDR) or other reference pharmacology book, obtain information on these drugs.

2. With a partner, practice identifying the correct sites for administering a subcutaneous (SC) and an intramuscular (IM) injection by palpating definite anatomic landmarks.

3. Practice preparing and administering medications by the routes discussed in this unit.

4. At the facility where you do your work experience check the supplies and drugs that are kept on the emergency tray. Compare your findings with the findings of others in your class. Discuss the purpose of each drug and piece of equipment kept on this tray.

STUDY QUESTIONS
Fill-In

In the blanks provided, write the answers that best complete the sentences:

1. _____ is the use of drugs to treat disease.

2. A _____ is the unusual or abnormal response or susceptibility to a drug that is peculiar to an individual.

3. Drug _____ is the decreased susceptibility to the effects of a drug after continued use.

4. _____ is an emotional dependence on a drug caused by repeated use, but without tendencies to increase the amount of the drug.

5. A _____ is an inactive substance resembling and given in place of a medication for its psychological effects to satisfy the patient's need for the drug.

6. A _____ is a response in addition to that for which the drug was used, especially an undesirable result.

7. A _____ is a system that supplies prepackaged, premeasured, prelabeled, individual portions of a medication for patient use.

8. Phamacology is _____ _____.

9. Describe the therapeutic uses of drugs.

   a. _____ _____

   b. _____ _____

   c. _____ _____

10. Prophylactically, drugs are used to _____ _____.

109

11. List the four main sources from which drugs are derived.

   a. _____

   b. _____

   c. _____

   d. _____

12. Explain the three names by which a typical drug may be known.

   a. Trade or brand name: _____

   _____

   b. Generic name: _____

   _____

   c. Chemical name: _____

   _____

13. Drugs having the potential for addiction and abuse, including narcotics, stimulants, and depressants, are termed _____ . Control of these drugs at all levels of manufacturing, distribution, and use is mandatory.

14. The Controlled Substance Act of 1970 is enforced by the _____ .

15. Under the CSA, drugs that are under federal control are classified into one of five schedules. Each schedule reflects decreasing levels of _____ , from Schedule I through Schedule V.

16. All controlled substances listed in the PDR are indicated with the symbol _____ with the Roman numeral _____, _____ , _____ , or _____ printed inside the _____ to designate the schedule in which the substance is classified.

17. Schedule _____ drugs have the highest potential for addiction and abuse, have not been accepted for medical use in the United States.

18. Schedule _____ drugs have a low potential for abuse and a limited addiction liability relative to drugs in the other schedules.

19. Prescription drugs may be obtained only when _____ .

20. Nonprescription drugs are frequently referred to as _____ drugs, because they can be obtained without a prescription (for example, vitamin tablets and aspirin).

21. Describe the various drug classifications.

   a. _____
   _____

   b. _____
   _____

   c. _____
   _____

   d. _____
   _____

22. A prescription is _____
   _____ .

23. Describe the seven parts of a prescription.

   a. _____
   _____

   b. _____
   _____

   c. _____
   _____

   d. _____
   _____

   e. _____
   _____

   f. _____
   _____

   g. _____
   _____

24. State regulations require the prescription form contain a statement indicating that a _____ _____ may be dispensed.

25. The same regulations also state that if a generic is not available, the physician must write out "_____ _____" or "dispense as written."

26. Once a prescription has been filled, the pharmacist must keep a record of that sale for _____ .

27. All prescriptions written for controlled substances in Schedule II must be wholly written and signed in _____ by _____ .

28. In the physician's office medications may be administered, dispensed, or prescribed. A medication is administered when it is _____ _____ .

29. A medication is dispensed when it is _____ _____ .

30. A medication is prescribed when _____ _____ .

31. Ideally, all medications should be stored in _____ and all must be kept in _____ .

32. When discarding outdated, opened drugs, you should pour liquids _____ ; drugs in the solid state should be crushed and then _____ .

33. To avoid medication errors, drugs for external use must be kept _____ from those to be used internally.

34. Any loss or theft of controlled substances must be reported by the _____ on discovery to the _____ .

35. The emergency tray kept in the physician's office or clinic must be checked frequently to _____ _____ .

36. Medications that are not clearly labeled must be _____ .

37. When pouring liquid medications from a bottle, the bottle should be held so that the label is facing _____ .

38. A running inventory of all narcotics and controlled substances must be kept for a period of _____ .

39. When a drug is given parenterally it is given by _____ .

40. List the five "rights" of proper medication administration.

    a. _____

    b. _____

    c. _____

    d. _____

    e. _____

    A sixth right added by many is:

    f. _____

41. A patient refuses to take a medication that has been poured for him. Describe what should be done with this mediation. _____ _____ .

42. After administering a medication, the medical assistant must record on the patient's chart the _____ , _____ , _____ , _____ , _____ , and _____ .

43. Name six factors that influence the prescribed dosage and anticipated action of a medication.

a. _____

b. _____

c. _____

d. _____

e. _____

f. _____

44. Give six reasons why medications are ordered to be administered by injection.

a. _____
_____

b. _____
_____

c. _____
_____

d. _____
_____

e. _____
_____

f. _____
_____

45. Describe seven dangers or complications of routine injections.

a. _____

b. _____

c. _____

d. _____

e. _____

f. _____

g. _____

46. List the areas to avoid when administering injections:

a. _____

b. _____

c. _____

d. _____

e. _____

f. _____

g. _____

h. _____

47. The most common sizes of syringes used in the physician's office are _____,

_____, _____, and

_____.

48. An 18-gauge needle has a (smaller *or* larger) _____ lumen than a 26-gauge needle.

49. When an oily medication is to be administered, a number _____ gauge needle may be used to withdraw the medication from the vial.

50. Before an injection is administered, the skin must be cleansed with a(n) _____ such as

_____.

51. Containers with multiple doses of a liquid medication to be administered by an injection are called

_____.

52. The main objective when administering an intramuscular mediation is to _____ .

53. Name four anatomic sites commonly used for administering intramuscular injections.

a. _____

b. _____

c. _____

d. _____

Be prepared to explain and demonstrate how to locate these sites on the patient.

54. The most common site for intramuscular injections is the _____ located in the

_____.

55. The objective of a subcutaneous injection is to

_____

_____ .

56. Describe most common and preferred sites for administering a subcutaneous injection.

　a. _____

　b. _____

　c. _____

57. Identify two additional sites that may be used for administering a subcutaneous injection, especially when the medication is self-administered, as by a diabetic.

　a. _____

　b. _____

58. The objective of an intradermal injection is to

_____ .

59. The amount of drug given by an intradermal injection is usually _____ to

_____ . A _____ syringe is to be used for this method because of its fine calibrations.

60. The most common and preferred site for administering an intradermal injection is the

_____ .

61. If, when administering an injection, the needle enters a blood vessel, the needle should be

_____

_____ .

62. The Z-tract intramuscular technique is used for

_____ .

63. The preferred site to administer a drug using the Z-tract technique is the _____

at a _____ -degree angle.

64. Allow the skin disinfectant to dry before giving an injection because _____

_____ .

65. Insert and remove the needle quickly when giving an injection so as to _____ .

66. Inject the medication slowly. Rapid injection of the medication would cause _____ .

67. *Rotating injection sites for insulin administration is no longer recommended* because _____

_____ .

However, *it is recommended* that each injection site be about _____ inch(es) from the last site used in the *same body area*.

68. When giving an insulin injection the _____ sites are preferred because absorption from those sites is rapid and unaffected by exercise. The

_____ are the second sites that provide the fastest absorption rate of insulin followed by

the _____ .

69. DO NOT rub the injection site after withdrawing the needle when giving insulin because _____

_____ .

70. When mixing regular insulin with a longer-acting insulin you must follow the manufacturer's recommendation which states that you must *always* first

draw up the _____ insulin into the syringe, then draw up the second insulin, such as NPH.

71. Oxygen is commonly used as a drug for patients with hypoxia (oxygen deficiency) or hypoxemia (deficiency of oxygen in the blood). Give the signs and symptoms of hypoxemia.

　a. _____

　b. _____

　c. _____

　d. _____

　e. _____

f. _____

g. _____

h. _____

72. List the conditions for which oxygen administration may be required.

   a. _____

   b. _____

   c. _____

   d. _____

   e. _____

   f. _____

   g. _____

   h. _____

   i. _____

Multiple Choice

Write the letter of the correct answer in the blank provided. There is only *one* correct answer.

_____ 1. An intramuscular injection should be inserted at a _____ -degree angle.
   A. 10 to 15
   B. 30
   C. 45
   D. 90

_____ 2. A subcutaneous injection should be inserted at a _____ -degree angle.
   A. 10 to 15
   B. 30
   C. 45
   D. 90

_____ 3. An intradermal injection should be inserted at a _____ -degree angle.
   A. 10 to 15
   B. 30
   C. 45
   D. 90

_____ 4. The needle should be inserted at a _____ -degree angle when administering an injection using the Z-tract technique.
   A. 10 to 15
   B. 30
   C. 45
   D. 90

_____ 5. A drug administered by the _____ method is placed under the patient's tongue and left to dissolve and be absorbed.
   A. Buccal
   B. Sublingual
   C. Inunction
   D. Instillation

_____ 6. A drug administered by the _____ method is applied or rubbed into the skin.
   A. Buccal
   B. Sublingual
   C. Inunction
   D. Instillation

_____ 7. A drug administered by the _____ method is placed between the cheek and gum to dissolve and be absorbed.
   A. Buccal
   B. Sublingual
   C. Inunction
   D. Instillation

_____ 8. An injection into a joint for local effects is called an _____ injection.
   A. Intradermal
   B. Interarticular
   C. Intraarterial
   D. Intracutaneous

_____ 9. The recommended size of needle used to administer a subcutaneous injection is a _____ needle.
   A. 1½-inch, 21-gauge
   B. ¼-inch, 21-gauge
   C. ⅝-inch, 22-gauge
   D. ½-inch, 25-gauge

_____ 10. The recommended size of needle used to administer an intramuscular injection is a _____ needle.
   A. 1-inch, 25-gauge
   B. 1½-inch, 21-gauge
   C. 1-inch, 18-gauge
   D. ½-inch, 22-gauge

_____ 11. The recommended size of needle used to administer an intradermal injection is a _____ needle.
A. ½-inch, 25-gauge
B. ¼-inch, 22 gauge
C. ½-inch, 26-gauge
D. 1-inch, 26-gauge

_____ 12. The recommended size of needle used to administer insulin is a _____ needle.
A. 1-inch, 21-gauge
B. 1½-inch, 21-gauge
C. ⅝-inch, 22-gauge
D. ½-inch, 25-gauge

_____ 13. A drug that is used to relieve pain is an:
A. Analgesic.
B. Anesthetic.
C. Antidepressant.
D. Antidote.

_____ 14. A drug that increases urinary output is called a(n):
A. Emetic.
B. Diuretic.
C. Miotic.
D. Styptic.

_____ 15. A drug that neutralizes a poison is called a(n):
A. Antidote.
B. Antiemetic.
C. Cathartic.
D. Hemostatic.

_____ 16. A drug that inhibits the growth and reproduction of or eliminates pathogenic microorganisms is a(n):
A. Disinfectant.
B. Antidote.
C. Antibiotic.
D. Hemostatic.

_____ 17. A drug used to dilate the pupils of the eye is a:
A. Mydriatic.
B. Miotic.
C. Hemostatic.
D. Cathartic.

_____ 18. A drug used to constrict the pupils of the eye is a:
A. Mydriatic.
B. Miotic.
C. Hemostatic.
D. Cathartic.

_____ 19. A drug used to inhibit the growth and spread of malignant cells is a(n):
A. Astringent.
B. Antineoplastic.
C. Cariogenic.
D. Anticoagulant.

_____ 20. Drugs that act as stimulants on the central nervous system are the:
A. Narcotics.
B. Antidepressants.
C. Antihistamines.
D. Amphetamines.

_____ 21. A drug that relieves constipation and promotes defecation is a(n):
A. Antacid.
B. Cytotoxin.
C. Cathartic.
D. Antidiarrheal.

_____ 22. A drug that arrests the flow of blood by helping coagulation is a:
A. Hemostatic.
B. Mydriatic.
C. Vasoconstrictor.
D. Vasodilator.

23. Some drugs, when taken together, may enhance or counteract the effect of the other. If the interaction is _____ , one drug augments the activity of the other drug; the action of the drugs is such that their combined effect is greater than the sum of their individual effects.
A. Additive
B. Antagonistic
C. Synergistic
D. Cumulative

24. A _____ action occurs when a drug is absorbed and circulates in the blood stream to produce a general effect, such as central nervous system stimulates and depressants do.
   A. Local
   B. Systemic
   C. Selective
   D. Cumulative

25. When a systemic effect is desired from an irritating drug, it should be given by a(n) _____ injection rather than by other parenteral routes.
   A. Subcutaneous
   B. Intradermal
   C. Intravenous
   D. Intramuscular

26. The most common site for administering intramuscular injections is the:
   A. Middletoid area.
   B. Gluteus medius.
   C. Ventrogluteal area.
   D. Vastus lateralis

27. The part of a prescription that gives the instructions to the patient is called the:
   A. Superscription.
   B. Inscription.
   C. Subscription.
   D. Signa.

28. The part of a prescription that gives directions to the pharmacist for compounding a drug is the:
   A. Superscription.
   B. Inscription.
   C. Subscription.
   D. Signa.

29. An unusual or abnormal response or susceptibility to a drug that is peculiar to the individual is called a drug:
   A. Tolerance.
   B. Contraindication.
   C. Idiosyncrasy.
   D. Side effect.

30. A patient who has been taking a medication regularly for an extended period of time may have developed a(n) _____ to the drug, and a larger dose may be required to obtain the desired results.
   A. Idiosyncrasy
   B. Potentiating effect
   C. Tolerance
   D. Antagonistic effect

31. A(n) _____ injection is usually administered in the outer surface of the upper arm, usually halfway between the shoulder and elbow.
   A. Subcutaneous
   B. Intramuscular
   C. Intradermal
   D. Intravenous

32. The most common and preferred site for intradermal injections is the:
   A. Ventral surface of the forearm, about 4 inches below the elbow.
   B. Outer surface of the upper arm, usually halfway between the shoulder and elbow.
   C. Upper outer quadrant of the buttock.
   D. Lateral aspect of the thigh.

33. When administering an intradermal to patients over 60 years of age, the _____ muscle may be used:
   A. Gluteus medius
   B. Deltoid
   C. Vastus lateralis
   D. Trapezius

34. A solution that is added to another to reduce the strength of the initial solution or mixture is a(n):
   A. Diluent.
   B. True solution.
   C. Emulsion.
   D. Solute.

116

Labeling

1. Label the parts of these syringes (Figure 7-1).

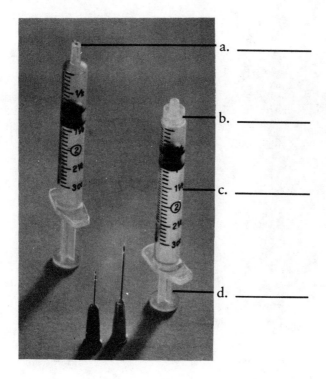

a. _____

b. _____

c. _____

d. _____

2. Label the parts of these needles (Figure 7-2).

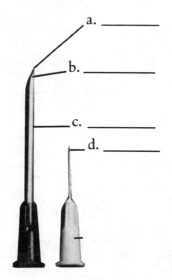

a. _____

b. _____

c. _____

d. _____

3. Label these containers of drugs that are supplied in a liquid form (Figure 7-3).

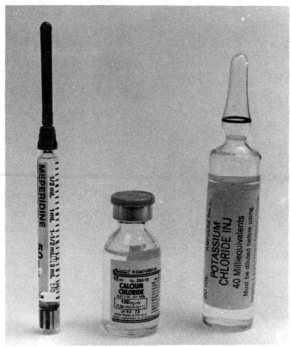

a. _____ b. _____ c. _____

4. State the type of injection that would be administered at the angles shown in the following diagram (Figure 7-4).

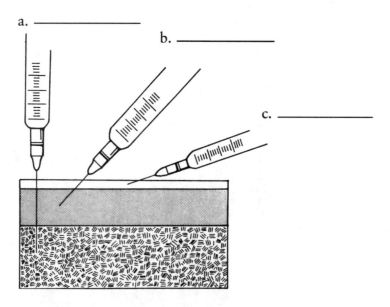

a. _____

b. _____

c. _____

PERFORMANCE TEST

In a skills laboratory, a simulation of a joblike environment, the medical assistant student is to demonstrate skill in preparing for and administering medication safely and efficiently by accomplishing the following.

1. Intramuscular injection in one of the four sites discussed in this unit; IM injection using the Z-tract technique.
2. Subcutaneous injection in the upper, outer part of the arm.
3. Loading and using a Tubex injector with a prefilled sterile cartridge-needle unit for an IM injection.

These procedures are to be performed without reference to source materials. For these activities, the student will need a person to play the role of the patient for demonstrating the correct positioning of the patient and to locate the correct anatomical site to be used for the injection. An artificial limb may be used for performing the actual injection. Time limits for the performance of the above procedure are to be assigned by the instructor.

The student is expected to perform these skills and record the procedures on the patient's chart with 100% accuracy.

PERFORMANCE CHECKLIST: Prepare and administer an intramuscular injection

DIRECTIONS: Evaluate student performance of each procedure using the following checklist. When you evaluate "not applicable," "unsatisfactory," or "not observed," please comment.

Checklist	S or NA*	U	N0	Comment
1. Washed hands. **Use appropriate Personal Protective Equipment (PPE) as dictated by facility.**				
2. Assembled equipment.				
3. Prepared syringe and needle for use.				
4. Checked physician's medication order with the label on the medication container.				
5. Checked the medication label three times when preparing the medication for administration.				
6. Calculated the correct dosage, if applicable.				
7. Took an alcohol sponge to clean ampule or vial.				
8. *For an ampule*: • Tapped the tip, cleaned the neck, filed, and broke the top off.				
• Removed the needle cover.				
• Inserted the needle into the vial, and withdrew the required amount of drug.				
• Removed the needle from the ampule, and replaced the cover over the needle. Used the one-handed method.				
• Placed the syringe with the needle and the alcohol sponge on a tray.				
• Checked the label on the ampule, discarded the ampule, and proceeded to the patient.				
9. *For a vial*: • Pulled the plunger on the syringe back to obtain a measured amount of air equal to the amount of mediation to be withdrawn from the vial.				
• Removed the needle cover, and inserted the needle through the cleansed rubber stopper of the vial, keeping the needle above the solution level.				
• Pushed the plunger to the bottom of the barrel of the syringe.				
• Inverted the vial, and with the needle opening in the solution, pulled the plunger back to withdraw the required amount of medication.				
• Removed the air bubbles in the syringe by tapping the barrel with fingertips until all air bubbles disappeared. Checked again that required amount of drug was withdrawn into the syringe.				

DIRECTIONS: Evaluate student performance of each procedure using the following checklist. When you evaluate "not applicable," "unsatisfactory," or "not observed," please comment.

Checklist	S or NA*	U	NO	Comment
• Removed the needle from the vial and replaced the cover over the needle.				
• Checked the label on the vial and replaced it in the storage area.				
• Proceeded to the patient.				
10. Identified and explained the procedure to the patient.				
11. Selected the injection site, and positioned the patient accordingly.				
12. Donned disposable single-use exam gloves.				
13. Cleaned the injection site.				
14. Removed the needle cover, and expelled air bubbles.				
15. Inserted the needle at a 90-degree angle with a quick thrust.				
16. Pulled back on the plunger; if no blood was aspirated, injected the medication slowly.				
17. Applied pressure to the injection site with an alcohol sponge, withdrew the needle quickly, and massaged the injection site.				
18. Assisted the patient as required, observed for any reactions, and left the patient with further instructions, if applicable.				
19. Removed used equipment and disposed of properly as indicated by the type of supplies used. Put disposable, uncapped needle and syringe in a puncture-resistant container for used sharps.				
20. Removed gloves and washed hands.				
21. Recorded the procedure on the patient's chart: date, time, name of medication, dosage, route used, site of injection, reason if applicable, and signature.				

Total Satisfactory Points _____

Comments

Student's signature: _____   Instructor's signature: _____
Date: _____
*S or NA, Satisfactory or not applicable; U, unsatisfactory; NO, not observed.

PERFORMANCE CHECKLIST: Prepare and administer a subcutaneous injection

DIRECTIONS: Evaluate student performance of each procedure using the following checklist. When you evaluate "not applicable," "unsatisfactory," or "not observed," please comment.

Checklist	S or NA*	U	NO	Comment
1. Washed hands **Use appropriate Personal Protective Equipment (PPE) as dictated by facility.**				
2. Assembled the equipment.				
3. Prepared the syringe and needle for use.				
4. Checked the label of medication three times when preparing the medication.				
5. Calculated dosage, if applicable.				
6. Cleaned the ampule or vial with an alcohol sponge.				
7. Inserted the needle into the ampule or vial, and withdrew the required amount of the drug.				
8. Checked the label, and replaced the vial in storage; or discarded the ampule.				
9. Identified and explained the procedure to the patient.				
10. Selected the injection site, positioned the patient, donned disposable, single use gloves, and cleaned the injection site.				
11. Expelled air bubbles from the syringe, and inserted the needle at a 45-degree angle.				
12. Pulled back on the plunger; injected the medication slowly.				
13. With an alcohol sponge, applied pressure to the injection site, and removed the needle quickly. Massaged the injection site, and observed the patient for any reactions.				
14. Left the patient safe and comfortable, providing any further instructions.				
15. Removed and disposed of equipment as indicated by the type used. *Did not* recap needle. Placed disposable syringe and needle in a puncture-resistant container for used sharps.				
16. Removed gloves and washed hands.				
17. Recorded the procedure, date, and signature on the patient's chart.				

Total Satisfactory Points   _____

Comments

Student's signature: _____ Instructor's signature: _____
Date: _____
*S or NA, Satisfactory or not applicable; U, unsatisfactory; NO, not observed.

PERFORMANCE CHECKLIST: Prepare and administer an injection using a Tubex injector and prefilled sterile cartridge-needle unit

DIRECTIONS: Evaluate student performance of each procedure using the following checklist. When you evaluate "not applicable," "unsatisfactory," or "not observed," please comment.

Checklist	S or NA*	U	NO	Comment
The method for administering the injection is basically the same as when using disposable or reusable syringes and needles. In loading and removing the Tubex injector with the prefilled sterile cartridge-needle unit:				
1. Turned the ribbed collar to the OPEN position until it stopped.				
2. Held the injector with the open end up and fully inserted the Tubex sterile cartridge-needle unit.				
3. Firmly tightened the ribbed collar in the direction of the CLOSE arrow.				
4. Threaded the plunger rod into the plunger of the Tubex sterile cartridge-needle unit until slight resistance was felt. The injector was now ready for use in the usual manner.				
AFTER USE				
5. *Did not* recap the needle. Disengaged the plunger rod.				
6. Held the injector, needle down, over a needle disposable container and loosened the ribbed collar. The Tubex cartridge-needle unit dropped into the container.				
7. Discarded the needle cover.				
8. Removed gloves and washed hands.				
9. Recorded the date, procedure, and signature on the patient's chart.				
10. Completed the procedure in the time limit set by the instructor.				

Total Satisfactory Points   _____

Comments

Student's signature:_____   Instructor's signature: _____
Date: _____
*S or NA, Satisfactory or not applicable; U, unsatisfactory; NO, not observed.

PERFORMANCE CHECKLIST: Prepare and administer an intramuscular injection using the Z-tract technique

DIRECTIONS: Evaluate student performance of each procedure using the following checklist. When you evaluate "not applicable," "unsatisfactory," or "not observed," please comment.

Checklist	S or NA*	U	NO	Comment
1. Followed steps 1 through 14 as listed under the checklist "Prepare and Administer an Intramuscular Injection" with the *exception* that the student changed needles after drawing the medication into the syringe.				
2. Moved the skin downward and toward the median.				
3. Inserted the needle at a 90-degree angle while maintaining traction on the tissue.				
4. Pulled back on the plunger; if no blood was aspirated, injected the medication slowly and smoothly while maintaining traction on the tissue.				
5. Waited 10 seconds, then withdrew the needle and immediately released the skin.				
6. *Did not massage the injection site.* If bleeding occurred, gently wiped the area with a dry sterile cotton ball or gauze.				
7. Advised the patient not to exercise or wear tight clothing immediately after the injection.				
8. Continued with steps 18 through 21 as given under the checklist "Prepare and Administer an Intramuscular Injection."				

Total Satisfactory Points _____

Comments

Student's signature:_____   Instructor's signature: _____
Date: _____
*S or NA, Satisfactory or not applicable; U, unsatisfactory; NO, not observed.

PERFORMANCE CHECKLIST: Reconstituting a powdered drug for administration

DIRECTIONS: Evaluate student performance of each procedure using the following checklist. When you evaluate "not applicable," "unsatisfactory," or "not observed," please comment.

Checklist	S or NA*	U	NO	Comment
1. Used a syringe and needle, inserted the needle through the cleaned rubber stopper of the vial containing the diluent.				
2. Withdrew the amount of liquid diluent that was to be added to the powdered drug.				
3. Added this liquid to the vial containing the powdered drug.				
4. With the needle above the fluid level in the vial, withdrew an amount of air equal to the amount of liquid diluent just added.				
5. Removed the needle from the vial.				
6. Discarded the syringe and needle in the used sharps container.				
7. Rolled the vial between the hands. This mixed the liquid with the powdered drug.				
8. Observed the solution obtained to make sure that all of the powdered drug was mixed and dissolved. The solution should be clear (or cloudy if it is a suspension).				
9. Labeled a multiple-dose vial with the date and time of preparation, the expiration date, the dilution/strength of the medication prepared.				
10. Stored any remaining drug according to the manufacturer's directions. Some drugs may have to be placed in a refrigerator.				
11. Completed procedure in the time limit set by the instructor.				

Total Satisfactory Points _____

Comments

Student's signature:_____ Instructor's signature: _____
Date: _____
*S or NA, Satisfactory or not applicable; U, unsatisfactory; NO, not observed.

Evaluation of student's technique   Name: _____   Date: _____

Satisfactory*   Unsatisfactory**

	Very Good	Good	Fair	Poor	Score
• IM injection	☐	☐	☐	☐	_____
• SR injection	☐	☐	☐	☐	_____
• Injections using the Tubex injector and prefilled cartridge-needle unit	☐	☐	☐	☐	_____
• IM injection using Z-tract technique	☐	☐	☐	☐	_____
• Reconstituting a powdered drug	☐	☐	☐	☐	_____

Very good = Perfect
Good   = Sufficient
Fair   = Not acceptable requires more practice
Poor   = Totally unacceptable
Pass* = Satisfactory
Fail** = Unsatisfactory

Comments:

Fill-In

1. Chemotherapy
2. Drug idiosyncrasy
3. Tolerance
4. Habituation
5. Placebo
6. Side effect
7. Unit-dose
8. The science that deals with the study of drugs—their origins, properties, uses, and actions
9. a. To treat or cure a disease or condition.
   b. To relieve undesirable symptoms such as pain.
   c. To provide substances that the body is not producing or not producing in sufficient amounts, for example, insulin, used for diabetes mellitus, and thyroid extract, used for hypothyroidism.
10. Prevent disease, for example, vaccinations
11. a. Plant
    b. Animal
    c. Mineral
    d. Synthetic
12. a. When a drug is developed and marketed, it is assigned a specific name that is patented by the pharmaceutical company that has manufactured it. This is called the trade or brand name of the drug and is the exclusive property of the manufacturer.
    b. Each drug has an official or nonproprietary name, which is also called the generic name. This name is often descriptive of the chemical composition or class of the drug and is assigned to the drug in the early stages of its development for general recognition purposes. After the patent on a brand name drug has expired, other companies may manufacture and sell the drug either under different brand names or under the drug's generic name. These exact copies of the original drug are often called generic drugs.
    c. The chemical name represents the drug's exact formula, that is, the chemical makeup or molecular structure.
13. Controlled substances
14. Drug Enforcement Administration (DEA) in the United States Department of Justice
15. Addiction and abuse potential
16. C; II, III, IV, V; C
17. I
18. V
19. Prescribed, administered, or dispensed by practitioners licensed by state law to prescribe drugs

20. Over-the-counter (OTC)
21. a. Drugs that have a principal action on the body; for example, analgesics, antidiarrheals
    b. Drugs used to treat or prevent specific diseases; for example, hormones, vaccines
    c. Drugs that act on specific organs or body systems; for example, cardiovascular drugs, gastrointestinal drugs
    d. Forms of drug preparations; for example, solids or liquids
22. A prescription is an order written by a licensed physician giving instructions to a pharmacist to supply a certain patient with a particular drug of specific quantity, prepared according to the physician's directions. It is a legal document.
23. a. Date, patient's name, and address (For children, the age should be given.)
    b. Superscription, consisting of the symbol Rx, from the Latin, *recipe*, meaning, "take thou"
    c. Inscription, specifying the ingredients and the quantities; the name of the drug, the dosage form, and the amount per dose
    d. Subscription, giving directions to the pharmacist on how to compound the drug(s). It generally designates the number of doses to be dispensed.
    e. *Signa* (Sig), from Latin, meaning "mark," which gives instructions to the patient indicating when and how to take the drug and in what quantities.
    f. Physician's signature, address, and phone number, registry number, and when prescribing controlled substances, the BNDD number
    g. Number of times, if any, that the prescription may be refilled
24. Generic equivalent
25. Do not substitute
26. 2 years (3 years in some states)
27. Ink or indelible pencil; the physician.
28. Actually given to the patient to take by mouth or when it is injected, inserted, or given by any other method used for administering medications
29. Given to a patient by the physician (or pharmacist at the pharmacy) to be taken at a later time
30. The physician gives the patient a written order, the prescription, to have filled by the pharmacist.
31. A separate room in a locked cabinet; their original container
32. Down the sink; flushed down the sink
33. Well separated
34. Physician; DEA field office in the area
35. Replace items that have been used and to discard outdated drugs or sterile supplies.
36. Discarded

37. The palm of the hand.
38. 2 years (3 years in some states)
39. Injection
40. a. Right drug
    b. Right dose
    c. Right route for administration
    d. Right time
    e. Right patient
    f. Right documentation
41. Discard the medication down a sink or toilet.
42. Date, time, drug, amount given, route of administration, and signature
43. a. Age
    b. Sex
    c. Weight
    d. Past medical history and drug tolerance
    e. Physical or emotional condition of the patient
    f. Drug idiosyncrasies or allergies
    g. Route of administration
    h. Time of administration
    i. Interactions of drugs
44. a. To achieve a rapid response to the medication. When injected, a medication enters the bloodstream quickly and therefore is more effective.
    b. To guarantee the accuracy of the amount of medication given
    c. To concentrate the medication in a specific area of the body, such as into a joint cavity, fracture, or lumbar puncture
    d. To produce local anesthesia to a specific part of the body
    e. To administer the medication when it cannot be given by mouth or by other methods, either because of the physical or mental condition of the patient or the nature of the drug
    f. To administer the medication when its effect would be destroyed by the digestive tract or lost through vomiting or when it would irritate the digestive system
45. a. Injury to superficial nerves or to a vessel
    b. Introduction of infection because of the improper disinfection of the injection site, and/or a contaminated needle, or syringe, or caused by an operator with unclean hands.
    c. Breakage of a needle in a tissue
    d. Injecting a blood vessel rather than a muscle or subcutaneous tissue
    e. Hitting a bone in a very thin patient
    f. Allergic reactions that may be mild, severe, or even fatal
    g. Toxic effects produced by the medication
    h. Too much air entering the bloodstream in a venipuncture

46. a. Burned areas
    b. Scar tissues
    c. Edematous areas
    d. Cyanotic areas
    e. Traumatized areas
    f. Areas near large blood vessels, nerves, and bones
    g. Areas in which there has been a change in skin texture or pigmentation
    h. Areas in which there are other tissue growths, such as a mole or wart
47. 2 cc, 3 cc, 5 cc, and 10 cc
48. Larger
49. 18
50. Antiseptic; isopropyl alcohol
51. Vials
52. Inject it deep into the muscle for gradual and optimal absorption into the bloodstream
53. a. Gluteus medius
    b. Middeltoid area
    c. Ventrogluteal area (von Hochstetter's site)
    d. Vastus lateralis
54. Gluteus medius; upper outer quadrant of the buttock
55. Deposit a relatively small amount of an aqueous solution under the skin for rapid absorption into the bloodstream
56. a. Outer surface of the upper arm, usually halfway between the shoulder and elbow
    b. Lateral aspect of the thigh
    c. Upper two thirds of the back
57. a. Areas on the abdomen
    b. Front aspect of the thigh
58. Inject a minute amount of solution between the layers of the skin
59. 0.1 ml to 0.3 ml. tuberculin
60. Ventral surface of the forearm, about 4 inches below the elbow
61. Withdraw a bit, redirected and again inserted. The plunger should be pulled back to determine if a second blood vessel has been entered. *Or* some recommend removing the needle and beginning the procedure again using new medication, syringe, and needle.
62. Medications such as Imferon, which may cause irritation of subcutaneous tissue and discoloration from leaking medications, or when complete absorption of the medication by the muscle tissue is crucial
63. Upper outer quadrant of the buttock; 90
64. If the skin is not dry before the injection is given, some of the disinfectant could be forced into subcutaneous tissue and cause more discomfort to the patient.

65. Help in reducing pain to the patient
66. Sudden distention of the tissue and more discomfort.
67. This can result in varying actions from the insulin and variable blood glucose levels. one
68. Abdominal. arms; thighs and buttocks
69. Rubbing the injection site can vary the absorption rate.
70. Clear Regular
71. a. Anxiety or a feeling of impending doom
    b. Confusion
    c. Cyanosis
    d. Dyspnea
    e. Increased BP
    f. Pale, cool extremities (due to vasoconstriction)
    g. Restlessness
    h. Tachycardia
72. a. Apnea
    b. Carbon monoxide poisoning
    c. Congestive heart disease
    d. Chronic obstructive pulmonary disease
    e. During surgical procedures
    f. Myocardial infarction
    g. Pulmonary edema
    h. Pneumonia
    i. Shock

Multiple Choice

 1. D
 2. C
 3. A
 4. D
 5. B
 6. C
 7. A
 8. B
 9. D
10. B
11. C
12. D
13. A
14. B
15. A
16. C
17. A
18. B
19. B
20. D
21. C
22. A
23. C
24. B
25. D
26. B
27. D
28. C
29. C
30. C
31. A
32. A
33. D
34. A

Labeling

1. a. Plain tip
   b. Luer-Lok tip
   c. Barrel
   d. Plunger
2. a. Point
   b. Bevel
   c. Cannula or shaft
   d. Lumen
   e. Hub
3. a. Cartridge
   b. Vial
   c. Ampule
4. a. Intramuscular
   b. Subcutaneous
   c. Intradermal

Unit 8

Diagnostic Allergy and Intradermal Skin Tests

SUGGESTED ACTIVITIES

1. With a partner, practice identifying the correct sites for administering an intradermal injection on a child, adult, and elderly adult.

2. With a partner, identify the sites used for a patch test, a scratch test, and a line tuberculin test.

3. Do you or does anyone you know have allergies? If the answer is yes, describe the signs and symptoms of the allergies. Discuss the method used to determine the cause of the allergies.

4. At the facility where you do your work experience, learn what action would be taken if a patient experienced an allergic reaction to a medication.

STUDY QUESTIONS
Fill-In

In the blanks provided, write the answers that best complete the sentences:

1. An _____ is the abnormal individual hypersensitivity to substances (allergens) that are usually harmless. _____ , substances capable of inducing hypersensitivity, can be almost any substance in the environment.

2. Give the signs and symptoms of allergies.

    a. _____

    b. _____

    c. _____

    d. _____

    e. _____

    f. _____

    g. _____

    h. _____

    i. _____

    j. _____

    k. _____

3. In order for the physician to correctly treat the patient's condition, the _____ responsible for the reaction must be identified.

4. Explain the principle involved in skin testing to diagnose allergies. _____
_____
_____.

5. Control tests using the diluent without the active allergen are essential in each type of testing because _____
_____.

6. Once the offending allergen has been identified the first step in treatment is to _____.

7. Often patients can be cured of allergies by
_____.
For these treatments patients are given _____
_____.

8. Allergies that are resistant to cure may be controlled with _____
_____.

9. Today the patch test is most often used to _____
   _____ .

10. To determine tissue hypersensitivity, using the patch test, gauze is impregnated with _____ and then applied and left in contact with an intact skin surface for _____ hours _____ .

11. Body sites used when administering the patch test are _____ . The _____ is the preferred site for adults; the _____ is preferred for children.

12. When determining allergies using the patch test as many as _____ to _____ patches may be applied at one time on _____ (body location).

13. When doing the scratch test, make one or more scratches in _____ then place a drop of the substance to be tested in the scratch for ____ minutes.

14. The scratch test is frequently used for detecting _____ .

15. When the commercially prepared kit for a scratch test is not used, the following equipment is needed:
    _____

16. When doing a scratch test make a _____-inch scratch with the needle supplied in the kit *or* with a 26-gauge needle *or* with a dull sterile knife.
    Then place _____ drop(s) of the allergen on the scratch.

17. When interpreting the scratch test results a *negative reaction* is _____ . A *positive reaction* is _____ .

18. In intradermal (intracutaneous) tests, a small amount of the substance under study is injected into _____ .

19. Intradermal skin tests are used to:
    a. _____
    b. _____

20. Describe the body sites to use for intradermal injections.
    a. _____
    b. _____

21. The angle used to insert the needle for an intradermal injection is _____ to the skin.

22. Many intradermal skin tests done to diagnose allergies are read as either positive or negative depending on _____ .

23. The standard test recommended by the American Lung Association to help detect people exposed to and infected with *Mycobacterium tuberculosis* is _____ .

24. The petrified protein derivative (PPD) skin test is performed by injecting intradermally _____ _____ .

25. A mantoux or PPD skin reaction is read _____ hours after the injection was given. Consider only _____ when interpreting the results.

26. When interpreting the Tuberculin skin test result a *positive reaction* is _____ _____ .
    A *doubtful reaction* is _____ _____ .
    A *negative reaction* is _____ _____ .

Multiple Choice

Write the letter of the correct answer in the blank provided. There is only *one* correct answer.

_____ 1. The patch test is most often used to diagnose:
- A. Skin allergies.
- B. Tuberculosis.
- C. Food allergies.
- D. Anaphylaxis.

_____ 2. The substance being tested in the patch test is left in contact with intact skin surface for _____ hours.
- A. 2
- B. 12
- C. 48
- D. 84

_____ 3. In the scratch test one or more scratches are made in the skin, then a drop of the substance to be tested is placed in the scratch and left for _____ minutes.
- A. 5
- B. 10
- C. 20
- D. 30

_____ 4. The _____ is the preferred site for a patch test for adults.
- A. leg
- B. forearm
- C. back
- D. upper outer part of the arm

_____ 5. An intradermal injection is inserted into the skin at a _____ -degree angle.
- A. 10 to 15
- B. 20 to 30
- C. 45
- D. 90

_____ 6. The _____ test is used to detect people who have been exposed to tuberculosis.
- A. Patch
- B. Scratch
- C. Mantoux
- D. Prick

_____ 7. A _____ syringe is used for intradermal skin tests.
- A. 2 cc
- B. 5 cc
- C. Tuberculin
- D. Insulin

_____ 8. In the PPD skin test 0.1 of tuberculin PPD is given:
- A. Intramuscularly.
- B. Intradermally.
- C. Subcutaneously.
- D. To a scratch made on the skin.

_____ 9. The reaction of the PPD test is read _____ hours after it is administered.
- A. 12 to 24
- B. 48 to 72
- C. 24 to 36
- D. 4 to 8

_____ 10. The patient who has a positive tuberculin test definitely has tuberculosis.
- A. True
- B. False

_____ 11. When reading the results of a Mantoux test only induration should be considered.
- A. True
- B. False

_____ 12. When reading the results of a Mantoux test disregard erythema of less than 10 mm.
- A. True
- B. False

PERFORMANCE TESTS

In a skill laboratory, a simulation of a joblike environment, the medical assistant student is to demonstrate knowledge and skill in performing the following procedures without reference to source materials. Time limits for the performance of each procedure are to be assigned by the instructor.

1. Select and prepare the supplies and equipment, then perform the following procedures:
   Patch test
   Scratch test
   Intradermal skin test (intradermal injection)
   Mantoux test
   Tine tuberculin test

2. Read and record the results of these tests.

   The student is expected to perform these skills with 100% accuracy.

PERFORMANCE CHECKLIST: Patch test

DIRECTIONS: Evaluate student performance of each procedure using the following checklist. When you evaluate "not applicable," "unsatisfactory," or "not observed," please comment.

Checklist	S or NA*	U	NO	Comment
1. Checked physician's order.				
2. Washed hands. **Use appropriate Personal Protective Equipment (PPE) as dictated by facility.**				
3. Assembled the equipment.				
4. Identified and prepared the patient; explained the procedure; positioned the patient.				
5. Cleaned the skin.				
6. Prepared the dressing with the allergen.				
7. Applied the impregnated dressing to the skin.				
8. Labeled the test allergen with name or number.				
9. Instructed the patient.				
10. Recorded the test on the patient's record.				
11. Removed the patch, and read the results.				
12. Instructed the patient.				
13. Left the treatment room clean.				
14. Washed hands.				
15. Recorded the procedure, date, time, and signature on the patient's record.				
16. Completed the procedure in the time limit assigned by the instructor.				

Total Satisfactory Points _____

Comments

Student's signature: _____ Instructor's signature: _____

Date: _____

*S or NA, Satisfactory or not applicable; U, unsatisfactory; NO, not observed.

PERFORMANCE CHECKLIST: Scratch test

DIRECTIONS: Evaluate student performance of each procedure using the following checklist. When you evaluate "not applicable," "unsatisfactory," or "not observed," please comment.

Checklist	S or NA*	U	NO	Comment
1. Checked physician's order.				
2. Washed hands.				
Use appropriate Personal Protective Equipment (PPE) as dictated by facility.				
3. Assembled the equipment.				
4. Identified and prepared the patient; explained the procedure, and positioned the patient with the test site exposed and supported.				
5. Donned disposable, single-use exam gloves.				
6. Washed the skin site.				
7. Wrote test numbers 2 inches apart on skin.				
8. Made a ⅛-inch scratch.				
9. Placed one drop of the allergen on the scratch.				
10. Made additional scratches, and applied over allergens as needed.				
11. Allowed the allergen to set for 30 minutes.				
12. Wiped off excess solution.				
13. Read the results.				
14. Instructed the patient.				
15. Removed used supplies. Left the treatment room clean.				
16. Removed gloves.				
17. Washed hands.				
18. Completed the procedure in the time limit assigned by the instructor.				

Total Satisfactory Points _____

Comments

Student's signature:_____   Instructor's signature: _____

Date: _____

*S or NA, Satisfactory or not applicable; U, unsatisfactory; NO, not observed.

136

PERFORMANCE CHECKLIST: Intradermal skin test and Mantoux test

DIRECTIONS: Evaluate student performance of each procedure using the following checklist. When you evaluate "not applicable," "unsatisfactory," or "not observed," please comment.

Checklist	S or NA*	U	NO	Comment
1. Washed hands. **Use appropriate Personal Protective Equipment (PPE) as dictated by facility.**				
2. Assembled the equipment.				
3. Prepared the syringe and needle for use.				
4. Checked the physician's order.				
5. Identified the medication label three times.				
6. Cleaned the stopper of the vial, inserted the needle, and withdrew the required amount of solution.				
7. Identified the patient, and explained the procedure.				
8. Selected the injection site, and positioned the procedure.				
9. Donned disposable single-use exam gloves.				
10. Cleaned the injection site. Allowed site to dry thoroughly.				
11. Removed the needle cover, and expelled excess air from the syringe.				
12. Facing the patient, grasped and supported the forearm to be injected with nondominant hand; pulled the anterior skin taut.				
13. Inserted the needle at a 10- to 15-degree angle.				
14. Injected the solution slowly.				
15. Withdrew the needle; wiped the injection site gently. *Did not* massage the injection site.				
16. Observed the patient for any unusual reaction; positioned the patient for safety and comfort.				
17. Instructed the patient.				
18. Removed and disposed of used needle and syringe correctly in container for used sharps.				
19. Removed gloves and washed hands.				
20. Recorded the procedure, date, time, results, and signature.				
21. Completed the procedure in the time limit assigned by the instructor.				

Total Satisfactory Points   _____

Comments

Student's signature: _____ Instructor's signature: _____
Date: _____
*S or NA, Satisfactory or not applicable; U, unsatisfactory; NO, not observed.

PERFORMANCE CHECKLIST: Tine tuberculin test

DIRECTIONS: Evaluate student performance of each procedure using the following checklist. When you evaluate "not applicable," "unsatisfactory," or "not observed," please comment.

Checklist	S or NA*	U	NO	Comment
1. Washed hands. **Use appropriate Personal Protective Equipment (PPE) as dictated by facility.**				
2. Assembled the equipment.				
3. Identified and prepared the patient; explained the procedure; positioned the patient with a forearm exposed.				
4. Donned disposable single-use exam gloves.				
5. Cleaned the skin on the forearm. Allowed skin to dry thoroughly.				
6. Removed the protective cap on the tine unit.				
7. Grasped the patient's forearm; with dominant hand, punctured the skin with the tine unit; held for 1 second before withdrawing.				
8. Discarded the tine unit in container for used sharps.				
9. Instructed the patient.				
10. Removed gloves and washed hands.				
11. Read the reaction in a good light; the patient's forearm should be slightly flexed.				
12. Recorded the procedure, date, time, results and signature on the patient's chart.				
13. Completed the procedure in the time limit assigned by the instructor.				

Total Satisfactory Points _____

Comments

Student's signature: _____ Instructor's signature: _____

Date: _____

*S or NA, Satisfactory or not applicable; U, unsatisfactory; NO, not observed.

Evaluation of student's technique   Name: _____   Date: _____

| | Satisfactory* | | Unsatisfactory** | | |

	Very Good	Good	Fair	Poor	Score
• Patch test	☐	☐	☐	☐	_____
• Scratch test	☐	☐	☐	☐	_____
• Intradermal skin test & Mantoux test	☐	☐	☐	☐	_____
• Tine tuberculin test	☐	☐	☐	☐	_____

Very good = Perfect
Good   = Sufficient
Fair   = Not acceptable requires more practice
Poor   = Totally unacceptable
Pass*   = Satisfactory
Fail**   = Unsatisfactory

Comments:

139

ANSWERS
Fill-In

1. allergy. Allergens
2. a. sneezing
   b. stuffed-up and running nose
   c. watery eyes
   d. itching
   e. coughing
   f. shortness of breath
   g. wheezing
   h. rashes
   i. skin eruptions
   j. slight local edema
   k. mild to severe anaphylactic shock, which can be fatal unless treated
3. allergen
4. When a minute amount of various suspected allergens is applied to the skin in these tests, a mild allergic reaction occurs at the site of the offending allergen without causing any serious symptoms.
5. Positive reactions at the other test sites can be compared with the appearance at the control site to verify that they are true allergic reactions and not merely irritating reactions to the diluent or trauma to the skin area.
6. Avoid it.
7. Receiving a series of densenitization treatments. the allergen(s) in gradually increasing amounts in order to reduce sensitivity to those substances, or to build up resistance to the point of immunity
8. Certain medications such as antihistamines, epinephrine, aminophylline, and cortisone preparations
9. Diagnose skin allergies, especially contact dermatitis
10. the substance to be tested; at least 24 to 27, but usually 48 hours
11. the anterior forearm or the upper back. forearm; back.
12. 23; 30; the back
13. the skin; 30
14. types of allergies
15. the bottles containing the allergens to be tested and 26-gauge needles (a dull, sterile knife may also be used.)
16. ⅔; one
17. No reaction after 30 minutes.
18. the substance of the skin
19. a. determine the patient's susceptibility to an infectious disease
    b. and to diagnose infectious diseases such as tuberculosis (the Mantoux test) and diphtheria (the Schick test).
20. a. The dorsal surface of the forearm, about 4 inches below the elbow
    b. The area over the trapezius muscle (on the back), just below the acromial process can be used for patients over 60 years of age
21. almost parallel—to 10-to 15-degree angle
22. the amount of redness (erythema) or hardening (induration)
23. the Mantoux test (also called the tuberculin or PPD skin test)
24. exactly 0.1 ml of tuberculin PPD. This dose contains 5 TU (tuberculin units) of tuberculin PPD.
25. 48 to 72; induration (area of hardened tissue)
26. induration measuring 10 mm or more indicates hypersensitivity to the tuberculin PPD and is interpreted as positive for present or past infection with Mycobacterium tuberculosis. A positive reaction does not necessarily signify active disease. Further diagnostic procedures must be performed before a diagnosis of tuberculosis is made.

   Induration measuring 5 to 9 mm means that retesting may be indicated using a different test site.

   Induration of less than 5 mm indicates a lack of hypersensitivity to the tuberculin, and tuberculosis infection is highly unlikely.

Multiple Choice

1. A
2. C
3. D
4. B
5. A
6. C
7. C
8. B
9. B
10. B
11. A
12. A

Unit 9

Instillations and Irrigations of the Ear and Eye

SUGGESTED ACTIVITIES

1. If you know someone who wears a hearing aid, ask the person to explain to you the difference it makes when listening or speaking with someone.

2. Put ear plugs in your ears, wear them for a few hours, then describe how it felt not to be able to hear sounds clearly or distinctly.

3. In a safe environment try blindfolding yourself for one half hour while you are speaking with someone. Describe how it felt not to be able to see the person with whom you were speaking.

4. Practice checking the otoscope and ophthalmoscope for proper functioning. Learn how to change the batteries in those instruments that require them.

5. With a partner, practice positioning and giving each other directions for instilling ear and eye drops.

STUDY QUESTIONS
Fill-In

In the blanks provided, write the answers that best complete the sentences:

1. Ear wax secreted by the glands of the external auditory meatus is called _____ .

2. The delicate membrane lining the eyelids and reflected onto the front of the eyeball is the

_____ .

3. A medication that causes the pupil of the eye to contract is called a _____ .

4. A medication that causes the pupil of the eye to dilate is called a _____ .

5. The study and science of the eye and its diseases is called _____ .

6. The study and science of the ear and its diseases is called _____ .

7. An instrument used for visual inspection of the ear is called _____ .

8. An _____is the dropping of a fluid into a body cavity; an _____ is the flushing or washing of a body cavity with a stream of fluid.

9. To lesson discomfort for the patient, the medications used for an ear instillation should be

_____ slightly before using. Solutions that are either too cold or too hot may cause a feeling of _____ in addition to pain.

10. Explain the reasons ear instillations are performed.

a. _____

b. _____

11. To straighten the external ear canal in adults gently pull the top of the earlobe_____ and

_____ .

12. When instilling ear drops, the dropper should be positioned so that the drops are instilled _____ of the ear canal.

13. An ear irrigation is _____ _____ .

14. Explain the reasons an ear irrigation is done.

   a. _____
      _____

   b. _____
      _____

   c. _____
      _____

   d. _____
      _____

   e. _____
      _____

15. Before an ear irrigation is done, all patients must be asked if they have a history of _____ and _____ . If the answer to either questions is "yes" the physician must be notified before giving this treatment.

16. When doing an ear irrigation, extreme care must be taken to prevent injury to the _____ and the spread of any infection to the _____ cavity.

17. When doing an ear irrigation, the patient should be positioned sitting with the head slightly tilted _____ the affected side.

18. To test the temperature of the solution used for an ear irrigation a few drops should be put on _____ . The solution should feel _____ .

19. Straightening the ear canal for an ear irrigation allows the irrigating solution to _____ .

20. During an ear irrigation the solution should be directed at the roof of the canal to prevent _____ , to prevent _____ , and to facilitate _____ .

21. Continue an ear irrigation until _____ _____ .

22. List the reasons eye instillations are performed.

   a. _____
   b. _____
   c. _____
   d. _____
   e. _____
   f. _____

23. When instilling eye drops, the dropper should be held _____ to the eye about ½-inch away from the inner canthus (the inner angle of the eyelids near the nose), and instill the drop(s) into the center of the _____ of the lower lid.

24. After instilling eyedrops, the patient should be instructed to _____ . This movement helps distribute the medication over the eyeball.

25. When instilling eyedrops and ointment at the same time the _____ should be instilled first and the _____ last.

26. Eye irrigations are performed to:

   a. _____
   b. _____
   c. _____
   d. _____
   e. _____

27. For an eye irrigation the patient should be instructed to assume a _____ position with the head tilted _____ the side being treated.

28. During an eye irrigation instruct the patient to look _____ , but not to _____ the eyelids.

29. During an eye irrigation hold the dropper or syringe parallel to the eye, and squeeze the solution into the eye, allowing it to flow _____ the nose. The dropper or syringe should be held _____ -inch from the eye, and the solution allowed to flow in a steady stream, but at low pressure.

30. An eye irrigation should be continued until _____ , or _____ , or _____ .

Multiple Choice

Write the letter of the correct answer in the blank provided. There is only *one* correct answer.

_____ 1. Ophthalmology is the study and science of the _____ and its diseases.
   A. Ear
   B. Eye
   C. Nose
   D. Nose and throat

_____ 2. _____ is the dropping of a fluid into a body cavity.
   A. Instillation
   B. Irrigation
   C. Parenteral administration
   D. Inunction

_____ 3. An otoscope is an instrument used for visual inspection of the:
   A. Eye.
   B. Mouth.
   C. Nose.
   D. Ear.

_____ 4. Another name for ear wax is:
   A. Conjunctiva.
   B. Canthus.
   C. Cerumen.
   D. Cathartic.

_____ 5. To straighten the external ear canal in adults the top of the earlobe should be pulled gently:
   A. Upward and backward.
   B. Downward and backward.
   C. Upward and forward.
   D. Downward and forward.

_____ 6. When giving ear drops to a child, the earlobe should be pulled gently:
   A. Upward and backward.
   B. Downward and backward.
   C. Upward and forward.
   D. Downward and forward.

_____ 7. Antibiotic solutions can be instilled into the ear canal to combat an ear infection.
   A. True
   B. False

_____ 8. Surgical aseptic technique is used when instilling solutions into the ear.
   A. True
   B. False

_____ 9. Medications instilled into the ear canal should be _____ to lessen discomfort for the patient.
   A. Cold
   B. Cool
   C. Warm
   D. Hot

_____ 10. When instilling ear drops the patient should be instructed to tilt the head toward the _____ side.
   A. Affected
   B. Unaffected

_____ 11. An _____ is the flushing or washing of a body cavity with a stream of fluid.
   A. Instillation
   B. Irritation
   C. irrigation
   D. Application

_____ 12. The fluid used for an ear irrigation should be at a temperature of approximately _____ degrees Fahrenheit.
   A. 60
   B. 38
   C. 80
   D. 100

_____ 13. Eye drops may be instilled to dilate the pupil of the eye before an examination.
  A. True
  B. False

_____ 14. The medical abbreviation for right eye is:
  A. RE.
  B. OS.
  C. OD.
  D. OU.

_____ 15. The medical abbreviation for left eye is:
  A. LE.
  B. OS.
  C. OD.
  D. OU.

_____ 16. When instilling drops into the right eye, the patient should be instructed to look:
  A. To the left.
  B. To the right.
  C. Downward.
  D. Upward.

_____ 17. After the instillation of eye drops the patient should be instructed to squeeze the eyelids.
  A. True
  B. False

_____ 18. When the patient is to have both medicated eyedrops and eye ointment, _____ is (are) to be put in first.
  A. Eye drops
  B. Eye ointment

_____ 19. For an eye irrigation the patient should be instructed to tilt the head backward and _____ the side being treated.
  A. Away from
  B. Toward

PERFORMANCE TEST

In a skills laboratory, the medical assistant student, with a partner, is to assemble supplies and demonstrate with 100% accuracy the correct procedure for the following, without reference to source materials. Time limits for the performance of each procedure are to be assigned by the instructor.
1. Ear instillation
2. Ear irrigation
3. Eye instillations
4. Eye irrigation

144

PERFORMANCE CHECKLIST: Ear instillation

DIRECTIONS: Evaluate student performance of each procedure using the following checklist. When you evaluate "not applicable," "unsatisfactory," or "not observed," please comment.

Checklist	S or NA*	U	NO	Comment
1. Checked the medication order.				
2. Washed hands. **Use appropriate Personal Protective Equipment (PPE) as dictated by facility.**				
3. Assembled supplies.				
4. Read the medication label three times.				
5. Identified the patient; explained the nature and purpose of the procedure.				
6. Positioned the patient in a sitting or side-lying position.				
7. Donned disposable single-use exam gloves.				
8. Instructed the patient to tilt the head toward the unaffected side.				
9. Stood at the patient's head.				
10. Withdrew the medication into the dropper; examined the dropper for defects.				
11. Straightened the patient's external ear canal.				
12. Placed the tip of the dropper slightly inside the ear canal and instilled the medication. *Did not* touch the ear canal.				
13. Instructed the patient to keep the head tilted (or remain lying on the side) for a few minutes.				
14. When ordered, placed a cotton ball over the ear opening.				
15. Discarded unused medication in the dropper before replacing the dropper in the bottle.				
16. Removed and discarded gloves and washed hands.				
17. Attended to the patient; provided further instructions when required.				
18. Replaced supplies.				
19. Recorded the procedure, date, time, and signature on the patient's chart.				
20. Completed the procedure in the time limit assigned by the instructor.				

Total Satisfactory Points   _____

Comments

Student's signature:_____ Instructor's signature: _____

Date: _____

*S or NA, Satisfactory or not applicable; U, unsatisfactory; NO, not observed.

PERFORMANCE CHECKLIST: Ear irrigation

DIRECTIONS: Evaluate student performance of each procedure using the following checklist. When you evaluate "not applicable," "unsatisfactory," or "not observed," please comment.

Checklist	S or NA*	U	NO	Comment
1. Checked the medication order.				
2. Washed hands. **Use appropriate Personal Protective Equipment (PPE) as dictated by facility.**				
3. Assembled supplies.				
4. Checked the solution label three times; warmed the solution.				
5. Identified the patient; explained the nature and purpose of the procedure.				
6. Positioned the patient with the head slightly tilted toward the affected side.				
7. Draped the patient's shoulder.				
8. Donned disposable single-use exam gloves.				
9. Had the patient hold the basin under the ear and against the neck.				
10. Cleaned the outer ear and external auditory meatus as necessary.				
11. Tested the temperature of the solution.				
12. Filled the syringe with irrigating solution and expelled air, if present.				
13. Straightened the patient's ear canal.				
14. Placed the tip of the syringe at the ear opening; gently directed a steady, slow stream of solution against the roof of the canal, not touching the canal itself.				
15. Observed the returning solution.				
16. Observed the patient for pain and/or dizziness.				
17. Continued until the desired results were obtained.				
18. Dried the external ear with a cotton ball.				
19. Had the patient maintain the position for a few minutes.				
20. Removed soiled drapes; provided for the patient's safety and comfort; provided further instructions as indicated.				
21. Returned supplies.				
22. Removed gloves and washed hands.				

146

Checklist	S or NA*	U	NO	Comment
23. Recorded the procedure, date, time, and signature on the patient's chart.				
24. Completed the procedure in the time limit assigned by the instructor.				

Total Satisfactory Points   _____

Comments

Student's signature:_____   Instructor's signature: _____

Date: _____

*S or NA, Satisfactory or not applicable; U, unsatisfactory; NO, not observed.

PERFORMANCE CHECKLIST: Instillation of eye drops and ointment

DIRECTIONS: Evaluate student performance of each procedure using the following checklist. When you evaluate "not applicable," "unsatisfactory," or "not observed," please comment.

Checklist	S or NA*	U	NO	Comment
1. Checked the medication order.				
2. Washed hands. **Use appropriate Personal Protective Equipment (PPE) as dictated by facility.**				
3. Assembled supplies.				
4. Checked the medication label three times.				
5. Identified the patient; explained the procedure and purpose.				
6. Positioned the patient in a supine or sitting position with the head tilted slightly backward.				
7. Donned disposable single-use exam gloves.				
8. Stood at the patient's head.				
9. Withdrew solution, and examined the dropper for defects.				
10. With fingers over a tissue, drew the lower lid down gently, and had the patient look up.				
11. Held the dropper parallel to the eye; instilled the correct amount of medication into the middle of the conjunctival sac of the lower lid. To instill ointment, gently squeezed a thin strip of ointment from the tube along the lower lid. *Did not* touch the eye or the lid.				
12. Instructed the patient to close the eyelids and move the eyeball, but not to squeeze the eyelids.				
13. Wiped excess solution off the cheek or eyelids.				
14. Discarded unused solution before replacing the dropper into the bottle, avoiding contamination of the dropper.				
15. Left the patient safe and comfortable; provided further instructions.				
16. Replaced supplies.				
17. Removed gloves and washed hands.				
18. Recorded the procedure, date, time, and signature on the patient's chart.				
19. Completed the procedure in the time limit assigned by the instructor.				

Total Satisfactory Points   _____

Comments

Student's signature: _____   Instructor's signature: _____

Date: _____

*S or NA, Satisfactory or not applicable; U, unsatisfactory; NO, not observed.

PERFORMANCE CHECKLIST: Eye irrigation

DIRECTIONS: Evaluate student performance of each procedure using the following checklist. When you evaluate "not applicable," "unsatisfactory," or "not observed," please comment.

Checklist	S or NA*	U	NO	Comment
1. Checked the medication order.				
2. Washed hands. **Use appropriate Personal Protective Equipment (PPE) as dictated by facility.**				
3. Assembled supplies.				
4. Checked the medication label three times.				
5. Identified the patient; explained the procedure and purpose. Instructed the patient not to squeeze the eyes during the treatment.				
6. Positioned the patient in a supine or sitting position with the head tilted slightly backward.				
7. Donned disposable single-use exam gloves.				
8. Positioned the basin to receive the irrigating solution; placed a towel under the basin.				
9. Stood in front of or to the side of the patient.				
10. Cleaned the eyelid.				
11. Filled the dropper or syringe with solution.				
12. Gently pulled the lower lid down and the brow down; instructed the patient to look up and not to squeeze the eyelids.				
13. Allowed the solution to flow in a steady stream at low pressure across the eye, away from the nose.				
14. Did not touch the eye or the eyelid with the syringe or dropper.				
15. Continued until desired results were obtained or until all the solution had been used.				
16. Gently dried the eye and cheek with a sterile cotton ball.				
17. Left the patient safe and comfortable; provided further instructions.				
18. Observed the drainage in the basin.				
19. Discarded the drainage and soiled disposable items; returned reusable supplies to the designated area.				
20. Removed gloves and washed hands.				

Checklist	S or NA*	U	NO	Comment
21. Recorded the date, procedure, time, signature, and the type and amount of solution used on the patient's card.				
22. Completed the procedure in the time limit assigned by the instructor.				

Total Satisfactory Points _____

Comments

Student's signature: _____ Instructor's signature: _____

Date: _____

*S or NA, Satisfactory or not applicable; U, unsatisfactory; NO, not observed.

Evaluation of student's technique   **Name:** _____ **Date:** _____

	Satisfactory*		Unsatisfactory**		
	Very Good	Good	Fair	Poor	Score

- Ear instillation   ☐   ☐   ☐   ☐   _____   Very good = Perfect
- Ear irrigation   ☐   ☐   ☐   ☐   _____   Good   = Sufficient
- Instillation of   ☐   ☐   ☐   ☐   _____   Fair   = Not acceptable; requires more practice
  eye drops and   Poor   = Totally unacceptable
  ointment   Pass* = Satisfactory
- Eye irrigation   ☐   ☐   ☐   ☐   _____   Fail** = Unsatisfactory

Comments:

ANSWERS
Fill-In

1. Cerumen
2. Conjunctiva
3. Miotic
4. Mydriatic
5. Ophthalmology
6. Otology
7. Otoscope
8. Instillation; irrigation
9. warmed. dizziness
10. a. To soften cerumen (ear wax) so that it can be removed easily later.
    b. To instill an antibiotic solution to combat an infection in the ear canal or eardrum.
11. Upward, backward. downward, backward
12. Along the side
13. The washing out of the external auditory canal with a stream of fluid
14. a. To clean the external auditory canal (external acoustic meatus).
    b. To relieve inflammation of the ear.
    c. To dislodge impacted cerumen or foreign bodies from the external auditory canal.
    d. To apply antiseptics to combat infection.
    e. To apply heat to the tissues of the ear canal.
15. Drainage from the ears; if they have ever had a perforation or other complications from a previous irrigation.
16. Tympanic membrane
    Mastoid
17. Toward
18. The inner aspect of your wrist and on the patient's wrist. warm
19. Reach all areas of the canal
20. Injury to the tympanic membrane; pushing material further into the canal; directing the inflow and outflow of the solution.
21. the desired results appear or the prescribed amount of solution has been used.
22. a. To dilate the pupil of the eye.
    b. To constrict the pupil of the eye.
    c. To relieve pain in the eye.
    d. To treat eye infections; relieve inflammation.
    e. To anesthetize the eye.
    f. To stimulate circulation in the eye.
23. Parallel; Conjunctival sac
24. Close the eyelids and move the eye; squeeze the eyelids.
25. Eye drops; ointment

26. a. Relieve inflammation of the conjunctiva.
    b. Remove inflammatory secretions.
    c. Prepare the eye for surgery.
    d. Wash away foreign material or injurious chemicals.
    e. Provide antibacterial and antifungal effects.
27. Lying or sitting; backward and toward
28. up; squeeze
29. away from; ½
30. The eye is free of secretions. The desired results occur. The prescribed amount of solution has been used.

Multiple Choice

1. B
2. A
3. D
4. C
5. A
6. B
7. A
8. B
9. C
10. B
11. C
12. D
13. A
14. C
15. B
16. D
17. B
18. A
19. B

Unit 10

Laboratory Orientation

SUGGESTED ACTIVITIES

1. Practice and then demonstrate proficiency in using and caring for a microscope.

2. Practice and then demonstrate proficiency in using and caring for a centrifuge.

3. Compare the classroom microscope and centrifuge with those that are at the facility where you do your work experience. Are there any differences in the function and use of these instruments? Discuss your findings with your classmates and instructor.

4. Have your instructor arrange a field trip to a large laboratory at a hospital. Observe the various departments in the laboratory and make a list of the tests performed in each one. Discuss your observations and findings with your classmates and instructor.

STUDY QUESTIONS
Fill-In

In the blanks provided, write the answers that best complete the sentences:

1. State three reasons for diagnostic studies.

    a. _____

    b. _____

    c. _____

2. List items that should be included on the requisition that accompanies a specimen to the laboratory.

    a. _____

    b. _____

    c. _____

    d. _____

    e. _____

    f. _____

    g. _____

3. Name six specialized departments common to all clinical laboratories.

    a. _____

    b. _____

    c. _____

    d. _____

    e. _____

    f. _____

4. The clinical laboratory area that deals with the study of blood is called _____ .

5. _____ involves laboratory tests that examine blood serum.

6. _____ deals with isolation and culture, microscopic identification, and biochemical tests to detect microorganisms that cause disease.

7. The study of bacteria is called _____

8. The study of viruses is called _____ .

9. The study of fungi is called _____ .

10. The study of rickettsiae is called _____ .

11. The study of protozoa is called _____ .

12. The study of algae is called _____ .

13. The study of parasites is known as

_____ .

14. _____ involves the study of specimens of tissue from any source in the body. Their form and structural changes are observed microscopically.

15. _____ is the study of the chemistry involved with immunity.

16. _____ involves the microscopic study of cells to detect abnormal or malignant changes.

17. Generally speaking, it is less expensive for the patient if simple laboratory tests are performed in the _____ .

18. State the medical assistant's responsibilities when dealing with a laboratory.

 a. _____

 b. _____

 c. _____

 d. _____

 e. _____

19. When unsure of the procedure for collecting or handling a specimen or what instructions are to be given to the patient, the medical assistant should

 _____ .

20. The container in which a specimen has been collected should always be labeled with the following information:

 a. _____

 b. _____

 c. _____

21. A microscope is a _____ .

22. The high power objective on a microscope is also called the _____ .

23. When carrying a microscope, one of your hands should be placed on the _____ of the microscope and your other hand on the _____ of the microscope.

24. The _____ of the microscope is the flat heavy part on which slides are placed for examination.

25. To clean the surface of the entrance lens of the eyepiece tube on a microscope, _____ should be used.

26. Before the microscope is put away, the nosepiece should be rotated so that the _____ objective is in position.

27. When a microscope is not in use it should be

 _____ .

28. The material to be examined under the microscope is placed on a _____ .

29. Centrifuges are used to _____ .

30. Name the procedures for which a centrifuge is used in a physician's office.

 a. _____

 b. _____

31. Capillary tubes are to be used in the _____-type centrifuges.

32. When using a centrifuge, it is important that tubes of the correct _____ and _____ for the required application are used.

33. When placing a specimen tube into the centrifuge, it must be counterbalanced with a _____ .

34. When operating a centrifuge, the cover must be

 _____ .

Multiple Choice

Write the letter of the correct answer in the blank provided. There is only *one* correct answer.

_____ 1. A _____ is a highly specialized laboratory worker who examines cells and tissues microscopically for the presence of cancer cells.
- A. Histological technician
- B. Cytotechnologist
- C. Clinical laboratory assistant
- D. Medical technician

_____ 2. A _____who is certified as a pathologist usually is the director of a clinical laboratory.
- A. Registered nurse
- B. Cytotechnologist
- C. Clinical laboratory assistant
- D. Medical technician

_____ 3. Reactions involving antibodies and antigens are observed and used to determine various types of infections in the _____ department of a clinical laboratory.
- A. Hematology
- B. Serology
- C. Clinical chemistry
- D. Cytology

_____ 4. In a physician's office correct labeling of a specimen and completion of the laboratory requisition are the responsibilities of the:
- A. Patient.
- B. Physician.
- C. Medical assistant.
- D. Laboratory technician.

_____ 5. When a laboratory report is received in the physician's office, it should be:
- A. Filed in the patient's chart.
- B. Filed in the patient's chart only if the results are normal.
- C. Given to the physician to review.
- D. Given to the physician only if the results are abnormal.

_____ 6. A microscope is used to:
- A. Store specimens until they are examined.
- B. Test blood for the chemical components.
- C. Separate solids from liquids in a specimen.
- D. View objects that are too small to be seen with the naked eye.

_____ 7. To remove finger marks from the lens surfaces on a microscope, use a soft cotton cloth that is lightly moistened with:
- A. Water.
- B. Xylene.
- C. Hydrogen peroxide.
- D. Absolute alcohol.

_____ 8. Solid material and fluid supernatant are separated in a specimen by the use of a(n):
- A. Centrifuge.
- B. Microscope.
- C. Capillary tube.
- D. Analyzer.

_____ 9. When placing a tube containing a specimen into the centrifuge, another tube of similar design and weight containing a liquid of equal weight should be placed:
- A. Directly opposite the tube containing the specimen.
- B. Right beside the tube containing the specimen.
- C. At a 45-degree angle from the tube containing the specimen.
- D. On the left side of the tube containing the specimen.

PERFORMANCE TEST

In a skill laboratory, a simulation of a joblike environment, the medical assistant student is to demonstrate knowledge and skill in performing the following procedures without reference to source materials:

1. Demonstrate proper use and care of a microscope.
2. Demonstrate proper use and care of a centrifuge.
3. Given sample laboratory requisitions and physician's orders, correctly complete each requisition to be sent to the laboratory along with a specimen.
4. Demonstrate the use of safety rules when working with laboratory equipment and specimens.

155

5. Demonstrate the use of commercial control products to check the reliability of test products and test results.

PERFORMANCE CHECKLIST

The medical assistant students are to design their own step-by-step procedures and performance checklists for the performance test in this unit.

ANSWERS
Fill-In

1. a. To determine (diagnose) the condition from which the patient is suffering so that treatment, if feasible, may be initiated
   b. To discover disease in its early stage before the patient experiences any signs or symptoms. This is called screening.
   c. To evaluate past or ongoing treatment received by the patient
2. a. The patient's full name, age, sex, and address
   b. The physician's full name (also address when sending specimens to outside laboratories)
   c. Date the specimen was collected; date the specimen was sent to laboratory if this differs from date of collection; time the specimen was collected.
   d. Source of the specimen
   e. Test(s) requested
   f. Possible diagnosis when feasible. This alerts the laboratory to watch for certain specifics.
   g. Medications or treatments the patient is receiving that may interfere with test results
3. a. Hematology
   b. Urinalysis
   c. Serology
   d. Blood banking
   e. Medical microbiology
   f. Clinical chemistry
4. Hematology
5. Serology
6. Medical microbiology
7. Bacteriology
8. Virology
9. Mycology
10. Rickettsiology
11. Protozoology
12. Phycology
13. Parasitology
14. Histology
15. Immunochemistry
16. Cytology
17. Physician's office or health care agency.
18. a. A basic knowledge of the various tests available
    b. Proper collection and handling of specimens that are to be forwarded to a laboratory
    c. Instructions to the patient preparing for certain tests
    d. Correct labeling of the specimen and completion of the laboratory requisition
    e. The handling of completed reports as they return to the office
19. Contact the laboratory for directions.
20. a. Date
    b. Patient's name
    c. Source of the specimen
21. Precise scientific instrument used in the laboratory when an enlarged image of a small (microscopic) object is required. When using the microscopic, details of structure not otherwise distinguishable are revealed.
22. Oil-immersion objective
23. Arm; base
24. Stage
25. Xylene
26. Low-power
27. Covered with the accessory vinyl cover and stored in a place free from moisture and fungus.
28. Glass slide
29. Separate components of varying densities contained in liquids by spinning them at high speeds. This process separates the solid material from the fluid supernatant.
30. a. To perform a microscopic analysis of urine
    b. to obtain serum for hematology or blood chemistry laboratory tests
31. Microhematocrit
32. Size and strength
33. Tube of similar design and weight.
34. Closed

Multiple Choice

1. B
2. C
3. B
4. C
5. C
6. D
7. D
8. A
9. A

Unit 11

Collecting and Handling Specimens

SUGGESTED ACTIVITIES

1. Make a list of procedures in this unit. Next to each list your responsibilities for these procedures.

2. Practice completing various types of requisition forms that accompany specimens sent to a laboratory.

3. With a partner demonstrate the correct technique and proper communication to the patient for collecting the specimens listed in this unit, preparing them to be sent to the laboratory, and completing the appropriate laboratory requisition form.

4. Make a chart of seven common sexually transmitted diseases. For each disease list:
   a. The cause
   b. The mode of transmission
   c. Signs and symptoms
   d. How the disease is diagnosed
   e. How the disease is treated

STUDY QUESTIONS
Fill-In

In the blanks provided, write the answers that best complete the sentences:

1. The study and identification of pathogens and the development of effective methods for their control or elimination is called _____.

2. Material spread thinly across a slide or culture medium with a swab, loop, or another slide in preparation for microscopic study is called _____.

3. The study of bacteria is called _____.

4. A commercial preparation used for the growth of microorganisms or other cells is called a _____.

5. The study of the microscopic form and structure of tissue is called _____.

6. An examination in which the specimen is visible only with the aid of a microscope is called a _____ examination.

7. The study of the structure and function of cells is called _____.

8. A culture made from suspected material that fails to reveal the suspected microorganism is called a _____ culture.

9. A culture that reveals the suspected microorganisms is called a _____ culture.

10. When pertaining to bacteriology, _____ refers to the period of culture development.

11. Once a specimen has been properly obtained, the medical assistant's responsibility is to ensure that it is _____ and _____ correctly for submission to the laboratory for examination.

12. Special preparation of the patient before a specimen is collected usually means:
    a. _____
    b. _____
    c. _____

157

13. Specimens collected for a smear or culture may be taken from _____ .

14. Samples of the following body fluids may be obtained for laboratory examination:

    a. _____

    b. _____

    c. _____

15. When it is not possible to examine a urine specimen immediately it must be put in _____ .

16. It is preferable to examine most blood specimens within _____ hours from the time they were collected.

17. Specimens should be handled and transported in an _____ position.

18. The medical assistant who touches some of a specimen while collecting it, must immediately

    _____ .

19. Fasting before a specimen is collected means abstaining from _____ usually for

    _____ to _____ hours before the specimen is collected.

20. The laboratory requisition that accompanies a specimen must always be filled out completely and accurately to include the following information:

    a. _____

    b. _____

    c. _____

    d. _____

    e. _____

    f. _____

21. To collect a _____ urine specimen, the patient voids at any time of the day or night, collecting a portion of the urine in a clean container.

22. To collect a _____ urine specimen, the patient voids after eating and collects this specimen.

23. To collect a timed specimen, the patient discards the _____ specimen and then collects all urine for exactly 24 hours.

24. To collect a _____ specimen, the patient starts to void into the toilet or bedpan; then, without stopping the process of voiding, a portion of the urine is collected in a clean container. The last part of the urine flow is passed into the toilet or bedpan.

25. The multiple-glass test is performed on men to evaluate _____ .

26. The _____ (time of day) urine specimen is the most concentrated; therefore, if at all possible, this specimen should be obtained for simple routine testing.

27. A signed, patient consent form may be needed for a _____ _____ specimen.

28. The amount of urine that is required for testing is usually _____ .

29. When collecting a urine specimen at home, the patient should be instructed to _____ .

30. When a 24-hour specimen is required, it is vital that the patient understand that:

    a. _____

    b. _____

    c. _____

    d. _____

    e. _____

31. A stool specimen is collected to help diagnose

    _____ .

32. A stool specimen should be collected in a

    _____ .

33. Sputum specimens are examined to _____ .

34. Other specimens that may be obtained if a patient is unable to produce sputum include:

   a. _____

   b. _____

   c. _____

35. Throat cultures are performed to determine _____.

36. When taking a throat culture, the patient should be instructed to assume a(n) _____ position.

37. A Hemoccult slide test is performed on a _____ specimen.

38. Whenever practical, patients who are to have a Hemoccult® slide test should be placed on the special diagnostic diet starting _____ and continuing through _____ .

39. Hemoccult II slides (should *or* should not) _____ be refrigerated after the specimen has been collected.

40. A wound culture is done to _____ .

41. After a smear has been obtained, it must be fixed immediately by _____ .

42. A smear must be fixed within _____ (time) to prevent drying and death of cells.

43. When spraying a smear, the can of fixative should be held at least _____ inches away from the slide.

44. To mail a slide with a smear on it to an outside laboratory, the slide should be placed inside a _____ once the fixative is dry.

45. A gram stain is performed to _____ .

46. Examples of gram-positive organisms are _____ , _____ , and _____ .

47. Gram-negative organisms are the _____ , _____ , and _____ .

48. A sensitivity study determines _____ _____ .

49. When the physician orders a C&S, a _____ test is to be performed.

50. Commercial culture media should be stored in _____ .

51. To inoculate a culture plate with a specimen, the applicator must be rolled in a large _____ pattern on the culture medium.

52. Vaginal smears and cultures are done to help diagnose and determine:

   a. _____

   b. _____

   c. _____

53. A patient should be instructed not to douche or use any vaginal medication for _____ hours before having a vaginal smear or culture taken.

54. According to the concept of Universal Precautions all human blood and other body fluids are treated as if known to be infectious for _____ , _____ , and _____ .

55. Gloves must be worn for handling specimens (when) _____ .

56. Specimens of blood or other potentially infectious materials are to be placed in _____ during collection, handling, processing, storage, transport, or shipping.

57. Specimen containers must be labeled or color coded before they leave the facility unless they are placed in _____ or _____ which may substitute for labels. The label must bear the legend _____ and must be fluorescent _____ color or predominately so, with lettering or symbols in a contrasting color.

58. Biohazard labels must also be affixed to refrigerators and freezers containing _____.

59. A very common infection especially in children and young adults is streptococcal pharyngitis, commonly referred to as _____.

60. Common signs and symptoms of strep throat include a _____, _____, _____, and _____.

61. Prompt diagnosis and treatment of strep throat is important because _____.

62. A patient must sign a consent form before a lumbar puncture is performed. (true *or* false)

_____

Multiple Choice

Write the letter of the correct answer in the blank provided. There is only *one* correct answer.

_____ 1. If when collecting a specimen, the medical assistant notices that the cap on the test tube is cracked, the cracked cap:
   A. May be used.
   B. Must be discarded.
   C. Should be replaced with a cotton ball.
   D. Should be replaced with a piece of *sterile* gauze.

_____ 2. To best demonstrate parasitic infection in stool, three fresh specimens must be collected:
   A. 3 hours apart.
   B. Every 3 hours for a 16-hour period.
   C. Every 3 hours for a 24-hour period
   D. On 3 different days.

_____ 3. In conditions in which the patient has _____, the stool is tarry black.
   A. Upper gastrointestinal bleeding
   B. Lower gastrointestinal bleeding
   C. Biliary obstruction
   D. Chronic ulcerative colitis

_____ 4. When cerebrospinal fluid has been obtained for laboratory examination, it should be kept _____ if testing is delayed.
   A. In a refrigerator
   B. At room temperature
   C. In a bacteriologic incubator
   D. In a freezer

_____ 5. To collect a _____ specimen, the patient starts to void into the toilet or bedpan; then without stopping the process of voiding, a portion of the urine is collected in a clean container. The last part of the urine flow is passed into the toilet or bedpan.
   A. Multiple-glass
   B. Clean-catch
   C. Midstream
   D. Timed

_____ 6. When urine is required for bacterial cultures, the patient collects a _____ specimen in a sterile container.
   A. Clean-catch
   B. Midstream
   C. Clean-catch midstream
   D. Spot

_____ 7. Microscopic examination of urine should be performed within _____ of collection.
   A. 1 hour
   B. 1½ hours
   C. 2 hours
   D. 3 hours

_____ 8. Two days before having a Hemoccult slide test, the patient may be instructed to:
   A. not eat fish.
   B. not eat rare red meats.
   C. not eat cooked fruits and vegetables.
   D. not eat canned fruits and vegetables.

_____ 9. After a fixative spray has been applied to a smear, it must be allowed to dry for:
   A. 1 to 2 minutes.
   B. 4 to 6 minutes.
   C. 15 minutes.
   D. 30 minutes.

_____ 10. When an order states "sputum cultures x3," it means that:
A. one specimen should be divided into three different containers.
B. The specimen should be cultured three times.
C. The specimens must all be collected on the same day.
D. Three different specimens should be collected at different times or on 3 successive days.

_____ 11. When preparing a smear for laboratory examination, the specimen must be smeared _____ on the glass slides.
A. Evenly and moderately thin
B. Evenly and thickly
C. Heavily at the frosted end
D. Heavily at the clear end

_____ 12. A smear obtained for cytology studies should be sprayed with a fixative spray or immersed in a bottle of fixative solution:
A. After the smear has dried.
B. 10 minutes after the smear is made.
C. 30 minutes after the smear is made.
D. Immediately (within 4 seconds).

_____ 13. The nation's most common sexually transmitted disease is now thought to be:
A. Herpes simplex type II.
B. Gonorrhea.
C. Syphilis.
D. *Chlamydia trachomatis.*

_____ 14. A laboratory method that is used to identify bacterial organisms and that permits the classification of bacteria into four basic groups is the:
A. Culture and sensitivity test.
B. Gram stain.
C. Tissue culture.
D. Cytology study.

_____ 15. A _____ determines the sensitivity of bacteria to antibiotics.
A. Sensitivity study
B. Gram stain
C. Bacterial culture
D. Bacteriology smear

_____ 16. Sputum cytology (exfoliative cytology) is performed to identify:
A. Tuberculosis.
B. Fungus infections.
C. Tumor cells.
D. Pertussis (whooping cough).

_____ 17. Throat cultures are frequently ordered for patients suspected of having:
A. A fungus infection.
B. Streptococcal pharyngitis.
C. Cancer of the throat.
D. Tuberculosis.

_____ 18. Medications that may interfere with obtaining accurate results for the Hemoccult slide test include:
A. Aspirin.
B. Antibiotics.
C. Vasodilators.
D. Vitamin B complex.

PERFORMANCE TEST

In a skill laboratory, a simulation of a joblike environment, the medical assistant student is to demonstrate knowledge and skill in performing the following procedures without reference to source materials. For these activities the student will need a person to play the role of the patient. Time limits for the performance of each procedure are to be assigned by the instructor.

1. Given an ambulatory patient and the appropriate supplies, prepare for, give explanations to the patient for, and obtain the following: (a) urine specimen, (b) stool specimen, (c) sputum specimen, (d) throat culture, (e) nasopharyngeal culture, (f) wound culture.
2. Given an ambulatory patient and the required equipment, prepare for, give explanations to the patient for, and assist with the following procedures:
   a. vaginal smears and cultures, b. preparing a smear from the specimen obtained by the physician, c. lumbar puncture.
3. Having obtained the above specimens, smears, and cultures, complete the appropriate laboratory requisition form, forward all to the laboratory for examination, and record the procedure on the patient's chart.
4. Given the required supplies, demonstrate the correct procedure for staining a smear using the Gram stain.
5. Given the required supplies, demonstrate the proper procedure for performing a Hemoccult slide test on a stool specimen.

6. Given the required supplies, demonstrate how to inoculate a culture medium.

The student is expected to perform the above with 100% accuracy 95% of the time (9 out of 10 times).

PERFORMANCE CHECKLIST: Clean-catch urine specimen

DIRECTIONS: Evaluate student performance of each procedure using the following checklist. When you evaluate "not applicable," "unsatisfactory," or "not observed," please comment.

Checklist	S or NA*	U	NO	Comment
1. Washed hands. **Use appropriate Personal Protective Equipment (PPE) as dictated by facility.**				
2. Assembled required equipment and supplies.				
3. Identified the patient, and explained the procedure. Supplied the patient with the appropriate supplies required to wash the genital area and collect the urine specimen.				
4. Donned disposable single-use exam gloves.				
5. Received the specimen from the patient.				
6. Labeled the specimen, and completed the laboratory requisition.				
7. Sent the specimen with the requisition to the laboratory.				
8. Removed gloves and washed hands.				
9. Recorded the procedure, date, time, and signature on the patient's chart.				

Total Satisfactory Points _____

Comments

Student's signature: _____ Instructor's signature: _____

Date: _____

*S or NA, Satisfactory or not applicable; U, unsatisfactory; NO, not observed.

PERFORMANCE CHECKLIST: Stool specimen collection

DIRECTIONS: Evaluate student performance of each procedure using the following checklist. When you evaluate "not applicable," "unsatisfactory," or "not observed," please comment.

Checklist	S or NA*	U	NO	Comment
1. Washed hands. **Use appropriate Personal Protective Equipment (PPE) as dictated by facility.**				
2. Assembled required equipment and supplies.				
3. Identified the patient, and explained the procedure.				
4. Prepared the label for the specimen container, and completed the laboratory requisition.				
5. Donned disposable single-use exam gloves.				
6. Received the bedpan with specimen from the patient, covered it, and took to work area.				
7. Transferred a portion of the specimen into the container, using a clean tongue blade as a spoon; placed the lid securely on the container.				
8. Discarded the used tongue blade in a bag, closed securely, and disposed of in a container for waste materials.				
9. Emptied and cleaned bedpan.				
10. Removed gloves and washed hands.				
11. Sent the specimen with a completed laboratory requisition to the laboratory.				
12. Washed hands again.				
13. Recorded the procedure, date, time, and signature on the patient's chart.				

Total Satisfactory Points _____

Comments

Student's signature:_____ Instructor's signature: _____
Date: _____
*S or NA, Satisfactory or not applicable; U, unsatisfactory; NO, not observed.

PERFORMANCE CHECKLIST: Sputum specimen collection

DIRECTIONS: Evaluate student performance of each procedure using the following checklist. When you evaluate "not applicable," "unsatisfactory," or "not observed," please comment.

Checklist	S or NA*	U	NO	Comment
1. Washed hands. **Use appropriate Personal Protective Equipment (PPE) as dictated by facility.**				
2. Assembled required equipment and supplies.				
3. Identified the patient, and explained the procedure.				
4. Donned disposable single-use exam gloves, lab coat, and face protection.				
5. Received the specimen from the patient; secured the container with paper tape.				
6. Labeled the container, completed the laboratory requisition, and sent together to the laboratory in a plastic bag in a secure transport container.				
7. Removed gloves, lab coat, and face protection and washed hands.				
8. Recorded the procedure, date, time, and signature on the patient's chart.				

Total Satisfactory Points _____

Comments

Student's signature: _____ Instructor's signature: _____

Date: _____

*S or NA, Satisfactory or not applicable; U, unsatisfactory; NO, not observed.

PERFORMANCE CHECKLIST: Throat culture

DIRECTIONS: Evaluate student performance of each procedure using the following checklist. When you evaluate "not applicable," "unsatisfactory," or "not observed," please comment.

Checklist	S or NA*	U	NO	Comment
1. Washed hands. **Use appropriate Personal Protective Equipment (PPE) as dictated by facility.**				
2. Assembled required equipment and supplies.				
3. Identified the patient, and explained the procedure.				
4. Had the patient sitting, facing student.				
5. Donned disposable single-use exam gloves.				
6. Had patient open mouth, extend tongue, and say "ah."				
7. Removed the sterile cotton-tipped applicator from the sterile tube.				
8. Depressed the patient's tongue with the tongue blade.				
9. Swabbed the back areas of the throat on both sides.				
10. Placed the applicator in a sterile tube, and secured the lid.				
11. Obtained two specimens, one from both the right and left tonsillar areas if this was required.				
12. Discarded the tongue blade in the container for waste supplies.				
13. Repositioned the patient if necessary.				
14. Removed gloves and washed hands.				
15. Labeled the culture tube(s), completed the laboratory requisition, and sent together to the laboratory.				
16. Recorded the procedure, date, time, and signature on the patient's chart.				

Total Satisfactory Points   _____

Comments

Student's signature: _____   Instructor's signature: _____

Date: _____

*S or NA, Satisfactory or not applicable; U, unsatisfactory; NO, not observed.

PERFORMANCE CHECKLIST: Nasopharyngeal culture after throat culture

DIRECTIONS: Evaluate student performance of each procedure using the following checklist. When you evaluate "not applicable," "unsatisfactory," or "not observed," please comment.

Checklist	S or NA*	U	NO	Comment
1. Wearing disposable single-use exam gloves, inserted a sterile cotton-tipped applicator through the patient's nose into the nasopharyngeal area.				
2. Rotated the applicator gently, and obtained the specimen.				
3. Removed the applicator, placed in the sterile culture tube, and secured the lid.				
4. Labeled the tube, completed the laboratory requisition, and sent together to the laboratory.				
5. Removed gloves and washed hands.				
6. Recorded the procedure, date, time and signature on the patient's chart.				

Total Satisfactory Points _____

Comments

Student's signature: _____ Instructor's signature: _____

Date: _____

*S or NA, Satisfactory or not applicable; U, unsatisfactory; NO, not observed.

PERFORMANCE CHECKLIST: Making a smear

DIRECTIONS: Evaluate student performance of each procedure using the following checklist. When you evaluate "not applicable," "unsatisfactory," or "not observed," please comment.

Checklist	S or NA*	U	NO	Comment
1. Washed hands. **Use appropriate Personal Protective Equipment (PPE) as dictated by facility.**				
2. Assembled the required equipment and supplies.				
3. Wrote the patient's name on the frosted end of the slide(s).				
4. Donned gloves.				
5. Received the applicator from the physician with dominant hand, grasping the distal end of the stick.				
6. Held the glass slide between thumb and index finger of nondominant hand.				
7. Spread the specimen across the slide, starting at the unfrosted end, using the correct method.				
8. Discarded the applicator.				
9. Fixed the smear by spraying it from a distance of 5 to 6 inches, using a continuous flow going right to left, then left to right (*or* placed the smear in a container of alcohol solution).				
10. Allowed the fixed smear to dry for 4 to 6 minutes.				
11. Removed gloves and washed hands.				
12. Prepared the smear to be sent to the laboratory immediately with a completed requisition. If the smear was to be mailed, placed it in the cardboard slide holder, secured it with a rubber band, and placed this with a completed requisition in the mailing envelope provided by the laboratory. Sealed and mailed.				
13. Recorded the procedure, date, time, and signature on the patient's chart.				

Total Satisfactory Points _____

Comments

Student's signature: _____ Instructor's signature: _____
Date: _____

*S or NA, Satisfactory or not applicable; U, unsatisfactory; NO, not observed.

PERFORMANCE CHECKLIST: Inoculating a culture medium

DIRECTIONS: Evaluate student performance of each procedure using the following checklist. When you evaluate "not applicable," "unsatisfactory," or "not observed," please comment.

Checklist	S or NA*	U	NP	Comment
1. Washed hands. **Use appropriate Personal Protective Equipment (PPE) as dictated by facility.**				
2. Assembled the required equipment for the examination to be done for inoculating the culture medium.				
3. Identified and prepared the patient. Explained the procedure. Had the patient disrobe and put the patient gown on. Had the patient void. Positioned the patient for the examination.				
4. Assisted the physician and patient as required.				
5. Donned disposable single-use examine gloves and lab coat.				
6. Received the applicator with the specimen from the physician.				
7. Removed top cover lid of culture plate, and placed it upside down on a flat surface.				
8. Inoculated the Thayer Martin culture plate; rolled the applicator in a large Z-pattern across the culture medium.				
9. Discarded the applicator.				
10. Replaced the cover lid on the culture plate.				
11. Obtained the wire loop and Bunsen burner; lit the burner, and heated the wire loop over the flame until it was red.				
12. Allowed time for loop to cool.				
13. Removed cover lid of culture plate, placing it upside down on a flat surface.				
14. Cross-streaked the inoculated culture in a criss-cross fashion over the Z with the wire loop.				
15. Replaced the cover lid over the culture medium.				
16. Reflamed the wire loop, and replaced it in the appropriate container in the correct position.				
17. Labeled the cover plate correctly and completely.				
18. Placed the culture plate in a candle jar with the medium on the top side of the plate.				
19. Removed gloves and washed hands.				

PERFORMANCE CHECKLIST: Inoculating a culture medium (continued)

Checklist	S or NA*	U	NO	Comment
20. Sent the culture plate in the candle jar to the laboratory with the correct completed laboratory requisition.				
21. Recorded the procedure, date, time, and signature on the patient's chart.				

Total Satisfactory Points _____

Comments

Student's signature: _____ Instructor's signature: _____

Date: _____

*S or NA, Satisfactory or not applicable; U, unsatisfactory; NO, not observed.

PERFORMANCE CHECKLIST: Vaginal smear for trichomoniasis vaginitis and candidiasis (monilial vaginitis)

DIRECTIONS: Evaluate student performance of each procedure using the following checklist. When you evaluate "not applicable," "unsatisfactory," or "not observed," please comment.

Checklist	S or NA*	U	NO	Comment
1. Washed hands. **Use appropriate Personal Protective Equipment (PPE) as dictated by facility.**				
2. Assembled and prepared the required equipment and supplies.				
3. Identified and prepared the patient. Explained the procedure. Had the patient void. Had the patient disrobe and put on a patient gown. Assisted the patient in assuming a lithotomy or dorsal-recumbent position for the vaginal exam. Draped the patient.				
4. Donned disposable single-use exam gloves.				
5. Assisted the physician as needed.				
6. Placed a small amount of saline on the glass slide. Added KOH (potassium hydroxide) if testing for candidiasis (monilial vaginitis).				
7. Received the applicator with the specimen from the physician.				
8. Dipped the applicator into the solution on the slide.				
9. Discarded the applicator.				
10. Placed a coverglass over the depressed area in the middle of the slide.				
11. Sent the specimen to the laboratory with a completed requisition.				
12. Assisted the patient as required.				
13. Assembled and disposed of used supplies according to office or agency policy.				
14. Removed gloves and washed hands.				
15. Replaced equipment and supplies as required.				
16. Recorded the procedure, date, time, and signature on the patient's chart.				

Total Satisfactory Points _____

Comments

Student's signature:_____ Instructor's signature: _____

Date: _____

*S or NA, Satisfactory or not applicable; U, unsatisfactory; NO, not observed.

PERFORMANCE CHECKLIST: Procedure for a Gram stain

DIRECTIONS: Evaluate student performance of each procedure using the following checklist. When you evaluate "not applicable," "unsatisfactory," or "not observed," please comment.

Checklist	S or NA*	U	NO	Comment
1. Washed hands. **Use appropriate Personal Protective Equipment (PPE) as dictated by facility.**				
2. Assembled and prepared the required equipment and supplies.				
3. Donned disposable single-use exam gloves.				
4. Made the smear and heat "fixed" it.				
5. Placed the slide on the staining rack, smear side up.				
6. Covered the slide with Gram crystal violet and allowed it to react for 1 minute.				
7. Grasped the slide with slide forceps and tilted it about 45 degrees to allow the Gram crystal violet to drain off.				
8. Rinsed the slide thoroughly with distilled water for 5 seconds.				
9. Replaced the slide on the staining rack.				
10. Covered the smear with Gram iodine solution allowing it to react for 1 to 2 minutes.				
11. Grasped the slide with the slide forceps and tilted it to a 45-degree angle to drain off the iodine solution.				
12. Rinsed the slide with distilled water in this position for 5 seconds.				
13. With the slide remaining tilted, slowly poured the alcohol-acetone solution over it.				
14. Rinsed the slide with distilled water for 5 seconds.				
15. Replaced the slide on the staining rack, covered it with safranin counterstain, and allowed it to react for 30 to 60 seconds.				
16. Using a slide forceps, tilted the slide and allowed the counterstain to drain off.				
17. Rinsed the slide thoroughly with distilled water for 5 seconds.				
18. Blotted the smear dry between the pages of the bibulous paper.				
19. Positioned the slide on the microscope to be examined.				
20. Removed gloves and washed hands.				

Checklist	S or NA*	U	NO	Comment
21. Notified the physician that the smear was ready to be examined.				
22. Replaced equipment and supplies as required.				
23. Recorded the procedure, date, time, and signature on the patient's chart (if this is one of the student's responsibilities).				

Total Satisfactory Points _____

Comments

Student's signature: _____ Instructor's signature: _____

Date: _____

*S or NA, Satisfactory or not applicable; U, unsatisfactory; NO, not observed.

PERFORMANCE CHECKLIST: Assisting with a lumbar puncture

DIRECTIONS: Evaluate student performance of each procedure using the following checklist. When you evaluate "not applicable," "unsatisfactory," or "not observed," please comment.

Checklist	S or NA*	U	NO	Comment
1. Washed hands. **Use appropriate Personal Protective Equipment (PPE) as dictated by facility.**				
2. Assembled and prepared the required equipment and supplies.				
3. Identified and prepared the patient, made sure the consent form was signed. Explained the procedure. Furnished a patient robe; had the patient disrobe and put the gown on with the opening in the back. Had the patient void, and saved the specimen if required.				
4. Summoned the physician into the room.				
5. Using aseptic technique, opened the sterile glove pack and the outer wrapping of the lumbar puncture tray.				
6. Positioned the patient correctly.				
7. Cleaned the skin with soap and water.				
8. Prepared the skin with an antiseptic solution. (Steps 7 and 8 may be done by the physician.)				
9. When using a stock supply of local anesthetic, checked the label, read aloud, and held the vial for the physician to identify and withdraw the solution with the needle and syringe.				
10. Helped the patient maintain the proper position.				
11. Gave appropriate instructions to the patient to remain still and to breathe slowly and deeply through the mouth when the needle is being inserted; once the needle is in place, instructed and helped the patient to straighten the legs and breathe normally.				
12. Donned gloves to receive the test tubes with the specimens from the physician.				
13. Checked the caps for secure closure.				
14. Placed the tubes in an upright position.				
15. Dated and labeled the tubes, CSF 1, 2, and 3, respectively.				
16. Assisted with the Queckenstedt test if it was performed.				
17. Observed the patient for any unusual reaction.				

PERFORMANCE CHECKLIST: Assisting with a lumbar puncture (continued)

Checklist	S or NA*	U	NO	Comment
18. Once the spinal needle was withdrawn, secured a Band-Aid or gauze dressing over the puncture site.				
19. Assisted the patient as required.				
20. Sent the specimen(s) to the laboratory with a completed requisition.				
21. Assembled and disposed of used equipment according to office or clinic policy.				
22. Removed gloves and washed hands.				
23. Replaced equipment as necessary.				
24. Charted the procedure, date, time, and signature on the patient's chart (if this is one of the student's responsibilities).				

Total Satisfactory Points _____

Comments

Student's signature:_____ Instructor's signature: _____

Date: _____

*S or NA, Satisfactory or not applicable; U, unsatisfactory; NO, not observed.

PERFORMANCE CHECKLIST: Wound culture and dressing change

DIRECTIONS: Evaluate student performance of each procedure using the following checklist. When you evaluate "not applicable," "unsatisfactory," or "not observed," please comment.

Checklist	S or NA*	U	NO	Comment
1. Washed hands. **Use appropriate Personal Protective Equipment (PPE) as dictated by facility.**				
2. Assembled the equipment.				
3. Identified the patient, and explained the procedure.				
4. Prepared the patient. Positioned as required, and draped the wound site if necessary.				
5. Prepared supplies for use.				
6. Donned disposable single-use exam gloves.				
7. Loosened the tape on the dressing.				
8. Removed the soiled dressing either with forceps, or wore a sterile disposable vinyl or rubber glove, or grasped the dressing with the hand in a plastic bag.				
9. Inspected the dressing for type and amount of drainage; then discarded it in the plastic bag.				
10. Observed the wound for the type and amount of drainage, the degree of healing, and presence of pus, necrosis, or a putrid odor. If sutures were present, noted if they were intact.				
11. Removed the sterile applicator from the tube, and swabbed the drainage area once to obtain a specimen.				
12. Placed applicator in the culture tube.				
13. Removed gloves and donned another pair.				
14. Cleaned the wound using aseptic technique.				
15. Applied fresh sterile dressing, and secured correctly with tape.				
16. Attended to the patient's comfort (student may reposition the patient if necessary.)				
17. Labeled the culture tube, and completed the laboratory requisition; sent both together to the laboratory.				
18. Assembled and disposed of used supplies according to office or agency policy.				
19. Removed gloves and washed hands.				

PERFORMANCE CHECKLIST: Assisting with a lumbar puncture (continued)

Checklist	S or NA*	U	NO	Comment
20. Replaced supplies as needed, leaving the room neat and tidy.				
21. Recorded the procedure, date, time, and signature on the patient's chart.				

Total Satisfactory Points _____

Comments

Student's signature:_____ Instructor's signature: _____

Date: _____

*S or NA, Satisfactory or not applicable; U, unsatisfactory; NO, not observed.

Evaluation of student's technique Name: _____ Date: _____

| | Satisfactory* | Unsatisfactory** | | | |

	Very Good	Good	Fair	Poor	Score
• Clean-catch urine specimen	☐	☐	☐	☐	_____
• Stool specimen collection	☐	☐	☐	☐	_____
• Sputum specimen collection	☐	☐	☐	☐	_____
• Throat culture	☐	☐	☐	☐	_____
• Nasopharyngeal culture	☐	☐	☐	☐	_____
• Making a smear	☐	☐	☐	☐	_____
• Inoculating a culture medium	☐	☐	☐	☐	_____
• Vaginal smear for trichomoniasis vaginitis and candidiasis (monilial vaginitis)	☐	☐	☐	☐	_____
• Gram stain	☐	☐	☐	☐	_____
• Assisting with a lumbar puncture	☐	☐	☐	☐	_____
• Wound culture and dressing change	☐	☐	☐	☐	_____

Very good = Perfect
Good   = Sufficient
Fair   = Not acceptable requires more practice
Poor   = Totally unacceptable
Pass* = Satisfactory
Fail** = Unsatisfactory

Comments:

1. medical microbiology
2. Smear
3. Bacteriology
4. Culture medium
5. Histology
6. Microscopic
7. Cytology
8. Negative
9. Positive
10. Incubation
11. Preserved and labeled
12. a. A modification in diet, *or*
    b. A period of fasting before the specimen is collected *or*
    c. medication restrictions
13. Any body opening
14. a. Urine
    b. Blood
    c. Cerebrospinal fluid
15. A refrigerator
16. 2 to 4
17. Upright
18. Wash the contact area thoroughly with an antiseptic soap. If the contact area was on a cut or scratch, apply tincture of iodine or another antiseptic solution to the area.
19. All food, gum, cigarettes, and fluids except water; 12 to 14
20. a. Date (time of day if relevant, for example, an early-morning specimen)
    b. Name of the patient, address, age, and sex
    c. Name of the attending physician and address
    d. Source of the specimen
    e. Name of laboratory test(s) to be performed
    f. If the patient is already taking antibiotics, a notation must be made
21. Random or spot
22. Postprandial
23. First morning
24. Midstream
25. A lower urinary tract infection
26. Early morning
27. Drug screen
28. 2 to 4 ounces
29. Use a thoroughly clean 3- to 4-ounce container in which to collect the specimen. Instruct the patient to boil the container to be sued for the collection for 20 minutes before using it. It is advisable to instruct the patient not to use a container that has held drugs or other solutions that may make the specimen unsuitable for examination.
30. a. All urine must be collected within a 24-hour period.
    b. The first early-morning specimen is discarded.
    c. All subsequent specimens are collected, including the first early-morning specimen the next day.
    d. The last specimen is collected 24 hours after collection was started.
    e. Urine is collected in a clean bottle into which a preservative has been added (preservative is prescribed by the laboratory). This bottle must be refrigerated or kept cold by placing it in a bucket of ice.
31. The presence of parasites and ova, occult blood, fecal urobilinogen, pus or mucus, membranous shreds, worms, infectious diseases, foreign bodies, and to detect the amount of fat being eliminated and various disorders of metabolism.
32. Waxed paper of glass container with a lid
33. Help determine the presence of infectious organisms or to identify tumor cells in the respiratory tract
34. a. Tracheal aspirates, collected by aspiration with a suction catheter
    b. Bronchial washings
    c. Transtracheal aspirates
35. The presence and the type of microscopic organism that is the cause of an infection
36. Upright sitting (facing the medical assistant)
37. Stool
38. 48 hours before; the test period
39. Should not
40. Determine the presence and the type of microorganism that is causing the infection
41. Spraying it with the fixative spray or by immersing it in the bottle of fixative solution obtained from the laboratory
42. 4 seconds
43. 5 to 6
44. Cardboard slide holder
45. Identify bacterial organisms
46. Staphylococci, streptococci, pneumococci
47. Gonococci, meningococci, and *Escherichia coli* (*E. coli*)
48. The sensitivity of bacteria to antibiotics
49. Culture and sensitivity
50. A refrigerator and warmed to room temperature before being used
51. Z

52. a. Trichomoniasis
    b. Candidiasis (moniliasis)
    c. Estrogen levels
    d. Sexually transmitted diseases (STD), for example, gonorrhea, herpes simplex type 2, and chlamydia
53. 24
54. HIV, HBV, other bloodborne pathogens
55. At all times
56. Containers which prevent leakage
57. Red bags, red containers, BIOHAZARD, orange or orange-red
58. Blood or other potentially infectious materials
59. Strep throat
60. Sore throat, fever, chills, swollen lymph nodes in the neck, nausea and vomiting
61. Complications such as rheumatic fever, otitis media, acute glomerulonephritis, or sinusitis may develop
62. True

Multiple Choice

1. B
2. D
3. A
4. C
5. C
6. C
7. A
8. B
9. B
10. D
11. A
12. D
13. D
14. B
15. A
16. C
17. B
18. A

Unit 12

Urinalysis

SUGGESTED ACTIVITIES

1. Practice and then demonstrate the correct procedure for performing a physical and chemical analysis of a urine specimen, and the correct procedure for preparing a urine specimen for microscopic examination.

2. Practice and then demonstrate the correct procedure for testing a urine specimen for the presence of glucose, acetone, and bilirubin using the Clinitest, Acetest, and Ictotest reagent tablets.

3. Practice and then demonstrate the correct procedure for testing a urine specimen for the presence of glucose using the Tes-Tape.

4. Discuss the advantage and use of quality control systems used in a laboratory.

5. Review laboratory results that have been received at the facility where you do your work experience. Determine if the results are normal. Discuss the significance of any abnormal results.

STUDY QUESTIONS
Fill-In

In the blanks provided, write the answers that best complete the sentences:

1. Name the organs of the urinary system.

    a. _____

    b. _____

    c. _____

    d. _____

2. Urine is formed in the _____ and passes through the _____ into the _____ , where it remains until the individual voids, and then it is excreted through the _____ .

3. The kidneys help maintain a state of homeostasis in the internal environment by _____ .

4. The functional unit of the kidney is called the _____ .

5. Give the main normal components of urine.

    a. _____

    b. _____

    c. _____

    d. _____

6. Urine is routinely examined as an aid in:

    a. _____

    b. _____

    c. _____

7. List general physical characteristics and measurements determined on a routine urinalysis.

    a. _____

    b. _____

    c. _____

    d. _____

    e. _____

8. List chemical examinations performed on a routine urinalysis.

   a. _____

   b. _____

   c. _____

   d. _____

   e. _____

   f. _____

   g. _____

   h. _____

   i. _____

9. Microscopic examination of the centrifuges sediment of urine will reveal the presence of the following items:

   a. _____

   b. _____

   c. _____

   d. _____

   e. _____

   f. _____

   g. _____

10. A freshly voided random urine specimen is collected in a _____ .

11. The above specimen should be examined within (amount of time) _____ to avoid changes to or deterioration of the contents. If the examination cannot be performed within this time, the specimen should be placed in _____ to preserve the specimen.

12. When performing a routine urinalysis, the first procedure is to note the _____ of the urine; the second is to measure the _____ ; the third is to _____ ; and the fourth is to _____ .

13. Abnormal cloudiness in the urine may be seen in patients who have _____ .

14. Normal, fresh, urine color ranges are described as _____ , _____ , or _____ , the result of the presence of the pigment urochrome.

15. The concentration of normal urine determines the degree of the color: very concentrated urine is _____ ; dilute urine is _____

16. Medications such as multivitamins may make the urine a very _____ color.

17. The average quantity of urine voided by an adult in a 24-hour period is about _____ and ranges from _____ to _____ .

18. Oliguria is the diminution of urinary secretions to between _____ and _____ ; more commonly defined as a scant amount of urine.

19. Polyuria is seen in patients who may have the conditions of _____ or _____ , or in patients who have ingested the type of medication known as a _____ .

20. Dysuria is symptomatic of many conditions such as _____ , _____ , and _____ .

21. The specific gravity of urine is _____ .

22. The specific gravity of urine indicates _____ _____ .

23. The normal specific gravity of urine is generally between _____ and _____ , although it may range from _____ to _____ , depending on the concentration of the urine.

24. The first morning urine specimen has the (highest *or* lowest) _____ specific gravity.

25. Abnormally low specific gravity values may be seen in patients who have _____, _____, _____, and _____.

26. Abnormally high specific gravity values are seen in patients with _____, _____, _____, _____, _____, or _____.

27. When there is an insufficient amount of urine to measure the specific gravity of urine with an urinometer, the medical assistant would then _____.

28. When a urinometer is not in use it should be placed in _____ and checked daily to test its reliability.

29. If an unusually high reading is found when testing the specific gravity of a urine specimen with an urinometer the medical assistant should _____.

30. pH is the symbol for the hydrogen-ion concentration that expresses _____.

31. The pH of solution is measured on a scale ranging from 0 to 14 with 7 being neutral; 0 to 7 is _____; and 7 to 14 is _____.

32. Usually freshly voided normal urine from patients on normal diets is (acidic *or* alkaline) _____, having a pH of _____, although normal kidneys are capable of secreting urine that may vary in pH from _____ to slightly higher than _____.

33. A reagent strip is a _____.

34. To determine the test results when using a reagent strip the medical assistant must _____.

35. Normal urine (may *or* may not) _____ contain protein after excessive muscular activity.

36. Normal urine usually (does *or* does not) _____ contain detectable glucose.

37. Glycosuria is _____.

38. Ingestion of large amounts of vitamins _____ may interfere with glucose testing in urine and produce a false positive result.

39. Acetonuria is the _____.

40. Ketonuria is seen in patients whose carbohydrate intake is (increased *or* decreased) _____.

41. Normally, bilirubin (does *or* does not) _____ appear in the urine.

42. Hematuria is the _____.

43. A positive nitrite result obtained from a urinalysis indicates _____.

44. Normal urine (does *or* does not) _____ contain a small amount of urobilinogen.

45. Increased amounts of urobilinogen in the urine are present in _____ and in _____.

46. When the presence of glucose in urine is determined by using a reagent strip, a more quantitative determination may be required. This can be accomplished by using the _____.

47. _____ drops of urine should be added to the test tube when using the Clinitest reagent tablet to determine the presence of glucose in urine.

48. To detect the presence of acetone and acetoacetic acid in urine, the _____ reagent tablet is used.

49. To detect liver function, a simple test on urine to determine the presence of bilirubin may be done with the use of the _____ reagent tablet.

50. Reagent tablets and reagent strips must be kept in _____.

51. The _____ is a roll of paper that is treated specifically for the analysis of glucose in urine.

52. The purpose of a microscopic examination of urine is to _____ _____ .

53. Organized sediment in urine includes

    _____ , _____ ,

    _____ , _____ ,

    _____ , _____ ,

    _____ , _____ , and

    _____ .

54. The presence of large numbers of white blood cells (WBCs) in the urine usually indicates the presence of a _____ .

55. The presence of numerous bacteria in the urine may indicate _____ .

56. Yeast may be seen as a contaminant in the urine of females who have a vaginal or urinary _____ infection.

57. Urine may be tested for the presence of the _____ hormone to determine pregnancy.

Multiple Choice

Write the letter of the correct answer in the blank provided. There is only *one* correct answer.

_____ 1. _____ is the absence of urine.
   A. Anuria
   B. Oliguria
   C. Polyuria
   D. Dysuria

_____ 2. When using the Acetest reagent tablet to detect the presence of acetone in urine, _____ drop(s) of urine are placed on the tablet.
   A. 1
   B. 2
   C. 5
   D. 10

_____ 3. When using the Clinitest reagent tablet to detect the presence of glucose in urine, _____ drop(s) of urine are put into a test tube.
   A. 1
   B. 2
   C. 5
   D. 10

_____ 4. When using the Acetest reagent tablet to determine the presence of acetone in urine, the results of the test should be read at:
   A. 10 seconds
   B. 30 seconds
   C. 1 minute
   D. 45 seconds

_____ 5. When using the Ictotest reagent tablet to determine the presence of bilirubin in a urine sample, _____ drop(s) of urine should be placed on the piece of special mat that is provided with the tablets.
   A. 1
   B. 2
   C. 5
   D. 10

_____ 6. The Tes-Tape is used to detect the presence of _____ in a urine sample.
   A. Bilirubin
   B. Acetone
   C. Protein
   D. Glucose

_____ 7. When using the Tes-Tape to test urine, wait _____ ; then compare any color change on the tape with the color chart on the dispenser.
   A. 30 seconds
   B. 15 seconds
   C. 45 seconds
   D. 60 seconds

_____ 8. The presence of blood in the urine is called:
   A. Pyuria.
   B. Hematuria.
   C. Uremia.
   D. Anemia.

_____ 9. A scant amount of urine is called:
   A. Anuria.
   B. Oliguria.
   C. Polyuria.
   D. Pyuria.

10. A synonym for micturition is:
    A. Urgency.
    B. Enuresis.
    C. Urination.
    D. Menstruation.

11. Pyuria refers to:
    A. Blood in the stool.
    B. Pus in the sputum.
    C. Pus in the urine.
    D. Blood in the vomitus.

12. A urinalysis which indicated glycosuria would mean that the urine contained:
    A. Albumin.
    B. Sugar.
    C. White blood cells.
    D. Red blood cells.

13. Patients who are taking multivitamins have urine that is a _____ color.
    A. Reddish brown
    B. Brown
    C. Reddish orange
    D. Very dark yellow

14. Normal specific gravity of urine is generally between:
    A. 1.005 and 1.050.
    B. 1.010 and 1.050.
    C. 1.025 and 1.500.
    D. 1.010 and 1.025.

15. A urinometer must be replaced when it does not read _____ when it is placed in distilled water.
    A. 1000
    B. 1500
    C. 500
    D. 1.5

16. Usually freshly voided normal urine from patients on normal diets will have a pH value of:
    A. 6.
    B. 7.
    C. 4.
    D. 5.

17. Normal kidneys are capable of secreting urine that may vary in a pH value of:
    A. 2 to 5.
    B. 3.5 to 7.
    C. 4.5 to 8.
    D. 6 to 8.

18. Normal urine does not contain any detectable glucose unless the concentration of blood glucose exceeds _____ ; at that point, glucose begins to spill into the urine.
    A. 50 to 100 mg/100 ml
    B. 100 to 150 mg/100 ml
    C. 140 to 160 mg/100 ml
    D. 160 to 180 mg/100 ml

19. If a urine sample cannot be examined for several hours after it has been collected it should be placed in the:
    A. Freezer.
    B. Refrigerator.
    C. Sunlight.
    D. Shaded area on the counter top.

20. The quantity of urine normally produced over a 24-hour period is highly variable but normal ranges are from:
    A. 750 to 2000 ml.
    B. 1000 to 1500 ml.
    C. 1500 ml to 1700 ml.
    D. 1700 to 2000 ml.

21. The average quantity of urine normally voided over a 24-hour period is:
    A. 750 ml.
    B. 1000 ml.
    C. 1500 ml.
    D. 2000 ml.

22. The Clinitest reagent tablet is used to determine the presence of _____ in urine.
    A. Glucose
    B. Acetone
    C. Ketone
    D. Bilirubin

23. A urine specimen should be examined within _____ hour(s) to avoid changes or deterioration to the contents.
    A. 1
    B. 2
    C. 4
    D. 6

24. An important symptom in diabetes mellitus is:
    A. Albuminuria.
    B. Ketonuria.
    C. Bilirubinuria.
    D. Hematuria.

25. The major cause of blycosuria is:
    A. Fad diets.
    B. Emotional stress.
    C. Toxemia of pregnancy.
    D. Diabetes mellitus.

26. A positive nitrite test on a urine specimen indicates:
    A. Congestive heart disease.
    B. Calculi in the urinary tract.
    C. Liver tissue damage.
    D. Urinary tract infection.

27. The desirable result for the test using the Clinitest reagent tablet is:
    A. 2%.
    B. 1%.
    C. ½%.
    D. 0%.

28. The desirable result for the test using the Acetest reagent table is recorded as:
    A. Negative.
    B. A small amount.
    C. A moderate amount.
    D. A large amount.

29. An example of unorganized sediment in the urine is :
    A. Red blood cells.
    B. Crystals.
    C. Bacteria.
    D. Yeasts and parasites.

30. The multiple-glass test is performed on men to evaluate:
    A. Congestive heart failure.
    B. Liver function.
    C. Lower urinary tract infection.
    D. Kidney function.

Labeling

1. Determine the specific gravity of urine for each
    of the following diagrams.

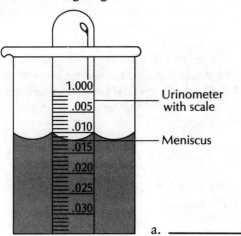

Urinometer with scale

Meniscus

a. _____

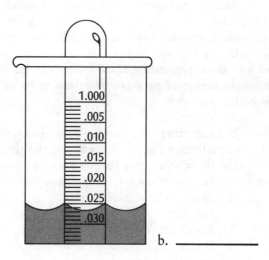

b. _____

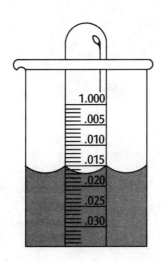

c. _____

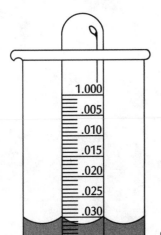

d. _____

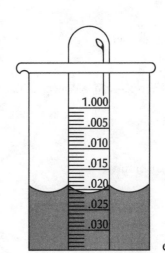

e. _____

PERFORMANCE TEST

In a skill laboratory, a simulation of a joblike environment, the medical assistant student is to demonstrate knowledge and skill in performing the following procedures without reference to source materials. For these activities, the student will require a fresh urine specimen or a synthetic preparation of the same. Time limits for the performance of each procedure are to be assigned by the instructor.

1. Given a fresh urine specimen and the required supplies, perform a routine physical and chemical analysis on the specimen and record the results, then prepare the specimen for a microscopic examination.

2. Given a fresh urine specimen and the required supplies, perform a Clinitest, Acetest, and Ictotest, and record the results.
3. Given a fresh urine specimen and Tes-Tape, test the urine for the presence of glucose, and record the results.
4. Given a fresh clean-catch midstream urine specimen and a Multistix-3 reagent strip, perform a semiquantitative culture test, and record the results.
5. Given a Dipper" or Dropper" urinalysis control kit, determine if the test reagent strips are reacting properly.
6. Given a Phenestix test reagent strip test a urine specimen for PKU.

The student is expected to perform these skills with 100% accuracy.

PERFORMANCE CHECKLIST: Routine urinalysis

DIRECTIONS: Evaluate student performance of each procedure using the following checklist. When you evaluate "not applicable," "unsatisfactory," or "not observed," please comment.

Checklist	S or NA*	U	NO	Comment
1. Washed hands. **Use appropriate Personal Protective Equipment (PPE) as dictated by facility.**				
2. Donned disposable single-use exam gloves.				
3. Checked physician's order.				
4. Obtained a urine specimen from the patient, and assembled the required equipment.				
5. Observed the specimen for the physical characteristics of appearance, color, and odor. Recorded observations.				
6. Poured the specimen into a graduated cylinder if the amount was to be recorded, and measured the quantity.				
7. Poured well-mixed urine into the 5-inch cylinder provided with the urinometer to within 1-inch from the top of the cylinder.				
8. Placed the urinometer into the urine, and spun it gently.				
9. Read the specific gravity value by noting the point where the lower middle part of the meniscus crosses the urinometer scale. Recorded the reading.				
10. Using the Multistix 10 SG, dipped the test areas of the strip into the urine specimen, and removed immediately.				
11. Tapped the strip against the side of the bottle to remove excess urine.				
12. Compared the test areas with the appropriate color chart on the Multistix 10 SG bottle at the specified times.				
13. Recorded the results accurately and promptly.				
14. Poured 10 to 15 ml of thoroughly mixed urine into a centrifuge tube and centrifuged for 5 minutes at the standard speed of 1500 rpm.				
15. Poured off the supernatant fluid.				
16. Allowed urine drops along the side of the tube to flow back into the sediment, and tapped the tube with finger to mix the contents.				
17. Placed a drop of the sediment on a glass slide and covered with a coverglass.				

Checklist	S or NA*	U	NO	Comment
18. Placed the slide on the microscope stage, and adjusted the low-power objective to examine the slide for casts; scanned the entire slide for an overall picture of the sediment after reducing the microscope light to a minimum.*				
19. Adjusted the microscope to the high-power field and examined the slide for specific cells and crystals.				
20. Estimated the approximate number of the various structures identified.				
21. Removed gloves and washed hands.				
22. Recorded the procedure, date, time, and signature on the patient's chart.				

Total Satisfactory Points   _____

Comments

Student's signature: _____ Instructor's signature: _____

Date: _____

*S or NA, Satisfactory or not applicable; U, unsatisfactory; NO, not observed.

*Frequently the actual examination of the slide is done by a laboratory technician or the physician. The medical assistant may be required only to prepare the specimen for the examination, which would then include just steps 1 through 18 and 21, and 22.

PERFORMANCE CHECKLIST: Clinitest

DIRECTIONS: Evaluate student performance of each procedure using the following checklist. When you evaluate "not applicable," "unsatisfactory," or "not observed," please comment.

Checklist	S or NA*	U	NO	Comment
1. Washed hands. **Use appropriate Personal Protective Equipment (PPE) as dictated by facility.**				
2. Donned disposable single-use exam gloves.				
3. Assembled required supplies, and obtained a urine specimen from the patient.				
4. Placed 5 drops of urine into a test tube.				
5. Rinsed dropper and added 10 drops of water to test tube.				
6. Placed Clinitest tablet in this test tube.				
7. Waited 15 seconds while boiling occurred.				
8. Shook tube gently and compared color of the contents with color chart.				
9. Removed gloves and washed hands.				
10. Recorded the procedure, date, time, and signature on the patient's chart.				
11. For the 2-drop method, used 2 drops of urine and 10 drops of water, and proceeded as above.				

Total Satisfactory Points _____

Comments

Student's signature: _____ Instructor's signature: _____

Date: _____

*S or NA, Satisfactory or not applicable; U, unsatisfactory; NO, not observed.

PERFORMANCE CHECKLIST: Acetest

DIRECTIONS: Evaluate student performance of each procedure using the following checklist. When you evaluate "not applicable," "unsatisfactory," or "not observed," please comment.

Checklist	S or NA*	U	NO	Comment
1. Washed hands. **Use appropriate Personal Protective Equipment (PPE) as dictated by facility.**				
2. Donned disposable single-use exam gloves.				
3. Assembled required supplies and obtained a urine specimen from the patient.				
4. Placed one tablet on clean, preferably white, paper.				
5. Placed 1 drop of urine on the tablet.				
6. At 30 seconds, compared the test results with the color chart.				
7. Removed gloves and washed hands.				
8. Recorded the procedure, date, time, and signature on the patient's chart.				

Total Satisfactory Points _____

Comments

Student's signature: _____   Instructor's signature: _____

Date: _____

*S or NA, Satisfactory or not applicable; U, unsatisfactory; NO, not observed.

PERFORMANCE CHECKLIST: Icotest

DIRECTIONS: Evaluate student performance of each procedure using the following checklist. When you evaluate "not applicable," "unsatisfactory," or "not observed," please comment.

Checklist	S or NA*	U	NO	Comment
1. Washed hands. **Use appropriate Personal Protective Equipment (PPE) as dictated by facility.**				
2. Donned disposable single-use exam gloves.				
3. Assembled required supplies and obtained a urine specimen from the patient.				
4. Placed 5 drops of urine on special mat provided with tablets.				
5. Placed one tablet in the center of wet area on mat.				
6. Put 2 drops of water onto the tablet.				
7. At 30 seconds, determined any color change on mat around the tablet, and compared with color chart.				
8. Removed gloves and washed hands.				
9. Recorded the procedure, date, time, and signature on the patient's chart.				

Total Satisfactory Points   ———

Comments

Student's signature:_____ Instructor's signature: _____
Date: _____
*S or NA, Satisfactory or not applicable; U, unsatisfactory; NO, not observed.

PERFORMANCE CHECKLIST: Testing for glucose using the Tes-Tape

DIRECTIONS: Evaluate student performance of each procedure using the following checklist. When you evaluate "not applicable," "unsatisfactory," or "not observed," please comment.

Checklist	S or NA*	U	NO	Comment
1. Washed hands. **Use appropriate Personal Protective Equipment (PPE) as dictated by facility.**				
2. Donned disposable single-use exam gloves.				
3. Assembled required supplies and obtained a urine specimen from the patient.				
4. Tore off 1½ inches of Tes-Tape paper.				
5. Dipped one end of tape into urine and removed.				
6. Waited 1 minute, then compared color changes with color chart on dispenser. Read results.				
7. Removed gloves and washed hands.				
8. Recorded the procedure, date, time, and signature on the patient's chart.				

Total Satisfactory Points _____

Comments

Student's signature: _____ Instructor's signature: _____

Date: _____

*S or NA, Satisfactory or not applicable; U, unsatisfactory; NO, not observed.

PERFORMANCE CHECKLIST: Multistix-3 culture strip method

DIRECTIONS: Evaluate student performance of each procedure using the following checklist. When you evaluate "not applicable," "unsatisfactory," or "not observed," please comment.

Checklist	S or NA*	U	NO	Comment
1. Washed hands. **Use appropriate Personal Protective Equipment (PPE) as dictated by facility.**				
2. Donned disposable single-use exam gloves.				
3. Assembled required supplies and obtained a clean-catch midstream urine specimen from the patient.				
4. Removed strip from wrapper.				
5. Dipped strip in urine for 5 seconds, then removed.				
6. Read nitrite test area 30 seconds later.				
7. Inserted strip into the sterile plastic pouch provided and sealed.				
8. Incubated pouch for 12 to 18 hours.				
9. Read results without removing strip from plastic pouch.				
10. Recorded the procedure, results, date, time, and signature on the patient's chart.				
11. Disposed of the still-sealed plastic pouch by incineration (or autoclaved and disposed of according to agency policy).				
12. Removed gloves and washed hands.				

Total Satisfactory Points _____

Comments

Student's signature: _____ Instructor's signature: _____

Date: _____

*S or NA, Satisfactory or not applicable; U, unsatisfactory; NO, not observed.

PERFORMANCE CHECKLIST: Urine pregnancy test—Wampole two-minute slide test

DIRECTIONS: Evaluate student performance of each procedure using the following checklist. When you evaluate "not applicable," "unsatisfactory," or "not observed," please comment.

Checklist	S or NA*	U	NO	Comment
1. Washed hands and assembled the equipment. **Use appropriate Personal Protective Equipment (PPE) as dictated by facility.**				
2. Allowed reagents and urine specimen to warm to room temperature.				
3. Donned disposable single-use exam gloves.				
4. Using disposable pipet placed one drop of urine within one of the circles on the glass slide.				
5. Added 1 drop of antiserum reagent to the urine. Held dropper at a 90-degree angle.				
6. Shook bottle of antigen to mix it well.				
7. Added 1 drop of antigen reagent to the urine and antiserum.				
8. Mixed reagents and urine well, spreading over entire circle.				
9. Gently rocked the slide for 2 minutes.				
10. Read the slide.				
11. Cleaned supplies and work area.				
12. Removed gloves and washed hands.				
13. Returned reagents to the refrigerator.				
14. Recorded the procedure, date, time, results, signature and date of the patient's last menstrual period on the patient's chart				
15. Completed procedure in time limit set by the instructor.				

Total Satisfactory Points _____

Comments

Student's signature: _____   Instructor's signature: _____
Date: _____
*S or NA, Satisfactory or not applicable; U, unsatisfactory; NO, not observed.

Evaluation of student's technique   **Name:** _____   **Date:** _____

	Satisfactory*		Unsatisfactory**		
	Very Good	Good	Fair	Poor	Score

- Routine urinalysis   ☐   ☐   ☐   ☐   _____   Very good = Perfect
- Clinitest   ☐   ☐   ☐   ☐   _____   Good   = Sufficient
- Acetest   ☐   ☐   ☐   ☐   _____   Fair   = Not acceptable requires more practice
- Ictotest   ☐   ☐   ☐   ☐   _____   Poor   = Totally unacceptable
- Glucose test using   ☐   ☐   ☐   ☐   _____   Pass*   = Satisfactory
  Tes-Tape
- Multistix-3 culture   ☐   ☐   ☐   ☐   _____
  strip
- Urine pregnancy test   ☐   ☐   ☐   ☐   _____

Comments:

ANSWERS
Fill-In

1. a. Two kidneys
   b. Two ureters
   c. One bladder
   d. One urethra
2. Kidneys; ureters; bladder; urethra
3. Selectively excreting or reabsorbing various substances according to the body's needs.
4. Nephron unit
5. a. Water (About 95% of urine is water.)
   b. Nitrogenous waste substances or the organic compounds, that is, urea, uric acid, and creatinine
   c. Mineral salts or the inorganic compounds, such as sodium chloride, sulfates, and phosphates of different kinds
   d. Pigment (Derived from certain bile compounds, pigment gives color to the urine.)
6. a. Diagnosis
   b. Monitoring the course of treatment of disease
   c. Providing a profile of the patient's health status
7. a. Appearance
   b. Color
   c. Odor
   d. Quantity
   e. Specific gravity
8. a. Reaction (pH)
   b. Protein
   c. Glucose
   d. Ketone
   e. Bilirubin
   f. Blood
   g. Nitrite
   h. Urobilinogen
   i. Special tests when indicated, such as for pregnancy, phenylketonuria, and porphyrinuria
9. a. Cells
   b. Casts
   c. Bacteria
   d. Parasites and yeasts
   e. Spermatozoa
   f. Crystals
   g. Artifacts and contaminates
10. Dry, clean container
11. 1 hour. a refrigerator at 41° F (5° C)
12. Physical characteristics; specific gravity; perform the series of chemical tests; prepare the specimen for the microscopic examinations
13. A urinary tract infection
14. Straw-colored, yellow, or amber
15. Dark; pale
16. Dark yellow
17. 1500 ml; 750 to 2000 ml
18. 100 and 400
19. Diabetes mellitus or chronic nephritis; Diuretic.
20. Cystitis, prolapse of the uterus, enlargement of the prostate, and urethritis.
21. Its weight compared with the universal standard weight of an equal amount of distilled water (expressed as 1.000).
22. The relative degree of concentration of dilution of the specimen, which in turn helps determine the kidney's ability to concentrate and dilute urine
23. 1.010 and 1.025; 1.005 to 1.030
24. Highest
25. Diabetes insipidus, pyelonephritis, glomerulonephritis, and various kidney anomalies.
26. Diabetes mellitus, congestive heart failure, hepatic disease, adrenal insufficiency, diarrhea and vomiting, or in patients who have lost an excessive amount of water through the skin during excessive perspiration
27. Record "quantity insufficient," *or* measure the specific gravity with a reagent strip.
28. Distilled water
29. Remove the urinometer and rinse it under cool water to remove all urine residue; then test the urine specimen in distilled water, and retest the specimen.
30. The degree of acidity or alkalinity of a solution
31. Acidic; alkaline
32. Acidic; 6; 4.5; 8
33. Clear plastic strip with up to 10 pieces of colored filter paper attached; identify different components in the urine. Every piece of filter paper is impregnated with various chemicals and changes color when dipped in the urine.
34. Compare the test areas to the appropriate color chart on the bottle at the specified times.
35. May
36. Does not
37. Abnormally high sugar content in the urine
38. C
39. Presence of acetone or ketone bodies in the urine.
40. Decreased
41. Does not
42. Presence of blood in the urine
43. Bacteriuria or a urinary tract infection
44. Does
45. Liver tissue damage and in congestive heart failure
46. Clinitest reagent tablet 5-drop method
47. Ten
48. Acetest
49. Ictotest

50. The bottles in which they are supplied with the cap secured tightly and at temperatures under 86° F (30° C)
51. Tes-Tape
52. Identify the type and the approximate number of formed elements present, which in turn helps the physician determine the presence of a disease process.
53. RBCs, WBCs, epithelial cells, casts, bacteria, parasites, yeast, fungi, and spermatozoa
54. Bacterial infection in the urinary tract, and/or pyuria
55. A urinary tract infection
56. Moniliasis
57. Human chorionic gonadotropin

Multiple Choice

1. A
2. A
3. C
4. B
5. C
6. D
7. D
8. B
9. B
10. C
11. C
12. B
13. D
14. D
15. A
16. A
17. C
18. D
19. B
20. A
21. C
22. A
23. A
24. B
25. D
26. D
27. D
28. A
29. B
30. C

Labeling

1. a. 1.012
    b. 1.027
    c. 1.017
    d. 1.032
    e. 1.021

Unit 13

Hematology

SUGGESTED ACTIVITIES

1. Practice and demonstrate the correct procedure for obtaining a blood sample from a patient by performing a skin puncture and a venipuncture.

2. Practice and demonstrate the correct procedure for determining the presence of glucose in blood by using a Dextrostix.

3. Practice completing requisition forms for blood work that would be performed in the hematology and chemistry departments of a laboratory.

4. Review laboratory results that have been received at the facility where you do your work experience. Determine if the results are normal. Discuss the significance of any abnormal results.

STUDY QUESTIONS
Fill-In

In the blanks provided, write the answers that best complete the sentences:

1. _____ is an increased number of RBCs.

2. _____ is the protein in a RBC that carries oxygen and carbon dioxide.

3. _____ is the destruction of RBCs with the release of hemoglobin into the plasma.

4. _____ is a state in which cells are equal in size, especially equality of size of RBCs.

5. _____ is an increased number of circulating WBCs.

6. _____ is a deficient number of circulating WBCs.

7. _____ is an increased number of platelets in the circulating blood.

8. _____ is the study of blood.

9. The formed elements in the blood are the _____, _____ , and _____ .

10. The average adult has approximately _____ quarts of blood.

11. The prime function of the RBC is to _____ _____ .

12. _____ is the result of too few RBCs in the circulating blood, or RBCs with reduced amounts of hemoglobin, or both.

13. Granular WBCs, sometimes called polymorphonuclear leukocytes, include the _____ , _____ , and _____ .

14. The agranular leukocytes are the _____ and _____ .

15. The prime function of WBCs is to _____ .

16. Platelets play a vital role in _____ .

17. For most routine hematological studies, blood may be obtained from a _____ or _____ .

18. Capillary blood is obtained by performing a _____ on the _____ .

19. When performing a skin puncture, the following areas on the body should be avoided:

_____, _____,

_____, _____, and

_____.

20. The most common sites for obtaining blood by a venipuncture are the _____ and _____ veins located in the _____.

21. The most common method for obtaining a blood sample is a _____.

22. A _____ would be performed to obtain the blood specimen when 10 cc of blood is needed for testing.

23. Alternative sites to use when blood cannot be obtained from a vein in the antecubital space are

_____, _____, or

_____.

24. Blood needed for blood gas studies is obtained from a(n) _____.

25. Generally, a blood collection tube (with *or* without) _____ an additive is used when a clot is needed to obtain serum for testing.

26. To separate serum from the blood clot in a collection tube the sample must be centrifuged for

_____ minutes.

27. Name the blood tests for which serum is needed.

a. _____

b. _____

c. _____

28. Blood collection tubes containing _____ are recommended for use when doing hematology studies.

29. A blood collection tube containing an anticoagulant additive, such as heparin, prevents _____.

30. A blood collection tube containing heparin (should *or* should not) _____ be used for hematology studies.

31. The amount of venous blood to be drawn when performing a venipuncture is _____ to _____, varying with the test(s) to be performed.

32. Depending on the test(s) to be performed, blood should be examined within _____ hours or less from the time it was collected.

33. The patient must fast for _____ hours before having blood drawn for a fasting blood sugar test.

34. A vacuum tube with a red top is used to collect a blood sample for tests done on _____.

35. A vacuum tube with a lavender top is used to collect a blood sample for tests done on _____ or _____.

36. A vacuum tube with a green top is used to collect a blood sample for tests done on _____ or _____.

37. When more than one tube of blood needs to be drawn the general order of draw is as follows:

a. First draw _____

b. Second draw _____

c. Third draw _____

d. Last draw _____

38. A vacuum collection tube without any additives would have a _____-colored top.

39. A vacuum collection tube with the additive EDTA would have a _____-colored top.

40. A vacuum collection tube with the additive sodium heparin would have a _____ -colored top.

41. A vacuum collection tube with the additives potassium oxalate and sodium fluoride would have a _____ -colored top.

42. Vacuum tubes used when drawing blood culture (do *or* do not) _____ contain an additive.

43. After blood has been drawn into a tube without an additive it (should *or* should not) _____ be inverted and shaken.

44. Tubes that contain an additive should be _____ to mix the blood with the additive.

45. Blood drawn for an electrolyte panel should be placed in _____ if it is not tested immediately.

46. A vacuum apparatus should not be used to draw blood from a small or constricted vein because this causes _____ .

47. If a venipuncture must be performed on a fragile, narrow vein, a _____ -gauge needle should be used rather than a _____ gauge needle.

48. When performing a venipuncture the vein must be palpated before inserting the needle to determine if _____ .

49. A sturdy-walled vein should be used for a venipuncture. The walls of sturdy veins feel _____ to the touch, and they exhibit _____ and when pressure is carefully applied.

50. A 1 inch, 1¼ inch, or 1½ inch, _____ -gauge needle should be used to perform a venipuncture.

51. Select the site for a venipuncture by palpating the _____ space.

52. For a venipuncture the tourniquet should be applied around the patient's arm _____ to _____ inches above the elbow.

53. For a venipuncture the needle should be inserted at a _____ -degree angle.

54. When performing a venipuncture release the tourniquet as soon as _____ .

55. When performing a venipuncture the tourniquet must be (on *or* off) _____ before the needle is withdrawn.

56. When using a vacuum tube for a venipuncture, the needle should be removed from the vein when _____ .

57. A sterile, disposable _____ is used to perform a fingertip skin puncture.

58. When performing a fingertip skin puncture, the first drop of blood that appears is not a desirable sample because _____ .

59. When performing a fingertip skin puncture (hard *or* gentle) _____ pressure should be applied above the puncture site to cause the blood to flow freely.

60. Blood tests that require the patient to fast beforehand include _____ , _____ , and _____ . At other times fasting tests are done according to the individual requests of the physician or laboratory.

61. The _____ is a reagent strip that measures blood glucose levels over a range of 45 to 250 mg/100ml of blood.

62. _____ (decreased *or* increased) numbers of RBCs will be seen in patients with some form of anemia.

63. A low hematocrit level is seen in patients who have _____ or _____ .

64. Pathologically, the WBC count increases in

_____ or _____ .

65. The differential is a blood test that determine

_____ .

66. Three types of specimens that can be obtained

from a venous blood sample are _____ ,

_____ , and _____ .

67. When serum is needed for a test it *must* be separated from the blood within_____

minutes after the sample has been collected.

68. Depending on the test(s) to be performed, blood

should be examined within _____ hours
or less from the time it was collected, and preferably within _____ hours of the time it
was drawn.

69. Do not use vacuum apparatus to draw blood from

a small or constricted vein because _____

_____ .

70. Blood glucose meters are designed for use with

_____ blood; using venous blood or

serum causes _____ .

71. Quality assurance is very important when using

blood glucose meters. This includes _____

_____ .

72. Blood group and blood typing is the classification

of blood based on _____ .

Multiple Choice

Write the letter of the correct answer in the blank
provided. There is only *one* correct answer.

_____ 1. Some of the tests done on a CBC include:
  A. WBC count.
  B. Hematocrit.
  C. Platelet count.
  D. Both A and B.
  E. A, B, and C

_____ 2. The most common sites used when performing a venipuncture for the purpose of withdrawing blood are the:
  A. Cephalic and basilic veins.
  B. Femoral and cephalic veins.
  C. Superior and inferior venae cavae.
  D. Saphenous veins.
  E. Brachial and basilic veins.

_____ 3. Granular WBCs, RBCs, and platelets are produced in the:
  A. Red bone marrow of bones such as the femur and humerus.
  B. Lymph nodes and other lymphoid tissue.

_____ 4. The normal values for a hematocrit performed on a female range from:
  A. 20% to 35%.
  B. 30% to 50%.
  C. 33% to 46%.
  D. 40% to 54%.
  E. 35% to 40%.

_____ 5. The body's primary lines of defense against infections are the:
  A. RBCs.
  B. Neutrophils.
  C. Basophils.
  D. Lymphocytes.
  E. Monocytes.

_____ 6. Increased levels of _____ are seen in the blood when a patient has a myocardial infarction.
  A. Total protein
  B. Serum asparate aminotransferase (AST), formerly called serum glutamic oxaloacetic transaminase (SGOT)
  C. Alkaline phosphatase
  D. Blood urea nitrogen (BUN)
  E. Creatinine

_____ 7. Capillary blood for testing is usually obtained:
  (1) By performing a skin puncture.
  (2) By performing a venipuncture.
  (3) From the lateral surface of a fingertip.
  (4) From the antecubital space.
  A. Both (2) and (4)
  B. Both (2) and (3)
  C. Both (1) and (3)
  D. Both (1) and (4)
  E. (1), (3), and (4)

8. When collecting a blood sample using the venipuncture technique, the tourniquet on the patient's arm should be released:
   A. As soon as the skin puncture is made.
   B. After the needle is removed from the vein.
   C. After the collection tube or syringe is full.
   D. As soon as blood starts to flow into the syringe or vacuum tube or before the needle is removed if taking multiple tubes.
   E. After the collection tube or syringe is half-filled.

9. When a patient is required to fast before a blood sample is drawn, this generally means that the patient:
   A. Must eat no food for 10 hours before the blood sample is drawn, but can have black coffee or water.
   B. Must abstain from all food, but may drink plain water and black coffee or tea until the time the blood is drawn.
   C. Must not eat breakfast the morning the blood sample is to be drawn.
   D. Must not eat lunch if the blood sample is to be drawn in the early afternoon.
   E. Must abstain from all food and liquids, except water, for up to 14 hours before the blood sample is drawn.

10. Laboratory blood tests that would require a collection tube without an additive would include:
    A. Hematology.
    B. Blood alcohol levels.
    C. Blood chemistries.
    D. Coagulation studies.

11. You would use a collection tube with the additive EDTA when you are collecting blood for:
    A. Hematology studies (e.g., WBCs, RBCs).
    B. Blood chemistries.
    C. Coagulation studies.
    D. Blood alcohol levels.

12. The reason why the vacuum tube that has heparin as the additive would not be used when you are collecting blood for hematology studies is because the heparin:
    A. Causes a clot to form.
    B. Causes serum to separate from the clot.
    C. Is not the choice of the laboratory.
    D. Causes distortion of the cells and lead, to false results.

13. After drawing a blood sample into a vacuum tube with an additive it must be:
    A. Centrifuged for 10 minutes.
    B. Vigorously shaken so that the blood would mix with the additive.
    C. Gently inverted 8 to 10 times.
    D. Immediately stood upright in a container until it is sent to the laboratory.

14. The angle for insertion of the needle when performing a venipuncture is:
    A. 15 to 30 degrees.
    B. 5 to 10 degrees.
    C. 30 to 50 degrees.
    D. 45 to 90 degrees.

15. When doing a multiple sample collection for various studies including a blood culture, the first tube in which to collect a specimen would be:
    A. A sterile blood culture tube.
    B. A tube with an additive.
    C. Coagulation tubes.
    D. A tube with no additive.

16. The usual size of the needle to use when performing a venipuncture is:
    A. ½-inch 25G
    B. 1½-inch 27G
    C. 1½-inch 21G
    D. 1-inch 17G

17. The tourniquet on the patient's arm should be placed approximately:
    A. ½ inch above the puncture site.
    B. 5 to 6 inches above the puncture site.
    C. 1 inch above the puncture site.
    D. 3 to 4 inches above the puncture site.

18. The correct position for the patient's arm when performing the venipuncture on one of the two recommended veins of the arm is:
    A. Slightly elevated from the side of the body.
    B. Parallel to the body.
    C. Perpendicular to the body.
    D. In a downward position.

19. When using a standard syringe and needle to perform the venipuncture, a vein may collapse if:
    A. The blood is withdrawn too slowly.
    B. The blood is withdrawn too quickly.
    C. Not enough blood is drawn off for the test.
    D. The patient's arm is in the wrong position.

20. The normal range of RBCs per cubic millimeter of blood for females is:
    A. 3,000,000 to 5,000,000.
    B. 4,000,000 to 5,000,000.
    C. 4,000,000 to 5,500,000.
    D. 4,500,000 to 5,500,000.

21. The normal range of RBCs per cubic millimeter of blood for males is:
    A. 4,000,000 to 5,000,000.
    B. 4,500,000 to 6,000,000.
    C. 4,500,000 to 6,500,000.
    D. 5,500,000 to 6,500,000.

22. The normal range of WBCs per cubic millimeter of blood for both females and males is:
    A. 3,000 to 5,000.
    B. 5,000 to 10,000.
    C. 15,000 to 20,000.
    D. 14,000 to 18,000.

23. The normal range of hemoglobin for females expressed as grams per 100 ml of blood is:
    A. 10 to 14.
    B. 10 to 20.
    C. 12 to 16.
    D. 14 to 18.

24. The normal range of hemoglobin for males expressed as grams per 100 ml of blood is:
    A. 10 to 14.
    B. 10 to 20.
    C. 12 to 16.
    D. 14 to 18.

25. The normal values for a hematocrit performed on a male range from:
    A. 25% to 45%.
    B. 35% to 55%.
    C. 35% to 45%.
    D. 40% to 54%.

26. The largest number of the different types of WBCs found when doing a differential test are the:
    A. Monocytes.
    B. Lymphocytes.
    C. Neutrophils.
    D. Basophils.

27. The smallest number of the different types of WBCs found when doing a differential test are the:
    A. Monocytes.
    B. Lymphocytes.
    C. Eosinophils.
    D. Basophils.

28. The normal range for a platelet count performed on whole blood per cubic millimeter of blood is:
    A. 1,000 to 10,000.
    B. 50,000 to 100,000.
    C. 100,000 to 300,000.
    D. 200,000 to 400,000.

29. The desirable blood cholesterol level expressed as mg/100 ml of blood for a 30-year-old person is:
    A. 120 to 230.
    B. Less than 200.
    C. 200 to 239.
    D. 240 or higher.

30. Decreased numbers of _____ may indicate disease of the spleen and also causes bleeding.
    A. WBCs
    B. Platelets
    C. RBCs
    D. Monocytes

_____ 31. Type _____ blood is known as the universal donor.
   A. 0.
   B. A.
   C. B.
   D. AB.

_____ 32. Type _____ blood is known as the universal recipient.
   A. 0.
   B. A.
   C. B.
   D. AB.

_____ 33. A patient is considered anemic if the hemoglobin value is below _____ g/100 ml of blood.
   A. 18.
   B. 14.
   C. 12.
   D. 16.

_____ 34. A decreased WBC count may be caused by:
   A. Infection.
   B. Leukemia.
   C. Exercise.
   D. Chemotherapy.

_____ 35. Decreased numbers of RBCs are seen in patients with some form of:
   A. Anemia.
   B. Leukemia.
   C. Erythrocytosis.
   D. Infection.

_____ 36. The hematocrit, or packed cell volume, represents the percentage of _____ in the total blood volume.
   A. RBCs.
   B. WBC.
   C. Platelets.
   D. Prothrombin.

_____ 37. The body's second line of defense against invasion by foreign substances is the:
   A. Monocytes.
   B. Neutrophils.
   C. Lymphocytes.
   D. Basophils.

_____ 38. When using the One Touch™ blood glucose meter test results appear in:
   A. 30 seconds.
   B. 45 seconds.
   C. 1 minute.
   D. 2 minutes.

_____ 39. A glucose tolerance test may be performed to aid in the diagnosis of:
   A. Kidney disease.
   B. Diabetes.
   C. Anemia.
   D. Heart disease.

PERFORMANCE TEST

In a skill laboratory, a simulation of a joblike environment, the medical assistant student is to demonstrate knowledge and skill in performing the following procedures without reference to source materials. For these activities, the student will need a person to play the role of a patient; *or* an artificial appliance representing a human arm and hand, and a blood sample. Time limits for the performance of each procedure are to be assigned by the instructor.

1. Given the required supplies and equipment, obtain blood samples from the patient by performing a fingertip skin puncture and a venipuncture. Then record these procedures on the patient's chart.
2. Having obtained a capillary blood sample in a nonheparinized capillary tube, perform a copper sulfate relative density test, and record the results on the patient's chart.
3. Having obtained a capillary blood sample in a heparinized capillary tube, perform a hematocrit test using the microhematocrit centrifuge, and record the results on the patient's chart.
4. Given a blood sample and a Dextrostix, test the sample for the presence of glucose, and record the results on the patient's chart.
5. Having obtained a blood sample by performing a fingertip skin puncture, test the blood for the presence and amount of glucose using an AccuChek III and a Chemstrip bG; using One Touch Basic or a One Touch II blood glucose meter and a test strip.

The student is expected to perform these skills with 100% accuracy.

PERFORMANCE CHECKLIST: Fingertip skin puncture to obtain blood sample

DIRECTIONS: Evaluate student performance of each procedure using the following checklist. When you evaluate "not applicable," "unsatisfactory," or "not observed," please comment.

Checklist	S or NA*	U	NO	Comment
1. Washed hands. **Use appropriate Personal Protective Equipment (PPE) as dictated by facility.**				
2. Assembled the required equipment and supplies.				
3. Identified the patient, and explained the procedure.				
4. Selected the correct site on fingertip.				
5. "Milked" the finger gently along the sides.				
6. Cleaned the puncture site with alcohol swab.				
7. Allowed the area to air dry.				
8. Donned disposable single-use exam gloves.				
9. Grasped the patient's finger on the sides near the fingertip.				
10. Took the lancet to make a quick in-and-out puncture on the patient's fingertip. (Held the lancet at a right angle to the lines on the patient's finger).				
11. Wiped off the first drop of blood with a clean sponge.				
12. Using gentle pressure above the puncture site, allowed the blood to flow freely.				
13. Collected a blood sample in a pipette.				
14. When more than one sample was required, wiped the finger with a clean cotton sponge between each sample collected to obtain fresh drops of blood each time.				
15. Applied pressure to the puncture site with a dry cotton sponge. Disposed of sponge and lancet with blood on it in a container labeled for bio-hazardous waste.				
16. Labeled the specimen(s) obtained; forwarded to the laboratory with a correct requisition.				
17. Disposed of lancet in puncture-resistant container for used sharps.				
18. Removed gloves and washed hands.				
19. Recorded the procedure, date, time, and signature on the patient's chart.				

Total Satisfactory Points　＿＿＿＿＿

Comments

Student's signature:＿＿＿＿＿＿＿＿＿＿＿＿＿　Instructor's signature: ＿＿＿＿＿＿＿＿＿＿＿＿＿

Date: ＿＿＿＿＿＿＿＿＿＿＿＿＿＿

*S or NA, Satisfactory or not applicable; U, unsatisfactory; NO, not observed.

PERFORMANCE CHECKLIST: Copper sulfate relative density test

DIRECTIONS: Evaluate student performance of each procedure using the following checklist. When you evaluate "not applicable," "unsatisfactory," or "not observed," please comment.

Checklist	S or NA*	U	NO	Comment
After obtaining the capillary blood sample in a non-heparinized capillary tube:				
1. Donned disposable single-use exam gloves.				
2. Held capillary tube vertically over the container of copper sulfate solution, allowing blood to drop into this solution.				
3. If blood did not drop freely into the solution, applied the bulb to the capillary tube, then squeezed the bulb to force blood into the solution.				
4. Determined the results.				
5. Disposed of used equipment correctly.				
6. Removed gloves and washed hands.				
7. Recorded the procedure, date, time, and signature on the patient's chart.				

Total Satisfactory Points _____

Comments

Student's signature: _____ Instructor's signature: _____
Date: _____

*S or NA, Satisfactory or not applicable; U, unsatisfactory; NO, not observed.

PERFORMANCE CHECKLIST: Venipuncture to obtain blood sample

DIRECTIONS: Evaluate student performance of each procedure using the following checklist. When you evaluate "not applicable," "unsatisfactory," or "not observed," please comment.

Checklist	S or NA*	U	NO	Comment
1. Washed hands. **Use appropriate Personal Protective Equipment (PPE) as dictated by facility.**				
2. Assembled the required equipment and supplies.				
3. Identified the patient, and explained the procedure.				
4. Had the patient seated with the arm well supported in a downward position.				
5. Prepared equipment for use: attached the needle to the syringe, and labeled the tube(s) with the date and the patient's name.				
6. Selected the site for the venipuncture, and palpated the anterior cubital space.				
7. Donned disposable single-use exam gloves.				
8. Applied the tourniquet around the patient's arm, above the elbow. Palpated the vein again.				
9. Cleaned the skin site with an alcohol sponge.				
10. Drew skin over the puncture site until tense.				
11. Gently and slowly inserted the needle into the vein.				
12. Slowly pulled on the plunger of the syringe to withdraw blood; released tourniquet as soon as blood flowed into the syringe.				
13. When the sample had been drawn, placed a dry sterile sponge over the puncture site and withdrew the needle.				
14. With this sponge, applied pressure over the puncture site for a few minutes. (Students may have the patient do this.)				
15. With the sponge in place and still applying pressure, had patient elevate the arm for a few minutes more.				
16. Injected the blood into the collection tube.				
17. Capped the tubes, then gently inverted tubes that contain an additive 8 to 10 times. Did not shake these tubes.				
18. Applied a Band-Aid to the puncture site if required. Disposed of sponge with blood on it in container marked for biohazardous waste.				
19. Destroyed and discarded disposable syringe and needle in designated container.				

Checklist	S or NA*	U	NO	Comment
20. Removed gloves and washed hands.				
21. Completed the laboratory requisition, and sent with sample(s) drawn to the laboratory.				
22. Recorded the procedure, date, time, and signature on the patient's chart.				

Total Satisfactory Points _____

Comments

Student's signature: _____ Instructor's signature: _____

Date: _____

*S or NA, Satisfactory or not applicable; U, unsatisfactory; NO, not observed.

PERFORMANCE CHECKLIST: Hematocrit

DIRECTIONS: Evaluate student performance of each procedure using the following checklist. When you evaluate "not applicable," "unsatisfactory," or "not observed," please comment.

Checklist	S or NA*	U	NO	Comment
After obtaining a capillary blood sample in a heparinized capillary tube: 1. Donned disposable single-use exam gloves.				
2. Sealed the dry end of the tube by sticking it into the Crito-seal clay tray or used self-sealing microhematocrit tube.				
3. With the sealed end facing toward the outer direction, placed the tube into a slot in the microhematocrit centrifuge.				
4. Closed and secured the lid of the centrifuge.				
5. Adjusted the timer, and spun down for 5 minutes.				
6. Read the results using the scale provided on the centrifuge, or used the microhematocrit card to read the results.				
7. Disposed of materials correctly.				
8. Removed gloves and washed hands.				
9. Recorded the procedure, date, time, and signature on the patient's chart.				

Total Satisfactory Points   _____

Comments

Student's signature:_____   Instructor's signature: _____
Date: _____
*S or NA, Satisfactory or not applicable; U, unsatisfactory; NO, not observed.

PERFORMANCE CHECKLIST: Test for blood glucose using the Dextrostix

DIRECTIONS: Evaluate student performance of each procedure using the following checklist. When you evaluate "not applicable," "unsatisfactory," or "not observed," please comment.

Checklist	S or NA*	U	NO	Comment
Given a blood sample and a Dextrostix: 1. Donned disposable single-use exam gloves.				
2. Placed a large drop of blood on the test area of the strip.				
3. Holding the strip horizontally, waited exactly 670 seconds.				
4. Holding the strip vertically, washed the blood off with a sharp stream of water from a wash bottle; 1 to 2 seconds was sufficient time.				
5. Compared the color on the test area to the color chart on the bottle.				
6. Recorded the procedure, date, time, and signature on the patient's chart.				
7. Disposed of lancet in biohazardous disposable sharps container. Disposed of test strip in container for biohazardous waste.				
8. Removed gloves and washed hands.				

Total Satisfactory Points _____

Comments

Student's signature:_____ Instructor's signature: _____
Date: _____

*S or NA, Satisfactory or not applicable; U, unsatisfactory; NO, not observed.

PERFORMANCE CHECKLIST: Test for blood glucose using the Accu-Chek III and Chemstrip bG

DIRECTIONS: Evaluate student performance of each procedure using the following checklist. When you evaluate "not applicable," "unsatisfactory," or "not observed," please comment.

Checklist	S or NA*	U	NO	Comment
1. Washed hands. **Use appropriate Personal Protective Equipment (PPE) as dictated by facility.**				
2. Assembled the equipment.				
3. Identified the patient and explained the procedure.				
4. Turned the meter on by pressing the ON/OFF button once.				
5. Placed the Chemstrip bG test strip on a flat work surface with test pads facing up.				
6. Donned disposable single-use exam gloves.				
7. Performed a skin puncture on the patient's fingertip.				
8. Lightly touched the blood drop to the test pads on the Chemstrip bG strip. Did not smear the blood. Completely covered both pads. Applied pressure over the puncture site with a clean, dry gauze pad or cotton ball.				
9. Pressed the TIME button on the meter. The meter counts to 60.				
10. When the display read 60 seconds, wiped the blood from the test pads with a clean, dry cotton ball using gentle pressure. *Did not* leave any blood on the test pads.				
11. While the meter is counting to 120 seconds, turned the test strip on its side with the test pads facing the ON/OFF button and inserted the reacted test strip into the test strip adaptor. *The test strip must be inserted before the display reads 120.*				
12. When the display reads 120, a high beep is emitted, followed by the blood glucose value displayed in mg/dl. Read the blood glucose value on the display screen.				
13. Recorded the procedure, date, time, and signature on the patient's chart.				
14. Turned the meter off. Removed the test strip from the meter. Disposed of lancet in biohazardous container for used, disposable sharps. Disposed of any sponge with blood on it and the test strip.				

PERFORMANCE CHECKLIST: Test for blood glucose using the Accu-Check III and Chemstrip bG (continued)

Checklist	S or NA*	U	NO	Comment
15. Attended to the patient.				
16. Cleaned and replaced equipment in storage area.				
17. Removed gloves and washed hands.				

Total Satisfactory Points _____

Comments

Student's signature:_____ Instructor's signature: _____

Date: _____

*S or NA, Satisfactory or not applicable; U, unsatisfactory; NO, not observed.

PERFORMANCE CHECKLIST: Test for blood glucose using the One Touch II Blood Glucose Meter

DIRECTIONS: Evaluate student performance of each procedure using the following checklist. When you evaluate "not applicable," "unsatisfactory," or "not observed," please comment.

Checklist	S or NA*	U	NO	Comment
1. Washed hands. **Use appropriate Personal Protective Equipment (PPE) as dictated by facility.**				
2. Assembled the equipment and supplies.				
3. Identified the patient and explained the procedure.				
4. Turned the meter on.				
5. Inserted test strip with test spot facing up.				
6. Donned disposable single-use exam gloves.				
7. Performed a skin puncture on the patient's fingertip. Turned the pricked area of finger downward. Squeezed firmly until a large hanging drop of blood formed.				
8. Immediately applied the blood to the Test Spot while APPLY SAMPLE was on the display.				
9. Covered the entire Test Spot with blood. *Did not* smear or rub blood on the Test Spot.				
10. Read results on the display. The meter display counts down from 45—then the result appeared.				
11. Recorded the procedure, date, time, and signature on the patient's chart.				
12. Attended to the patient.				
13. Cleaned and replaced equipment and supplies in the proper storage area.				
14. Removed gloves and washed hands.				

Total Satisfactory Points _____

Comments

Student's signature: _____   Instructor's signature: _____
Date: _____
*S or NA, Satisfactory or not applicable; U, unsatisfactory; NO, not observed.

216

Evaluation of student's technique　　Name: _____　Date: _____

	Satisfactory*		Unsatisfactory**		
	Very Good	Good	Fair	Poor	Score
• Fingertip skin puncture	☐	☐	☐	☐	_____
• Venipuncture	☐	☐	☐	☐	_____
• Copper sulfate relative density test	☐	☐	☐	☐	_____
• Hematocrit	☐	☐	☐	☐	_____
• Dextrostix	☐	☐	☐	☐	_____
• Accu-Chek III and Chemstrip bG	☐	☐	☐	☐	_____
• One Touch II Blood Glucose Meter	☐	☐	☐	☐	_____

Very good = Perfect
Good　 = Sufficient
Fair　 = Not acceptable requires more practice
Poor　 = Totally unacceptable
Pass*　 = Satisfactory
Fail**　= Unsatisfactory

Comments

1. Erythrocytosis
2. Hemoglobin
3. Hemolysis
4. Isocytosis
5. Leukocytosis
6. Leukopenia
7. Thrombocythemia
8. Hematology
9. RBCs, WBCs, and platelets
10. 5 to 6
11. Transport oxygen from the lungs to the body cells and carbon dioxide from the cells back to the lungs to be exhaled.
12. Anemia
13. Eosinophils, basophils, and neutrophils
14. Monocytes and lymphocytes
15. Protect the body against infection and disease
16. Initiating the clotting process of blood
17. Capillary or vein
18. Skin puncture on the palmar surface of the fingertip or on the ear lobe. For infants, the skin puncture is done on the plantar surface of the great toe or heel.
19. Cyanotic, scarred, traumatized, edematous, and heavily calloused
20. Basilic and cephalic veins located in the antecubital area of the arm, which is at the inner aspect of the arm opposite the elbow
21. Venipuncture
22. Venipuncture
23. The veins on the top of the hand, in the wrist, or even in the foot
24. Artery
25. Without
26. 10
27. a. Most blood chemistries (varying with the laboratory's preference)
    b. Serology tests
    c. Rh-factor testing
28. EDTA anticoagulant additive
29. The blood from clotting
30. Should not
31. 3 to 30 ml
32. 8
33. 8 to 14
34. Serum
35. Whole blood or plasma
36. Whole blood or plasma
37. a. Blood culture tubes
    b. Tubes with no additives
    c. Coagulation tubes
    d. Tubes with additives
38. Red
39. Lavender
40. Green
41. Gray
42. Do not
43. Should not
44. Gently inverted 8 to 10 times
45. A refrigerator
46. The vein to collapse
47. 23; 21
48. The vein is patent.
49. Firm; elasticity; resilience
50. 21
51. Antecubital
52. 3 to 4
53. 15
54. Blood starts to flow into the syringe.
55. Off
56. The vacuum is exhausted and blood stops flowing into the tube.
57. Lancet
58. It contains tissue fluid.
59. Gentle
60. Fasting blood sugar, glucose tolerance test, and any type of lipid analysis, such as cholesterol and triglycerides.
61. Dextrostix
62. Decreased
63. anemia or leukemia
64. infections and leukemia
65. The percentage of each of the five different types of WBCs in the blood.
66. serum, whole blood, plasma
67. 30 to 45
68. 8, 2 to 4
69. This causes the vein to collapse.
70. Capillary, inaccurate readings
71. Regular cleaning and maintaining the instrument, and using control solutions periodically to test the accuracy of the meter
72. the presence or absence of antigens on the surface of the RBCs

Multiple Choice

1. D
2. A
3. A
4. C
5. B
6. B
7. C
8. D
9. E
10. C
11. A
12. D
13. C
14. A
15. A
16. C
17. D
18. D
19. B
20. C
21. B
22. B
23. C
24. D
25. D
26. C
27. D
28. D
29. B
30. B
31. A
32. D
33. C
34. D
35. A
36. A
37. A
38. B
39. B

Unit 14

Diagnostic Radiology, Radiation Therapy, and Nuclear Medicine

SUGGESTED ACTIVITIES

1. Have your instructor arrange for a field trip to a radiology department at a hospital. Observe the equipment and techniques for the many radiological procedures. Discuss your observations when returning to your classroom.

2. In the classroom have another student play the role of the patient. Practice explaining the various radiological procedures and related information to the patient.

3. Practice scheduling patients for various radiological diagnostic procedures.

4. Practice and demonstrate preparing and assisting a patient for various radiological procedures that may be performed in a clinic or physician's office.

5. Practice and demonstrate proficiency in handling and storing x-ray films received in the physician's office or clinic.

STUDY QUESTIONS
Fill-In

In the blanks provided, write the answers that best complete the sentences:

1. Radiology is the specialty of medical science that deals with the _____ _____ .

2. Radiology procedures can be divided into three specialties: _____ , _____ , and _____ .

3. A fluoroscope is used during x-ray examinations for _____ .

4. Fluoroscopy is the _____ .

5. An oscilloscope is used for _____ .

6. Ionizing radiation is _____ .

7. A radiogram is a _____ .

8. Radiography is the _____ .

9. X-rays are also called _____ .

10. The major advantage of the fluoroscope over the usual type of x-ray film is that _____ _____ .

11. A contrast medium is a _____ _____ .

12. Positive contrast media include barium sulfate and iodine compounds. Because these media are dense, they absorb more of the _____ . They appear _____ (color) on x-ray images.

13. Negative contrast media include air, gas, and carbon dioxide. They appear _____ (color) on x-ray images.

14. Barium sulfate is an opaque medium that is used for two main types of x-ray and fluoroscopic examinations. These examinations are a _____ _____ and a _____ .

15. A barium meal or upper GI series is the oral ingestion of the barium mixture to outline the _____, and if ordered, the _____, depending on the physician's request.

16. A lower GI series outlines the _____ for study after the instillation of the barium mixture through an _____ .

17. A barium swallow is done to outline the _____ _____ .

18. The iodinated contrast media interfere with _____ studies performed by the nuclear medicine department; therefore procedures using the iodinated contrast media should not be performed when the patient is having _____ tests.

19. Air, oxygen, and carbon dioxide are negative contrast media that can be used for x-ray examinations of the _____ and _____ .

20. A myelogram is an x-ray record of the _____ _____ .

21. An _____ is an x-ray record of a joint after injecting air or another gas into the articular capsule.

22. _____, an x-ray examination of the breast to identify breast lesions or tumors, involves detection of radiodense tissue or calcifications.

23. _____ is the most effective method for detecting early and curable breast cancer.

24. The patient who is having a mammogram should be asked not to wear any _____ or _____ on the day of the examination, because these products sometimes show up as artifacts on the x-ray images.

25. Tomography can be used in any part of the body, but is most effective in areas of high contrast, such as in the _____ and _____ _____ .

26. Computed tomography (CT) provides valuable clinical information in the early detection, differentiation, and demarcation of disease of the _____ and _____ .

27. When having a CT scan performed the patient (will or will not) _____ be hospitalized.

28. A CT scan takes _____ to _____ minutes or longer to complete all the slices required for a complete examination.

29. Some facilities require the patient to have nothing by mouth for _____ hours before a CT scan is performed if a contrast medium is used.

30. Magnetic resonance (MR) is a computer-based, cross-sectional imaging modality that examines the interactions of _____ and _____ with tissue to obtain its images.

31. One advantage of MR is that x-rays (are or are not) _____ used to obtain the MR image.

32. MR is a (painful or painless) _____ and noninvasive procedure.

33. Magnetic resonance is used to detect _____ in soft tissue.

34. MR (can or cannot) _____ detect septal defects in the heart.

35. MR (can or cannot) _____ see the hard part of bones.

36. Diagnostic ultrasound uses _____ that bounce off the body to record information on the structure or internal organs.

37. Diagnostic ultrasound procedures produce a record that is called a(n) _____ or _____ .

38. Diagnostic ultrasound procedures (are or are not) _____ safe to use on a woman who is pregnant.

39. Diagnostic ultrasound procedures are (painful *or* painless) _____ procedures.

40. An x-ray record of the chest is obtained with the patient in the _____ position. Generally, a lateral view is also taken.

41. X-ray records are made of bones suspected of disease or trauma, such as _____ and _____ or _____ .

42. Radiography of the neck are referred to as _____ x-ray films.

43. Radiographs of the middle back are referred to as _____ x-ray films, and those of the lower back are referred to as _____ x-ray films.

44. When radiation goes beyond a safe limit, body tissues may begin to break down. Blood cells, skin, eyes, and reproductive cells are some of the tissues most sensitive to radiation. Overexposure to radiation can result in: _____

_____

_____

_____

_____

_____

_____

_____

_____ .

45. Describe the hazards of x-rays.

a. _____

b. _____

46. _____ are used to separate x-ray personnel operating the controls of the machine from the patient receiving the radiation.

47. The abdomen and reproductive organs should be shielded with a _____ when a patient is having an x-ray examination.

48. The medical assistant's responsibilities relating to radiological procedures used in the physician's office or clinic are to _____ and _____ .

49. Give the medical assistant's responsibilities relating to radiological procedures performed at an outside source.

a. _____
_____

b. _____
_____

c. _____
_____

d. _____
_____

50. X-ray examinations not using a contrast medium are done (before *or* after) _____ examinations that do use a contrast medium.

Multiple Choice

Write the letter of the correct answer in the blank provided. There is only *one* correct answer.

_____ 1. A radiopaque substance that is used in diagnostic radiology to permit a more accurate visualization of internal body parts and tissues in contrast to their adjacent structures is called a(n):
A. Oscilloscope.
B. Density.
C. Contrast medium.
D. Cassette.

_____ 2. An example of a positive contrast medium is:
A. Barium sulfate.
B. Air.
C. Gas.
D. Carbon dioxide.

_____ 3. A lower GI series is performed to outline the
_____ for study.
   A. Ileum
   B. Duodenum
   C. Stomach
   D. Colon

_____ 4. A barium sulfate mixture is ingested by a
patient who is having a _____
performed.
   A. Cholecystogram
   B. Lower GI series
   C. Pyelogram
   D. Upper GI series

_____ 5. Iodine radiopaque contrast media are used
for the following test:
   A. Mammogram
   B. Upper GI series
   C. Hysterosalpingogram
   D. Tomography

_____ 6. A cholecystogram is performed in order to
view the:
   A. Kidneys.
   B. Gallbladder.
   C. Common bile ducts.
   D. Urinary bladder.

_____ 7. An arthrogram is an x-ray record of a(n):
   A. Artery.
   B. Joint.
   C. Great vessel from the heart.
   D. Blood vessel in the brain.

_____ 8. An x-ray record of the spinal cord after
injection of a contrast medium into the
subarachnoid space through a lumbar punc-
ture is a:
   A. Diskogram.
   B. Myelogram.
   C. Urogram.
   D. Mammogram.

_____ 9. A hysterosalpingogram is performed after the
injection of a contrast medium:
   A. Into the brachial artery.
   B. Into the brachial vein.
   C. Through the vagina into the uterus.
   D. Through the urethra into the urinary
bladder.

_____ 10. Which of the following examinations is
performed without the use of a contrast
medium?
   A. Arthrogram
   B. Barium enema
   C. Urogram
   D. Mammogram

_____ 11. Fallopian tubal patency may be demonstrat-
ed by:
   A. Hysterosalpingogram.
   B. Urogram.
   C. Lymphangiogram.
   D. Pelvimetry.

_____ 12. The most effective x-ray examination used
for detecting early and curable breast cancer
is:
   A. Xeroradiography.
   B. Thermography.
   C. Mammography.
   D. Tomography.

_____ 13. A patient should be instructed not to wear
any body powder or deodorant on the day
of the following examination:
   A. Mammography
   B. Tomography
   C. CT scan
   D. MRI

_____ 14. The American Cancer Society recommends
that women without symptoms of breast
cancer, ages 40 to 49, should have a mam-
mogram performed:
   A. Every 1 to 2 years.
   B. Every 2 to 4 years.
   C. Every year.
   D. Every 3 years.

_____ 15. Xeroradiography is used mostly for exami-
nations of the:
   A. Breast.
   B. Kidneys.
   C. Liver.
   D. Stomach.

_____ 16. Tomography is most effective for x-rays of
the:
   A. Breast.
   B. Kidneys.
   C. Gallbladder.
   D. Lungs and bones.

17. The radiologic technique that provides images of soft tissue in three dimensions is:
    A. Ultrasound procedures.
    B. CT scan.
    C. Tomography.
    D. Thermography.

18. The imaging modality that examines the interactions of magnetism and radio waves with tissue to obtain its images is the:
    A. CT scan.
    B. MRI.
    C. Ultrasound.
    D. Sonogram.

19. _____ does not use ionizing radiation to diagnose or treat disease but uses very high frequency inaudible sound waves.
    A. Magnetic resonance imaging
    B. Computer tomography
    C. Diagnostic ultrasound
    D. Tomography

20. Patients who have stomach ulcers frequently have a(n) _____ performed.
    A. Urogram
    B. Lower GI series
    C. Barium enema
    D. Upper GI series

21. The position in which the x-ray beam is directed from front to back is called:
    A. Anteroposterior.
    B. Posteroanterior.
    C. Lateral.
    D. Oblique.

22. Studies have shown that massive and prolonged exposure to radiation can result in a higher incidence of:
    A. An increased number of white blood cells.
    B. Cancer.
    C. An increased number of red blood cells.
    C. Arthritis.

23. The medical assistant can inform a patient that a barium enema takes approximately:
    A. 1½ hours.
    B. 2 hours.
    C. 30 to 60 minutes.
    D. 15 minutes.

24. The medical assistant can inform a patient that a CT scan of the lower back takes approximately:
    A. 2 hours.
    B. 1 to 2 hours.
    C. 15 minutes.
    D. 5 minutes.

25. The medical assistant can inform a patient that a myelogram takes approximately:
    A. 2 hours.
    B. 3 hours.
    C. 1½ hours.
    D. 1 hour.

26. X-ray films must be stored in a:
    A. Warm atmosphere.
    B. Warm and moist atmosphere.
    C. Dark, but warm place.
    D. Dry, cool place.

PERFORMANCE TEST

In a skills laboratory, a simulation of a joblike environment, the medical assistant student is to demonstrate skill in performing the following activities without reference to source materials. Time limits for each of the following activities are to be assigned by the instructor.

1. Communicate proper preparation for x-ray procedures to the patient.
2. Prepare the patient for and assist the patient during an x-ray examination.
3. Position the patient for the anterioposterior, posterionterior, left lateral, and right lateral x-ray exposure, if licensed to do so.
4. Care for and store an x-ray film in the office.
5. Demonstrate safety hazards and precautionary measures relevant to x-ray equipment.

The student is expected to perform these skills with 100% accuracy.

PERFORMANCE CHECKLIST

The medical assistant students are to design their own performance checklists for the performance test.

225

ANSWERS
Fill-In

1. Study, diagnosis, and treatment of disease by using x-rays, radioactive substances, and other forms of radiant energy such as gamma rays, ultraviolet rays, alpha and beta particles, and sound waves
2. Diagnostic radiology, radiation therapy (radiation oncology), and nuclear medicine
3. Visual observation of the internal body structures. The body part to be viewed is placed between the x-ray tube and a fluorescent screen. As x-rays pass through the body, shadowy images of the internal organs are projected on the screen. Usually a contrast medium is used.
4. Visual examination by means of an image intensifier
5. Visualizing the shape or wave form of sound waves, as in ultrasonography, or of electric currents, as when monitoring heart action and other body functions
6. Radiant energy given off by radioactive atoms and x-rays
7. Picture of internal body structures produced by the action of gamma rays or x-rays on a special film
8. Taking of radiograms.
9. Roentgen rays
10. The action of organs, joints, or entire body systems can be observed in motion.
11. Radiopaque substance that is used in diagnostic radiology to permit a more accurate visualization of internal body parts and tissues in contrast to their adjacent structures
12. Radiation. white
13. Black
14. Barium meal or upper GI series; barium enema
15. Esophagus, stomach, and small intestine
16. Colon; enema
17. Esophagus
18. Thyroid; thyroid function
19. Spinal cord and joints
20. Spinal cord
21. Arthrogram
22. Mammography
23. Mammography
24. Powder or deodorant
25. Lungs and bones
26. Head and body
27. Will not
28. 15 to 30
29. Four
30. Magnetism and radio waves
31. Are not
32. Painless

33. Tumors
34. Can
35. Cannot
36. Very high frequency inaudible sound waves
37. Echogram or sonogram
38. Are
39. Painless
40. Posteroanterior erect
41. Tumors and fractures or displacement
42. Cervical
43. Thoracic; lumbosacral
44. In a lowered RBC and WBC count because of disturbances of bone marrow and other blood-forming organs; burns on the skin, and cancer; damage to the germinal cells in the ovaries and testes; and also damage to a fetus, especially in the first 3 months of pregnancy. Radiation also apparently predisposes individuals to the development of cataracts. Studies have shown that massive and prolonged exposure to radiation can result in a higher incidence of cancer, especially of the lymph glands, and the various types of leukemia.
45. a. The direct x-ray beam itself from the x-ray machine, which travels through an opening in the x-ray tube
    b. Scattered radiation
46. Lead screens or shields
47. Lead apron or cover
48. Prepare the patient, provide reassurance when needed, and employ the safety measures relevant to x-ray equipment. When the physician employs an x-ray technician, the assistant may not do any of these functions.
49. a. Call the radiologist's office or hospital x-ray department to schedule the examination.
    b. Furnish the patient's name, the referring physician's name, and the type of examination(s).
    c. Inform the patient of the approximate amount of time the examination(s) takes.
    d. Give the patient any special directions required for the examination(s).
50. Before

Multiple Choice

1. C
2. A
3. D
4. D
5. C
6. B
7. B
8. B
9. C
10. D
11. A
12. C
13. A
14. A
15. A
16. D
17. B
18. B
19. C
20. D
21. A
22. B
23. C
24. B
25. D
26. D

Unit 15

Physical Therapy

SUGGESTED ACTIVITIES

1. Arrange a field trip to a physical therapy facility to observe the use of the various modalities and techniques.

2. Practice and then demonstrate proficiency in communicating proper preparation of the patient for physical therapy treatments.

3. Design step-by-step procedures for each procedure discussed in this unit.

4. Practice assisting a person to get in and out of a wheelchair. Use good body mechanics throughout this procedure.

5. Practice measuring a friend for the correct size crutches.

6. Practice walking with crutches that have been properly measured for you.

STUDY QUESTIONS
Fill-In

In the blanks provided, write the answers that best complete the sentences:

1. Physical medicine or physiatrics is _____ _____ .

2. Physical therapy is _____ _____ .

3. The purpose and aim of physical therapy is to _____ .

4. Arthritis is the _____ _____ .

5. A modality is a _____ _____ .

6. Phototherapy is _____ _____ .

7. Psoriasis is _____ _____ .

8. A sprain is _____ _____ .

9. A strain is _____ _____ .

10. Tendinitis is _____ _____ .

11. Ultraviolet rays are used therapeutically in the treatment of _____ , _____ , _____ , _____ . The purposes of this treatment are to _____ and to _____ _____ .

12. The light source of ultraviolet rays must be placed at least _____ inches away from the patient and directed only on the area(s) to be treated.

13. Excessive exposure to ultraviolet light can cause

_____ .

14. Diathermy is the therapeutic use of _____ ,
whose purpose is _____ .

15. The duration of a diathermy treatment is usually

_____ minutes and should be timed
carefully.

16. Diathermy must not be applied to areas of the skin

that are _____ or _____ .

17. Ultrasound treatment uses _____

to penetrate _____ .

18. List the reasons ultrasound is used.

a. _____

b. _____

c. _____

d. _____

e. _____

f. _____

19. The ultrasound applicator must be in constant

motion when used to prevent _____

_____ .

20. The length of any ultrasound treatment is usually

under _____ minutes.

21. When heat is applied to a body part the blood

vessels in the area (dilate *or* constrict) _____ .

22. When cold applications are applied to the ankle,
the blood vessels in the area (dilate *or* constrict)

_____ .

23. Generally, compresses and packs cool off within

_____ minutes and then have to be
reheated and reapplied.

24. Give the reasons for using local heat applications.

a. _____

b. _____

c. _____

d. _____

25. Infrared radiation is dry heat application by means

of a _____ .

26. Heat lamps must be kept at least _____
(distance) away from the skin, varying with the
type and intensity of the lamp used.

27. The duration of time for treatment with a heat lamp

is usually _____ .

28. The accepted temperature ranges for water that is

put into a hot water bottle are from _____

for patients 2 years and older, and from _____
for children under 2 years and elderly patients.

29. Electric heating pads must be placed in _____
before being applied to a dry skin area.

30. The reason why the temperature of water in a hot
water bottle must be lower for children under 2
years of age and elderly patients is because these

patients tend to be _____ .

31. A hot water bottle must be placed into a _____
before it is applied to the patient.

32. After use, a hot water bottle must be _____

_____ before being stored for future use.

33. Name the types of moist heat applications
commonly used.

a. _____

b. _____

c. _____

34. The solution used for a hot soak should be at a

temperature of _____ .

35. Unless otherwise ordered, a body part is kept

immersed in a hot soak for _____
minutes.

36. Hot soaks can be used for heat applications to the

    _____ , _____ ,

    _____ or _____ (areas of
    the body).

37. During a hot soak some of the cooled-down solution should be removed and an additional hot solution should be added to the container at a

    point _____ the patient's skin and
    stirred quickly into the cooler solution.

38. On completion of a hot soak, the limb should be

    dried with a towel by (patting *or* rubbing) _____

    _____ the skin.

39. Soaks differ from compresses and packs in that

    soaks are used for _____

    _____ .

40. Explain two basic differences between hot moist compresses and packs.

    a. _____

    b. _____

41. A compress used for the application of moist heat

    is prepared by _____

    _____ .
    This material is then applied to a limited body area, such as the finger or a small area on the arm, for a designated period of time.

42. A pack used for the application of moist heat is prepared in the same manner as a compress except

    that _____ materials are used.

43. The recommended temperature for hot compresses

    and packs is _____ .

44. A plastic covering can be placed over or wrapped

    around a compress or pack to _____

    _____ .

45. During a hot compress or pack treatment, the patient's skin should be checked frequently to ensure that it is not burning and to observe for

    signs of _____ .

46. Generally hot packs or compresses are prescribed

    for _____ minutes, but at times they may

    be applied for _____ .

47. On completion of a hot pack or compress treatment, the skin should be (patted *or* rubbed)

    _____ dry.

48. Cryotherapy is the therapeutic use of _____ .

49. Explain the reasons cold applications are used.

    a. _____

    b. _____

    c. _____

    d. _____

    e. _____

50. Cold applications are commonly used on

    _____ , _____ , and

    _____ and for _____ .

51. The selection of the temperature used for cold applications depends on the following:

    a. _____

    b. _____

    c. _____

    d. _____

52. An ice massage is given for _____
    minutes. A cold compress or pack is applied for

    _____ minutes.

53. Name the types of dry cold applications commonly used.

    a. _____

    b. _____

54. Describe signs excessive coldness of the skin resulting from a dry cold application.

    a. _____

    b. _____

55. List the types of moist cold applications commonly used.

    a. _____

    b. _____

    c. _____

56. A moist cold application is generally applied to the skin for _____ minutes and then repeated every _____ hours.

57. Ice packs are generally applied for _____ minutes.

58. The basic use for galvanic and faradic currents in physical therapy is for _____ .

59. Faradic current is used mainly for _____ _____ .

60. Electromyographic examinations measure very specifically the _____ and also the _____ . The recording obtained is called the

    _____ . This recording helps to distinguish any weakness from neuropathy from that of other causes.

61. Nerve conduction studies are performed to _____ _____ .

62. Hydrotherapy is _____ .

63. Traction is _____ , as applied to the musculoskeletal system.

64. List the reasons traction is used.

    a. _____

    b. _____

    c. _____

    d. _____

    e. _____

    f. _____

    g. _____

    h. _____

65. Massage is _____ _____ .

66. State the purposes of massage.

    a. _____

    b. _____

    c. _____

    d. _____

    e. _____

    f. _____

67. State the purposes of therapeutic exercise, the performance of prescribed physical exertion.

    a. _____

    b. _____

    c. _____

    d. _____

    e. _____

    f. _____

    g. _____

    h. _____

68. _____ is movement of a body part away from the midline of the body, as when moving the arm out to the side.

69. _____ is movement of a body part toward the midline of the body, as when bringing a raised arm down to the side of the body.

70. _____ is movement of a joint that opens it or that increases the angle between the bones.

71. _____ is the bending of a joint so that the angle between bones is reduced, as in bending the arm at the elbow or the leg at the knee or the toes.

72. _____ is movement that turns a body part outward; movement of the ankle that turns the foot outward.

73. _____ is movement that turns a body part inward; movement of the ankle that turns the foot inward.

74. _____ is movement of the arm to face the palm downward.

75. _____ is movement of the arm to face the palm upward. It is the opposite of pronation.

76. Safe body mechanics include the principles of _____ , _____ , and _____ .

77. An important reason for using correct body mechanics to prevent _____ , _____ , _____ , and _____ .

78. Crutches are wooden or metal supports used to _____ .

79. The type of crutch used depends on _____ _____ .

80. Axillary crutches should be measured for each patient so that they do not cause pressure on _____ .

81. The patient who needs crutches must be instructed not to rest the body's weight on the axillary bars of the crutch for more than a few minutes at a time because _____ _____ . The patient should be instructed to bear weight on the _____ .

82. In crutch-walking gaits, each foot and crutch is called a _____ .

83. Before crutch walking begins, the patient should assume the _____ .

84. Patients who need help with _____ or who have _____ may use a cane to provide additional support.

85. Always hold a single crutch or cane on the _____ side of the body.

86. Walkers are used by patients who need _____ , or who need _____ _____ .

Multiple Choice

Write the letter of the correct answer in the blank provided. There is only *one* correct answer.

_____ 1. Diathermy is used to:
A. Generate heat within a part of the body and to increase the circulation.
B. Diagnose a joint disease.
C. Treat pain syndromes.
D. Break up calcium deposits.

_____ 2. The medical discipline that uses physical and mechanical agents in the diagnosis, treatment, and prevention of disease processes and bodily ailments is:
A. Physiatrics.
B. Psychology.
C. Psychiatry.
D. Physiology.

_____ 3. The various types of therapeutic agents used in physical therapy are referred to as:
A. Modules.
B. Modalities.
C. Physical agents.
D. Mechanical agents.

_____ 4. In many facilities diathermy has been replaced by:
A. Cryotherapy.
B. Thermotherapy.
C. Ultrasound.
D. Ultraviolet light.

_____ 5. When treatment is given with the use of an ultraviolet light, the light must be placed at least _____ inches away from the patient and directed only on the area(s) to be treated.
A. 10
B. 20
C. 30
D. 36

6. Duration of a treatment using diathermy is usually:
   A. 30 seconds.
   B. 1 minute.
   C. 10 minutes.
   D. 15 to 20 minutes.

7. Ultrasound therapy uses _____ to penetrate deep tissue layers.
   A. Ultraviolet rays
   B. Ultraviolet light
   C. Heat-inducing wavelengths
   D. High frequency sound waves

8. The length of time of any treatment using ultrasound depends on the size of the area being treated, but is usually under _____ minutes.
   A. 5
   B. 10
   C. 15
   D. 20

9. After use, the sound head from the ultrasound equipment should be cleaned:
   A. With a low-sudsing detergent.
   B. By autoclaving for 10 minutes.
   C. With alcohol.
   D. By boiling for 20 minutes.

10. A physiological reaction produced by heat applications is:
    A. Dilation of blood vessels in the area.
    B. Constriction of blood vessels in the area.
    C. Elevation of blood pressure.
    D. A decrease in respiratory rate.

11. A physiological reaction produced by cold applications is:
    A. Dilation of blood vessels in the area.
    B. Constriction of blood vessels in the area.
    C. Lowered blood pressure.
    D. Lowered respiratory rate.

12. Ultrasound can be used to:
    A. Treat acne.
    B. Treat psoriasis.
    C. Relax muscle spasms.
    D. Heal wound infections.

13. It is important to keep the patient _____ during thermotherapy.
    A. Warm
    B. Cool
    C. Chilled
    D. Uncovered

14. Infrared radiation is a form of _____ application.
    A. Moist heat
    B. Dry heat
    C. Dry cold
    D. Moist cold

15. Heat lamps must be kept at least _____ away from the patient's skin.
    A. 12 inches
    B. 2 to 4 feet
    C. 6 inches
    D. 5 feet

16. The accepted temperature ranges for water placed into a hot water bottle to be applied to a 30-year-old patient are:
    A. 90° to 95° F.
    B. 100° to 105° F.
    C. 105° to 115° F.
    D. 115° to 125° F.

17. The accepted temperature ranges for water placed into a hot water bottle to be applied to an elderly patient are:
    A. 90° to 95° F.
    B. 100° to 105° F.
    C. 105° to 115° F.
    D. 115° to 125° F.

18. Unless otherwise ordered, a body part is kept immersed in a hot soak for:
    A. 5 to 10 minutes.
    B. 10 to 15 minutes.
    C. 15 to 20 minutes.
    D. 30 to 45 minutes.

19. The solution used for a hot soak should be at a temperature of:
    A. 90° to 95° F.
    B. 100° to 105° F.
    C. 105° to 115° F.
    D. 115° to 125° F.

20. The process of having immersed the body in water from the neck down in a special tank called the Hubbard tank or immersing the body or limb in a whirlpool tank is commonly referred to as:
    A. Hydrotherapy.
    B. Cryotherapy.
    C. Thermotherapy.
    D. Electrotherapy.

21. Hot soaks differ from hot compresses and packs in that soaks are used:
    A. For longer periods of time.
    B. Only on the limbs.
    C. For higher temperatures.
    D. For shorter period of time.

22. Generally hot compresses or packs are prescribed for:
    A. 10 to 15 minutes.
    B. 15 to 20 minutes.
    C. 20 to 30 minutes.
    D. 25 to 30 minutes.

23. The therapeutic use of cold is referred to as:
    A. Cryotherapy.
    B. Thermotherapy.
    C. Hydrotherapy.
    D. Electrotherapy.

24. Cryotherapy is commonly used:
    A. To generate heat within a part of the body.
    B. To increase circulation to a body part.
    C. To stimulate growing epithelial cells and cause capillary hyperemia.
    D. For muscle spasm and tenderness.

25. An ice massage is given for _____ minutes.
    A. 5
    B. 10
    C. 15
    D. 20

26. A cold compress or pack is usually applied for:
    A. 5 to 15 minutes.
    B. 10 to 20 minutes.
    C. 20 to 30 minutes.
    D. 30 to 40 minutes.

27. A cold compress may be repeated every:
    A. 30 minutes.
    B. 1 hour.
    C. 45 minutes.
    D. 2 hours.

28. Galvanic and faradic currents are used for:
    A. Muscle relaxation.
    B. Muscle stimulation.
    C. Decreasing blood supply to a muscle.
    D. The stimulation of strong muscles.

29. Electromyographic examinations measure very specifically the electrical activity in:
    A. The heart muscle.
    B. The brain.
    C. A muscle.
    D. A nerve.

PERFORMANCE TEST

In a skills laboratory, the medical assistant student is to demonstrate skill and knowledge in performing the following activities without reference to source materials. The student will need a partner to play the role of the patient. Time limits for the performance of each procedure are to be assigned by the instructor.

1. To the outer aspect of the patient's right forearm, and to the inner aspect of the patient's left lower leg, prepare, apply, and remove the following:
   a. Hot water bottle
   b. Hot compress
   c. Ice bag
   d. Cold compress
2. Discuss the purpose and physiological effects of hot and cold treatments with your instructor.
3. Demonstrate with a partner:
   a. Active exercises of the right arm
   b. Passive exercises to the right arm
   c. Active-resistant exercises to the patient's right hand
4. Using the information provided in this unit, correctly write out the procedural steps and a performance checklist for the following applications of heat or cold:
   a. Heating pad
   b. Hot water bottle
   c. Hot moist compress
   d. Hot soak
   e. Ice bag
   f. Ice pack
   g. Moist cold compress
   h. Alcohol sponge bath

i. Chemical cold pack

5. Using the information you outlined in No. 4, design a teaching-instruction sheet for the patient to use at home for each of the hot and cold applications listed.

6. Demonstrate safe and effective body mechanics when lifting a patient or heavy object.

7. Assist patients in learning how to walk with crutches, and with a cane.

8. Assist patients getting in and out of a wheelchair.

9. Measure and determine the correct size of crutches, a cane, and a walker for a patient.

PERFORMANCE CHECKLIST

Medical assistant students are to design their own step-by-step procedures and performance checklists for the performance test.

ANSWERS
Fill-In

1. The medical discipline that uses physical and mechanical agents in the diagnosis, treatment, and prevention of disease processes and bodily ailments

2. The therapeutic use of physical and mechanical agents in conjunction with patient education and rehabilitation programs (rather than by medicinal or surgical means)

3. Relieve pain, increase circulation, restore and improve muscular function, build strength, and increase the range of motion or mobility of a joint.

4. Inflammation of a joint

5. Therapeutic agent used in physical medicine and physical therapy

6. The use of light rays in the treatment of disease processes. By custom, this includes the use of ultraviolet and infrared or heat rays (radiation).

7. A chronic inflammatory recurrent skin disease characterized by scaly, red patches on the body surfaces

8. A joint injury in which some fibers of a supporting ligament are torn or wrenched and partially ruptured, but continuity of the ligament remains intact. There may also be damage to the associated muscles, tendons, nerves, and blood vessels.

9. An overexertion or overstretching of some part of a muscle

10. Inflammation of a tendon; one of the most common causes of acute pain in the shoulder

11. Acne, psoriasis, pressure sores, and wound infections. Stimulate growing epithelial cells and cause capillary hyperemia; increase cellular metabolism and vascular engorgement, which increases the skin's defenses against bacterial infections

12. 30

13. Severe sunburn up to second- and third-degree burns.

14. A high frequency current; to generate heat within a part of the body and to increase the circulation

15. 15 to 20

16. Broken down or inflamed

17. High frequency sound waves; deep tissue layers

18. a. The treatment of pain syndromes
    b. To relax muscle spasm
    c. To provide deep penetration of heat and stimulate circulation in small areas, as when used to increase blood supply to tissues in patients with vascular disorders
    d. Breaking up calcium deposits
    e. Loosening scars
    f. Increasing elasticity of tissues with collagen, such as tendons and ligaments, so that they respond better to stretching

19. Internal burns or tissue damage

20. 10

21. Dilate

22. Constrict

23. 15 or 20

24. a. Relieve pain.
    b. Promote muscle relaxation and reduce spasm.
    c. Increase circulation to an area to relieve congestion and swelling by dilating the blood vessels.
    d. Speed up the inflammatory process to promote suppuration (pus formation) and drainage from an infected area. In addition, *dry heat* applications are used to dry and heal surgical incision and sutures, perineal lacerations, and skin ulcers.

25. Heat lamp

26. 2 to 4 feet

27. 15 to 20 minutes

28. 115° to 125° F (46° to 52° C); 105° to 115° F (41° to 46° C)

29. A protective covering, such as a towel or pillow case

30. More sensitive to applications of heat and to cold

31. Protective covering, such as a pillow case or towel

32. Washed thoroughly with warm water and detergent, rinsed, and allowed to dry

33. a. Hot soaks
    b. Hot compresses
    c. Hot packs

34. 105° to 110° F (41° to 44° C)
35. 15 to 20
36. Hands, arms, feet, or legs
37. Farthest away from
38. Patting
39. Shorter periods of time and usually at lower temperatures
40. a. Different materials are used for each.
    b. A pack is usually applied to a more extensive body area than a compress is.
41. Taking a soft square of gauze or similar absorbent material (a clean washcloth can also be used), soaking it in hot water, then wringing it out manually or with the use of forceps to avoid excessive wetness
42. Flannel or similar
43. 105° to 110° F (41° to 44° C)
44. Concentrate and hold the heat over the area treated for as long a time as possible
45. Increased redness or swelling
46. 15 to 20; 1 hour
47. Patted
48. Cold
49. a. Prevent edema or swelling.
    b. Relieve pain or tenderness (cold produces a topical anesthetic effect).
    c. Reduce inflammation and pus formation (cold inhibits microbial activity in the early stages of the infectious process).
    d. Control bleeding (the peripheral vessels constrict with the application of cold, thus resulting in a decreased blood flow).
    e. Reduce body temperature.
50. Strains, sprains, bruises, and for muscle spasm and tenderness.
51. a. Condition of the patient
    b. Sensitivity of the patient's skin
    c. Area to be covered
    d. Method to be used
52. 5; 20 to 30
53. a. Ice bags
    b. Ice collars
54. a. Mottled and pale skin
    b. Excessive numbness in the body part
55. a. Cold compress
    b. Cold packs
    c. Ice massage
56. 20 to 30; 2
57. 20 to 30
58. Muscle stimulation, used to retrain patients who have had nerve injuries

59. The stimulation of weak muscles that have a normal nerve supply. This current causes contractions, which in turn increase blood supply to the muscle and thus help the muscle gain strength.
60. Electrical activity in a muscle as a result of nerve conduction; general electrical excitability of the muscle cells; electromyogram
61. Test the speed with which the nerve is conducting; this helps the physician diagnose.
62. The use of water in the treatment of disease processes
63. The process of pulling or drawing
64. a. Obtain and maintain proper position.
    b. Correct or prevent a deformity.
    c. Decrease or overcome muscle spasms.
    d. Lessen or prevent contractures (an abnormal shortening of muscle tissue).
    e. Facilitate healing.
    f. Achieve relief of compression at vertebral joints.
    g. Promote better movement of the area.
    h. Lessen and prevent severe stiffening of peripheral joints.
65. A systematic and methodical pressure applied to bare skin by stroking, rubbing, kneading or rolling, tapping or pounding with the fingers or cupped hand, or by quick tappings with alternating fingertips
66. a. Aid circulation by removing blood and waste products from injured tissues and by bringing fresh blood to the injured part, which helps the healing process.
    b. Relax muscles and relieve spasms.
    c. Reduce pain.
    d. Help restore motion and function to the affected part.
    e. Decrease swelling.
    f. Reduce edema.
67. a. Improve one's general health status.
    b. Improve one's general health status after being afflicted with disabilities affecting the neuromuscular, skeletal, cardiovascular, integumentary, respiratory, and urinary systems, in addition to treatment for congenital defects, prenatal and postnatal care, and psychiatric problems.
    c. Correct a physical deformity.
    d. Improve muscle tone and strengthen muscles.
    e. Restore the strength of muscles that have atrophied or weakened because of disease processes.
    f. Restore motion after a fracture, injury, or any form of immobilization
    g. aid circulation.

    h. Improve coordination.
68. Abduction
69. Adduction
70. Extension
71. Flexion
72. Eversion
73. Inversion
74. Pronation
75. Supination
76. Proper body alignment, balance, and movement
77. Muscle and back fatigue, pain, strain, and injury
78. Aid a person in walking
79. The patient's disability
80. The axillae
81. Pressure on the axillae causes pressure on the brachial plexus. Excessive pressure on the brachial plexus can cause numbness and tingling, and can lead to severe and sometimes permanent paralysis in the arms.
    Palms and the hands
82. Point
83. Tripod position
84. Balance; one-sided weakness
85. Opposite side of the injury
86. Help when standing or walking; help in maintaining balance

26. C
27. D
28. B
29. C

Multiple Choice

1. A
2. A
3. B
4. C
5. C
6. D
7. D
8. B
9. C
10. A
11. B
12. D
13. A
14. B
15. B
16. D
17. C
18. C
19. C
20. A
21. D
22. B
23. A
24. D
25. A

Unit 16

Electrocardiography

SUGGESTED ACTIVITIES

1. Practice and then demonstrate proficiency in communicating proper preparation of the patient for electrocardiography and in preparing the room and equipment.

2. Practice and then demonstrate the proper procedures for applying the electrodes and lead wires to the patient, recording the EKG with a standard electrocardiograph and the Phone-A-Gram system, mounting the finished product, and caring for the equipment after use.

3. Observe the different types of electrocardiographs at the facilities where you do your work experience. Discuss the similarities, differences, and advantages, if any, of each type of electrocardiograph.

4. Discuss methods to use to prevent artifacts from occurring on an electrocardiogram.

5. Practice changing the EKG paper in the electrocardiograph.

6. Develop a reference card plan that you can see when taking a patient's EKG. Include the:
   a. Purpose of the procedure
   b. Explanation to the patient about the procedure and equipment
   c. Preparation of the patient
   d. Questions to ask the patient before the EKG is performed
   e. Care and instructions to the patient after the recording has been completed

STUDY QUESTIONS
Fill-in

In the blanks provided, write the answers that best complete the sentences:

1. An arrhythmia is a _____
   _____.

2. The upper chambers of the heart are called
   _____ ,
   and the lower chambers are called _____
   _____.

3. The _____ atrium receives deoxygenated blood from the body, whereas the _____ atrium receives oxygenated blood from the lungs.

4. Cardiac arrest is the _____
   _____.

5. Fibrillation is a cardiac arrhythmia characterized by
   _____
   _____.

6. Defibrillation is _____
   _____.

7. The heart muscle is called the _____ .

8. A myocardial infarction is _____
   _____.

9. The abbreviations for electrocardiogram are
   _____.

10. An EKG is _____
_____.

11. The term *cardiac cycle* refers to _____,
which consists of _____.

12. The normal EKG cycle consists of waves that
have been arbitrarily labeled P, QRS, and T
waves. Each wave corresponds to a particular part
of the cardiac cycle. The P wave reflects
_____.

13. The QRS wave (complex) reflects _____
_____.

14. The T wave reflects _____
_____.

15. A T wave follows every _____ wave.

16. The P-R interval reflects _____
_____.

17. The P-R interval is measured from _____
_____.

18. The ST segment reflects _____
_____.

19. The ST segment is measured from _____
_____.

20. The Q-T interval reflects _____
_____.

21. The Q-T interval is measured from _____
_____.

22. The baseline on an EKG is _____
and is known as the _____ line.

23. Specialized masses of tissue in the heart form the
conduction system, regulating the sequence of
events of the cardiac cycle. These include the
_____ , _____ ,
_____ and the _____ .

24. The pacemaker of the heart is the _____
node.

25. The electrical impulse of the cardiac cycle travels
first to the _____ node, from which
wavelike impulses are sent through the atria.

26. Each cardiac cycle takes approximately _____
seconds. At this rate, the heart beats _____
times per minute.

27. Typical sounds of the heart as heard through a
stethoscope are described as _____ .

28. The first or systolic sound of the heart is believed
to be caused by _____
_____.

29. The second or diastolic sound of the heart is
thought to be caused by _____ .

30. The electrocardiograph (can *or* cannot) _____
pick up the heart sounds discussed in questions 27,
28, and 29.

31. When the physician interprets an EKG, the following factors are usually determined:

a. _____
_____

b. _____
_____

c. _____
_____

d. _____
_____

32. To determine if heart rhythm is irregular, the
distance between each _____ wave is
measured to determine _____ rhythm,
and the distance between each _____
wave is measured to determine _____
rhythm.

33. Artifacts on an EKG are _____ _____.

34. The most common types of artifacts seen on EKGs are _____, _____, and _____.

35. Somatic tremor artifacts on an EKG are caused by _____.

36. List the causes of a wandering baseline on an EKG.

   a. _____

   b. _____

   c. _____

   d. _____

   e. _____

37. State the common causes of alternating current interference artifacts.

   a. _____

   b. _____

   c. _____

   d. _____

   e. _____

   f. _____

   g. _____

38. When taking a patient's EKG you notice that a straight line is being recorded but no tracing. This is caused by _____ .

39. Electrodes are _____ _____.

40. The standard 12-lead EKG has _____ electrodes.

41. When recording an EKG, apply the electrodes to _____, _____ , and _____.

42. To help conduct the electric current in the electrocardiograph an _____ is applied to each electrode.

43. Electrolytes are available in the form of _____ _____.

44. The first three leads to be recorded on a standard EKG are known as _____, _____, and _____.

45. Lead I records electrical activity between the _____ and _____ .

46. Lead II records electrical activity between the _____ and _____ .

47. Lead III records electrical activity between the _____ and _____ .

48. The augmented leads are designated as _____, _____ , and _____ .

49. Lead aV$_R$ records electrical activity from _____ _____.

50. Lead aV$_L$ records electrical activity from _____ _____.

51. Lead aV$_F$ records electrical activity from _____ _____.

52. The last six leads of the standard 12-lead electrocardiograph are the _____ or _____ leads. These leads are designated as _____, _____, _____, _____, _____, and _____ .

53. The third set of leads records electrical activity between six points on the _____ and a point within _____ .

54. The universal standard of electrocardiographic measurement is _____ .

55. Before any EKG is recorded, the machine must be standardized; that is, it must be checked to determine _____ .

56. The universal standard for recording an EKG is at a speed of _____ .

57. During the recording of an EKG a patient (will *or* will not) _____ experience shock, pain, or other sensation.

58. A patient (may *or* may not) _____ chew gum during the recording of an EKG.

59. When a woman is to have an EKG she (has to *or* does not have to) _____ remove sheer nylon stockings.

60. When using presaturated electrolyte pads rather than a gel or paste, rub _____ before placing the pad on the skin.

61. If taking an EKG on a patient who has a lower leg amputation, place the electrode _____ . The electrode for the other extremity must then be placed _____ .

62. While Leads I, II, and so on are recording the chest electrode should remain _____ , or _____ .

63. Before beginning recording an EKG, routinely check:

   a. _____
   b. _____
   c. _____

64. The time to mark the identification code for each lead is _____ , unless the machine does it automatically.

65. When the physician requires proof of standardization for each lead, the standardization mark should be inserted between the _____ wave of one complex and the _____ wave of the next complex.

66. Mounting the EKG is important so that the recording can be:

   a. _____
   b. _____
   c. _____

67. Use only _____ or _____ to clean the electrodes after use.

68. The term *normal sinus rhythm* refers to an EKG that is within _____ limits. In normal sinus rhythm the heart rate is _____ beats per minute and the rhythm is _____ .

69. _____ is a regular sinus rhythm of 100-180 beats per minute.

70. _____ is a regular sinus rhythm of less than 60 beats per minute.

71. _____ is an irregular sinus rhythm in which the cycle lengths vary.

72. Name three arrhythmia that originate outside of the sinus node and above the branching portion of the bundle of His:

   a. _____
   b. _____
   c. _____

73. Name three types of ventricular arrhythmias.

   a. _____
   b. _____
   c. _____

74. Ambulatory cardiac monitoring, frequently referred to as Holter monitoring (named after the inventor), is _____ .
By using a special monitor the activity of the patient's heart can be recorded during _____

_____ .

75. Explain the reasons that ambulatory cardiac monitoring is done:

a. _____

b. _____

c. _____

76. The treadmill stress test helps the physician to determine an appropriate _____ program for the patient. It is also used to assess _____ after heart surgery, to diagnose _____ , and to diagnose the possible causes of _____ pain.

77. A signed informed consent form is required before the treadmill stress test can be performed. (True *or* False) _____

Multiple Choice

Write the letter of the correct answer in the blank provided. There is only *one* correct answer.

_____ 1. An appropriate abbreviation for an electrocardiogram is:
   A. EEG.
   B. EGG.
   C. EKG.
   D. EMG.

_____ 2. The heart muscle is called the:
   A. Endocardium.
   B. Precardium.
   C. Pericardium.
   D. Myocardium.

_____ 3. A patient suffering from rapid heart action is experiencing:
   A. Tachycardia.
   B. Bradycardia.
   C. Defibrillation.
   D. Fibrillation.

_____ 4. A patient suffering from abnormally slow heart action is experiencing:
   A. Tachycardia.
   B. Bradycardia.
   C. Fibrillation.
   D. Defibrillation.

_____ 5. The graphic representation of the electrical activity produced by the heart during the processes of contraction and relaxation is the:
   A. EKG.
   B. EMG.
   C. EEG.
   D. BMR.

_____ 6. A cholecystogram is performed in order to view the:
   A. Abnormal breathing rate.
   B. Abnormal rapidity of the heart rate.
   C. Abnormally slow heart rate.
   D. Abnormally high blood pressure.

_____ 7. The term _____ refers to one complete heartbeat.
   A. Systole
   B. Diastole
   C. Systolic
   D. Cardiac cycle

_____ 8. The _____ wave on an EKG reflects contraction (depolarization) of the atria of the heart.
   A. P
   B. QRS
   C. T
   D. U

_____ 9. The _____ wave on an EKG reflects the contraction of the ventricles.
   A. P
   B. QRS
   C. T
   D. U

_____ 10. The _____ wave on an EKG reflects ventricular recovery (repolarization of the ventricles).
   A. P
   B. QRS
   C. T
   D. U

11. The _____ on an EKG reflects the time it takes from the beginning of the atrial contraction to the beginning of ventricular contraction.
   A. QRS complex
   B. ST segment
   C. Q-T segment
   D. P-R interval

12. The pacemaker of the heart is the:
   A. Sinoatrial node.
   B. Atrioventricular node.
   C. Bundle of His.
   D. Purkinje fibers.

13. Each cardiac cycle takes approximately:
   A. 1 second.
   B. 0.8 second.
   C. 1 minute.
   D. 80 seconds.

14. With the time limit mentioned in question 13, the heart will beat _____ times per minute.
   A. 60
   B. 70
   C. 75
   D. 80

15. _____ artifacts on an EKG can be caused when the patient moves or talks.
   A. Wandering baseline
   B. Somatic tremor
   C. Baseline shift
   D. Alternating current

16. The electrodes must be kept clean, therefore after each use they must be washed and occasionally cleaned with:
   A. Steel wool.
   B. Alcohol.
   C. Kitchen cleanser.
   D. A disinfectant.

17. When the stylus heat is too low, one of the following will result:
   A. An indistinct tracing.
   B. A straight line but no tracing.
   C. A break between the complexes.
   D. A break between the P and QRS waves.

18. A standard EKG recording has _____ leads.
   A. 6
   B. 8
   C. 10
   D. 12

19. The first group of leads to be recorded on a standard EKG are:
   A. The augmented leads.
   B. Leads V_1 through V_4
   C. Leads I, II, and III.
   D. Leads V_1 through V_6.

20. To record only the augmented leads on an electrocardiogram, you would record:
   A. Leads I, II, and III.
   B. Leads aV_R, aV_L, and aV_F.
   C. Leads V_1 through V_6.
   D. Leads I, II, III, aV_R, aV_L, and aV_F.

21. The second group of leads to be recorded on a standard EKG are:
   A. The chest leads.
   B. The precordial leads.
   C. Leads I, II, and III.
   D. The augmented leads.

22. Lead V_2 in an EKG recording is:
   A. The second limb lead.
   B. The second chest lead.
   C. The second augmented lead.
   D. The second code lead.

23. For the universally accepted standardization of the electrocardiograph the stylus should deflect precisely:
   A. 10 mm.
   B. 5 mm.
   C. 10 ml.
   D. 10 cm.

24. The universal standard for recording an EKG is at a speed of:
   A. 25 mm/second.
   B. 50 mm/second.
   C. 10 mm/second.
   D. 5 mm/second.

25. When segments of the EKG are close together or when the heart rate is very rapid, the physician may want a few leads recorded at a faster rate; therefore the machine should be run at a speed of:
   A. 10 mm/second.
   B. 25 mm/second.
   C. 50 mm/second.
   D. 75 mm/second.

26. The patient should assume the _____ position for an EKG.
   A. Prone
   B. Semi-Fowler's
   C. Fowler's
   D. Recumbent

27. The standard EKG has _____ electrodes.
   A. 2
   B. 3
   C. 4
   D. 5

28. When doing an EKG, which of the following is applied to the patient first?
   A. Electrodes
   B. Electrolyte
   C. Rubber straps
   D. Cable lead wires

29. The height of the standardization measurement should be 10 mm or _____ from the baseline on the EKG paper.
   A. One large square
   B. Two large squares
   C. 1½ large squares
   D. Three large squares

30. When all the leads for an EKG have been recorded satisfactorily, turn the lead selector to _____, the recorder switched to OFF, and unplug the power cord.
   A. STD
   B. Lead I
   C. Lead AVR
   D. Lead V₁

31. There are _____ electrodes in the Phone-A-Gram system for EGs.
   A. 3
   B. 5
   C. 6
   D. 10

32. Lead V_2 is located at the:
   A. Fourth intercostal space at the right margin of the sternum.
   B. Fourth intercostal space at the left margin of the sternum.
   C. Fifth intercostal space at the junction of the left midclavicular line.
   D. At the horizontal level of position 4 at the left anterior axillary line.

Labeling

1. Label the following on the EKG cycle: (Figure 16-1)
   a. P Wave
   b. QRS wave (complex)
   c. T wave
   d. Atrial depolarization
   e. Ventricular depolarization
   f. Ventricular repolarization

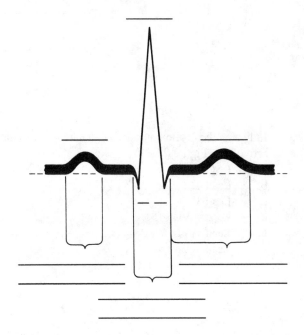

2. Label the following on the EKG cycle: (Figure 16-2)
   a. P-R interval
   b. Q-T interval
   c. S-T segment

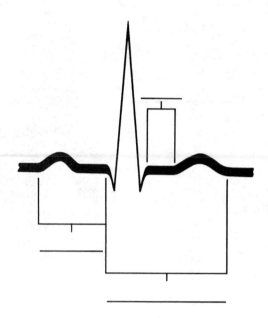

3. Indicate the following leads on the diagrams provided: (Figure 16-3)
   a. Lead I
   b. Lead II
   c. Lead III
   d. Lead AVR
   e. Lead AVL
   f. Lead AVF

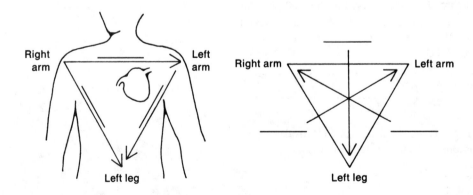

4. Label and explain the location of chest leads on the following diagram: (Figure 16-4)

a. _____

b. _____

c. _____

d. _____

e. _____

f. _____

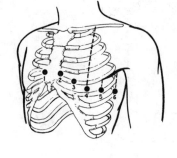

5. Label the following photograph. (Figure 16-5)

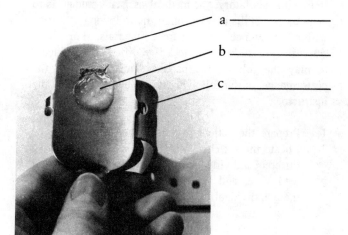

a _____

b _____

c _____

List the marking codes for all of the leads for a standard 12-lead EKG.

a. _____

b. _____

c. _____

d. _____

e. _____

f. _____

g. _____

h. _____

i. _____

j. _____

k. _____

l. _____

PERFORMANCE TEST

In a skills laboratory, the medical assistant student is to demonstrate skills in performing the following activities without reference to resource materials. For these activities the student will need five different individuals to play the role of the patient. Time limits for the performance of the following are to be assigned by the instructor.

1. Prepare the patient for an electrocardiogram.
2. Locate the six chest lead positions on at least five different individuals; then apply the electrodes and lead wire, and record the electrocardiograms of these individuals.
3. Mount the recordings obtained in No. 2
4. Correctly care for the equipment after use.
5. Apply a Holter monitor to a patient.
6. Give the patient instructions to follow when wearing a Holter monitor.

The student is expected to perform these skills with 100% accuracy 90% of the time (9 out of 10 times).

PERFORMANCE CHECKLIST: Obtaining an electrocardiogram

DIRECTIONS: Evaluate student performance of each procedure using the following checklist. When you evaluate "not applicable," "unsatisfactory," or "not observed," please comment.

Checklist	S or NA*	U	NO	Comment
1. Assembled supplies; prepared the room and equipment for use.				
2. Prepared the patient.				
a. Explained the nature and purpose of the EKG.				
b. Had the patient disrobe and put the patient gown on with the opening in the front; jewelry that would interfere with the electrodes had been removed.				
c. Positioned and draped the patient.				
d. Located and marked the six chest positions.				
e. Explained that the patient must remain still and not talk during the recording.				
f. Gave reassurance as needed.				
g. Asked if the patient has any questions before beginning the recording.				
3. Applied electrodes with electrolyte to the four limbs.				
4. Attached the patient cable lead wires to the electrodes.				
5. Plugged the patient cable into the patient cable jack on the machine.				
6. Checked once more to ensure that all electrodes and lead wires were correctly and securely attached.				
7. Set the lead selector to STD and the recorder switch to ON. (Some machines require a warm-up period.				
8. Turned the recorder switch to RUN.				
9. Centered the baseline by turning the position control knob.				
10. Checked the standardization.				
11. Turned the lead selector to Lead I.				
12. Marked the identification code and recorded 8 to 10 inches of Lead I.				
13. Inserted standardization mark between the T wave of one complex (or the U wave if present) and the P wave of the next complex when this was required by the physician.				
14. Continued recording Leads II, III, aV_R, aV_L, and aV_F in the same manner, but turned the lead selector to the appropriate position, and marked the identification code for each lead. Recorded only 5 to 6 inches of the augmented leads.				

Checklist	S or NA*	U	NO	Comment
15. Turned the machine off.				
16. Positioned the chest electrode for the first chest lead.				
17. Turned the lead selector to STD, the recorder switch to RUN, and depressed the standardization button.				
18. Turned the recorder switch to OFF.				
19. Turned the lead selector switch to V.				
20. Turned the recorder switch to ON.				
21. Marked the identification code for the chest lead, and inserted standardization marks if required (see step 13).				
22. Recorded 5 to 6 inches.				
23. Turned the recorder switch off.				
24. Moved the chest lead to the next position. Started again with step 19; repeated until all the chest leads had been recorded.				
25. Turned the lead selector to STD, the recorder switch to OFF, and unplugged the power cord.				
26. Disconnected the lead wires, unfastened the rubber straps, and removed the electrodes from the patient.				
27. Wiped any electrolyte off the patient's skin; assisted the patient as needed, and provided further instructions.				
28. Labeled the recording.				
29. Cleaned the equipment, and returned it to the storage area.				
30. Washed hands.				
31. Recorded the procedure, date, time, and signature on the patient's chart.				
32. Mounted the recording and labeled it.				
33. Gave the mounted recording to the physician.				

Total Satisfactory Points _____

Comments

Student's signature:_____ Instructor's signature: _____

Date: _____

*S or NA, Satisfactory or not applicable; U, unsatisfactory; NO, not observed.

PERFORMANCE CHECKLIST: Procedure and Patient Care For Holter Monitoring

DIRECTIONS: Evaluate student performance of each procedure using the following checklist. When you evaluate "not applicable," "unsatisfactory," or "not observed," please comment.

Checklist	S or NA*	U	NO	Comment
1. Washed hands. **Use appropriate Personal Protective Equipment (PPE) as dictated by facility.**				
2. Assembled and prepared equipment.				
3. Inserted a fully charged *new* battery into the monitor.				
4. Identified the patient and explained the procedure.				
5. Instructed the patient about the care of the monitor.				
6. Taught the patient how to maintain the diary. Stressed the need to record significant symptoms and events.				
7. Had the patient remove clothes from the waist up and put on a patient gown with the opening in the front.				
8. Had the patient lie down on the examining table.				
9. Prepared the patient's skin for electrode placement.				
10. Removed the protective backing from the electrode and applied it to the chest position. Pressed on the electrodes adhesive ring first. Avoided pressing the center gel cap.				
11. Repeated step 10 until all five electrodes were in place on the patient's chest.				
12. Attached the lead wires to the electrodes.				
13. Place a strip of adhesive tape over the wire just below each electrode.				
14. Attached the EKG cable connector to the monitor.				
15. Followed the start up procedure for the system that was used.				
16. Examined the EKG printout and assessed it with the criteria given with the system that was used. Most systems automatically switch over to monitoring once the system is started.				
17. Recorded the start time in the patient diary.				
18. Had the patient redress.				
19. Placed the recorder in the holder bag and attached it to the patient's belt or to a shoulder harness. Ensured that there was no pulling or strain on the lead wires or cable connector.				
20. Reminded the patient of the special instructions that must be followed.				
21. Answered any questions that the patient had.				

PERFORMANCE CHECKLIST: Procedure and Patient Care For Holter Monitoring (continued)

Checklist	S or NA*	U	NO	Comment
22. Gave the diary to the patient and reviewed the instructions for maintaining this record.				
23. Informed the patient when to return to have the monitor removed.				
24. Washed hands.				
25. Recorded the procedure, date, time, and signature on the patient's chart.				
26. Completed the procedure in the limit set by the instructor.				

Total Satisfactory Points _____

Comments

Student's signature: _____ Instructor's signature: _____

Date: _____

*S or NA, Satisfactory or not applicable; U, unsatisfactory; NO, not observed.

Evaluation of student's technique   Name: _____   Date: _____

	Satisfactory*		Unsatisfactory**		
	Very Good	Good	Fair	Poor	Score
• Obtaining an EKG	☐	☐	☐	☐	_____
• Mounting an EKG	☐	☐	☐	☐	_____
• Procedure and patient care for Holter monitoring	☐	☐	☐	☐	_____

Very good = Perfect
Good   = Sufficient
Fair   = Not acceptable requires more practice
Poor   = Totally unacceptable
Pass*   = Satisfactory
Fail** = Unsatisfactory

Comments:

ANSWERS

1. Variation from the normal or an irregular rhythm of the heartbeat
2. Atria; ventricles
3. Right; left
4. Sudden and often unexpected cessation of the heartbeat
5. Rapid, irregular, and ineffective electrical activity in the heart
6. The application of electrical impulses to the heart to stop heart fibrillation
7. Myocardium
8. The death of cells in an area of the heart muscle due to oxygen deprivation which in turn is caused by an interference of blood supply to the area
9. ECG and EKG
10. A graphic representation of the electrical activity (currents) produced by the heart during the processes of contraction and relaxation. More precisely, the EKG records the amount of electrical activity, the time required for this activity to travel through the heart during each complete heartbeat, and the rate and rhythm of the heartbeat.
11. One complete heartbeat; contraction (systole) and relaxation (diastole) of both atria and both ventricles
12. Contraction (depolarization) of the atria
13. The contraction (depolarization) of the ventricles
14. Ventricular recovery (repolarization of the ventricles)
15. QRS
16. The time it takes from the beginning of the atrial contraction to the beginning of ventricular contraction
17. The beginning of the P wave to the beginning of the QRS complex
18. The time interval from the end of the ventricular contraction (depolarization) to the beginning of ventricular recovery (repolarization)
19. The end of the S wave (of the QRS complex) to the beginning of the T wave
20. The time it takes from the beginning of ventricular depolarization to the end of ventricular repolarization
21. The beginning of the QRS complex to the end of the T wave
22. A flat horizontal line that separates the waves; isoelectric
23. Sinoatrial node (SA node), atrioventricular node (AV node), bundle of His (or atrioventricular bundle), Purkinje fibers
24. SA
25. SA
26. 0.8; 75
27. "Lubb dupp"
28. The contraction of the ventricles and vibrations from the closing of the cuspid valves
29. The vibrations of the closure of the semilunar valves (pulmonic and aortic valves)
30. Cannot
31. a. *Rate.* How many beats per minute; determined are the atrial rate and the ventricular rate
    b. *Rhythm.* Whether the heart rhythm is regular or irregular; determined are the atrial rhythm and the ventricular rhythm
    c. *Conduction time.* How long it takes for the impulse originating at the SA node to simulate ventricular contraction (review the conduction system); determined are the P-R interval, and the QRS duration
    d. *Configuration and location* of each wave, the ST segment, the P-R interval, and sometimes the Q-T interval
32. P; atrial; R; ventricular
33. Defects (unwanted activity) on the electrocardiograph *not* caused by the electrical activity produced during the cardiac cycle
34. Somatic tremor (muscle movement), wandering baseline (baseline shift), and alternating current interference
35. Muscle movement, either voluntary or involuntary
36. a. Electrodes that are applied too tightly or too loosely
    b. Tension on an electrode as a result of an unsupported lead wire that is pulling the electrode away from the patient's skin
    c. Too little or poor quality electrolyte gel or paste on an electrode
    d. Corroded or dirty electrodes
    e. Skin creams or lotions present on the area to which the electrode is applied
37. a. Improper grounding of the electrocardiography
    b. Presence of other electrical equipment in the room
    c. Electrical wiring in walls or ceilings
    d. X-ray or other large electrical equipment being used in adjacent rooms
    e. Lead wires crossed and not following the contour of the patient's body
    f. Corroded or dirty electrodes
    g. Faulty technique of the operator
38. The patient cable not being plugged in correctly
39. Small metal plates placed on the patient to pick up the electrical activity of the heart and conduct it to the electrocardiograph
40. 5

41. The fleshy part of the arms, the fleshy part of the legs, and in six different positions on the chest when recording the chest leads
42. Electrolyte
43. Gels, pastes, or flannel materials presaturated with an electrolyte solution
44. Lead I, Lead II, and Lead III
45. Right arm and left arm
46. Right arm and left leg
47. Left arm and left leg
48. aV_R, aV_L, and aV_F
49. The midpoint between the left arm and left leg to the right arm
50. The midpoint between the right arm and left leg to the left arm
51. The midpoint between the right arm and left arm to the left leg
52. Chest or precordial leads; V_1, V_2, V_3, V_4, V_5, and V_6
53. Chest wall; the heart
54. One millivolt of cardiac electrical activity; this deflects the stylus precisely 10 mm (1 cm) high which is equal to 10 small blocks on the electrocardiograph paper.
55. If it is set to record according to the universal measurement
56. 25 mm/second
57. Will not
58. May not
59. Does not have to
60. The skin with the pad
61. Above the affected area; in the same location opposite the first
62. Unattached but not touching a direct surface, or positioned on the first chest position using the electrolyte of choice
63. a. That all connections are secure
    b. That the patient cable is supported on the table or over the patient's abdomen to prevent pulling of the cable
    c. To see if the patient has any questions
64. Immediately after the lead is selected
65. T (or U wave when present); P
66. a. Protected
    b. Easily seen by the physician
    c. Inserted into the patient's medical record after the physician has it reviewed and interpreted
67. Alcohol or soap and water
68. Normal; 60 to 100; regular.
69. Sinus tachycardia
70. Sinus bradycardia
71. Sinus arrhythmia

72. a. Premature atrial contractions
    b. Paroxysmal atrial tachycardia
    c. Atrial fibrillation
73. a. Premature ventricular contractions
    b. Ventricular tachycardia
    c. Ventricular fibrillation
74. A continuous recording of the electrical activity of the patient's heart (an EKG) for 24 to 48 hours. unrestricted activity, rest, and sleep for future observation and study
75. a. Detect any cardiac rhythm disturbances and correlate them with patient symptoms of chest pain, palpitations, dizziness, syncope, or fatigue.
    b. Assess the effectiveness of antiarrhythmic medication therapy.
    c. Assess the function of a new or old pacemaker.
76. exercise; cardiac function; heart disorders; chest
77. True

Multiple Choice

1. C
2. D
3. A
4. B
5. A
6. C
7. D
8. A
9. B
10. C
11. D
12. A
13. B
14. C
15. B
16. C
17. A
18. D
19. C
20. B
21. D
22. B
23. A
24. A
25. C
26. D
27. D
28. B
29. B
30. A
31. D
32. B

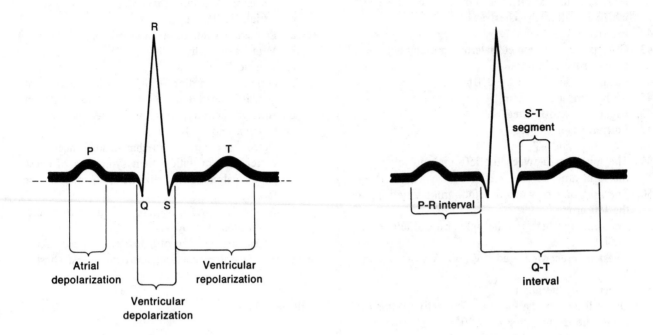

Answer to Figure 16-1

Answer to Figure 16-2

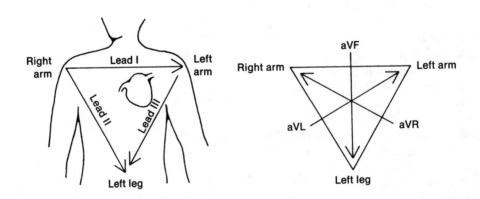

Answer to Figure 16-3

Standard or bipolar limb leads	Electrodes connected	Marking code	Recommended positions for multiple chest leads (Line art illustration of chest positions)
Lead I	LA & RA	1 dot	
Lead II	LL & RA	2 dots	
Lead III	LL & LA	3 dots	

Augmented unipolar limb leads			
aVR	RA & (LA-LL)	1 dash	V₁ Fourth intercostal space at right margin of sternum
aVL	LA & (RA-LL)	2 dashes	V₂ Fourth intercostal space at left margin of sternum
aVF	LL & (RA-LA)	3 dashes	V₃ Midway between position 2 and position 4

Augmented unipolar limb leads

aVR — RA & (LA-LL) — 1 dash

aVL — LA & (RA-LL) — 2 dashes

aVF — LL & (RA-LA) — 3 dashes

Chest or precordial leads

V — C & (LA-RA-LL) — (See data on right)

Dash—1 dot

V_1 Fourth intercostal space at right margin of sternum

V_2 Fourth intercostal space at left margin of sternum

V_3 Midway between position 2 and position 4

V_4 Fifth intercostal space at junction of left midclavicular line

V_5 At horizontal level of position 4 at left anterior axillary line

V_6 At horizontal level of position 4 at left midaxillary line

Answer to Figure 16-4

Answer to Figure 16-5

a. Electrode
b. Electrolyte gel
c. Rubber strap

Unit 17

Common Emergencies and First Aid

SUGGESTED ACTIVITIES

1. Practice and then demonstrate on a partner the proper first aid care to be used for all of the medical emergencies presented in this chapter.

2. Practice and then demonstrate on a partner how to locate the seven pressure points to be used when controlling severe bleeding.

3. Enroll in a cardiopulmonary resuscitation (CPR) course if you have not been certified in this procedure or enroll in a recertification program if it has been over 1 year since you were certified.

4. Check at the facility where you do your work experience for the policy and protocols for emergency situations. Develop a plan of action and policy for emergencies that you think would be appropriate. Include:
   a. Routine plan
   b. Protocols
   c. Emergency tray: equipment, drugs, and how and when it is checked
   d. Duties of the medical assistant when the physician is present
   e. Duties of the medical assistant when the physician is absent
   f. Charting procedures

5. Develop a list of emergency situations that may be called into the office by a patient; for example, "My husband is experiencing severe chest pain and feels nauseated." For each situation on the list develop a list of questions to ask the telephone caller. State what to tell the caller to do after answering the questions.

6. Try to visit an emergency care facility or have a paramedic or an emergency care physician or registered nurse speak to your class.

STUDY QUESTIONS
Fill-In

In the blanks provided, write the answers that best complete the sentences:

1. First aid is defined as _____ _____.

2. Describe the aspects of an emergency.
   a. _____
   b. _____
   c. _____

3. State the fundamental rules and general procedures to follow in an emergency.
   a. _____
   b. _____
   c. _____
   d. _____

4. CPR is _____ _____.

5. The goal of CPR is _____ _____.

6. Once started, CPR must be continued until one of the following has occurred:
   a. _____

b. _____

c. _____

d. _____

7. Give the basic ABC steps in CPR.

a. _____

b. _____

c. _____

8. List signals that indicate a person may be having a heart attack.

a. _____

b. _____

c. _____

d. _____

e. _____

f. _____

9. When performing one-rescuer CPR on an adult, the ratio of compressions to breaths is

_____, and the rate of compressions is

_____ .

10. During two-rescuer CPR on an adult, the ratio of compressions to breaths is _____, and the rate of compressions is _____ .

11. When performing CPR on an infant, depress the sternum _____ inch at a rate of _____ compressions per minute.

12. When performing CPR on a child, depress the sternum _____ inch(es) at a rate of _____ compressions per minute.

13. If you suspect that the victim has suffered a neck injury, open the airway by _____ to perform CPR.

14. When an adult is choking and is unable to speak or cough effectively, perform the _____ maneuver which consists of _____ _____ .

15. Shock is _____ _____ .

16. Name the five basic types of shock.

a. _____

b. _____

c. _____

d. _____

e. _____

17. Describe the most outstanding signs and symptoms of severe shock or the later stages of shock.

a. _____

b. _____

c. _____

d. _____

e. _____

f. _____

g. _____

h. _____

i. _____

j. _____

k. _____

l. _____

18. Explain the objectives for preventing or treating shock that should be met.

a. _____

b. _____

c. _____

d. _____

19. For abdominal pain caused by trauma, keep the patient (lying flat *or* sitting) _____ if possible, in case of internal bleeding.

20. _____ and _____ are often administered as the treatment for an anaphylactic reaction.

21. Three types of bleeding can be observed from open wounds. Spurting of bright red blood from a wound indicates _____ bleeding; continuous flow of dark red blood indicates _____ bleeding; and oozing of blood indicates _____ bleeding.

22. State the objectives of wound care.

    a. _____

    b. _____

    c. _____

    d. _____

23. Cite the methods used to control severe bleeding in order of preference.

    a. _____

    b. _____

    c. _____

    d. _____

24. Name the seven pressure points used to control severe bleeding.

    a. _____

    b. _____

    c. _____

    d. _____

    e. _____

    f. _____

    g. _____

25. People with known allergies and diabetes should be encouraged to wear a _____ bracelet or necklace.

26. First-degree or superficial burns involve only the _____ of the skin. The skin is reddened (with *or* without) _____ blister formation and is painful.

27. Second-degree or partial thickness burns involve deeper layers of the epidermis, (are *or* are not) _____ painful, and usually (do *or* do not) _____ form blisters.

28. Third-degree or full-thickness burns are (painful *or* painless) _____ , and usually (do *or* do not) _____ form blisters.

29. When more than _____ percent of total body surface is burned, it is considered a severe burn.

30. State the objectives for the care of first degree or superficial burns.

    a. _____

    b. _____

31. List objectives for treating second- and third-degree burns (partial and full-thickness burns).

    a. _____

    b. _____

    c. _____

32. When a person has been burned with a chemical, immediately wash the area with copious amounts of _____ .

33. When giving first aid care for second- and third-degree (partial and full thickness) burns, (break *or* do not break) _____ any blisters that are present.

34. When giving first aid care for burns, (remove *or* do not remove) _____ any pieces of cloth or bits of debris or dirt that are stuck to the burn.

35. Chest pain can be associated with _____ and _____ disease.

36. Convulsions are _____ _____ .

37. The primary effort in first aid for convulsions is to

_____ .

38. The term *epistaxis* means _____ .

39. The term *syncope* means _____ .

40. The first step in first aid care for a nosebleed is

_____ .

41. When the care given in No. 40 does not control

the bleeding you should _____

_____ .

42. Fainting is _____

_____ .

43. A person who has fainted should be positioned

_____ .

44. When a person is in a sitting position and begins

to feel faint you should _____

_____ .

45. The first aid if a foreign body in the ear is a live

bug or insect is to _____

_____ .

46. For a head injury keep the patient at rest in a

_____ position if the face is ashen and

gray, or _____ if the face is flushed.

47. After a head injury the patient (should *or* should

not) _____ be given fluids by mouth.

48. For an unconscious patient who has had a head

injury, gently turn the head to one side to prevent

_____ .

49. Immediate first aid treatment for someone who is

hyperventilating is to _____

_____ .

50. The signs and symptoms of insulin reaction or hypoglycemia and diabetic coma or hyperglycemia are:

Insulin Reaction (Hypoglycemia)	Diabetic Coma (Hyperglycemia)
Onset	
_____	_____
_____	_____
Skin	
_____	_____
_____	_____
Behavior	
_____	_____
_____	_____
Gastrointestinal tract	
_____	_____
_____	_____
Vision	
_____	_____
_____	_____
Respiration	
_____	_____
_____	_____
Pulse	
_____	_____
_____	_____
Speech	
_____	_____
_____	_____
Breath	
_____	_____
_____	_____
Level of consciousness	
_____	_____
_____	_____

Insulin Reaction   Diabetic Coma
(Hypoglycemia)   (Hyperglycemia)

Blood glucose

_____   _____

_____   _____

Urine test

_____   _____

_____   _____

51. The first aid to give for a conscious patient who is having an insulin reaction is to _____ _____ .

52. The first aid treatment for diabetic coma is ____ _____ .

53. List five types of wounds.

    a. _____

    b. _____

    c. _____

    d. _____

    e. _____

54. Wounds bleeding severely (should *or* should not) _____ be cleansed by a first aider.

55. A patient who has suffered from a severe laceration may need to have a _____ immunization.

56. Describe the objectives of first aid measures for poisoning.

    a. _____

    b. _____

    c. _____

    d. _____

57. First aid for poisoning depends on _____ _____ .

58. The telephone number for your poison control center is _____ .

59. When specific directions cannot be obtained, vomiting should not be induced in a victim who has swallowed a poison if the person:

    a. _____

    b. _____

    c. _____

    d. _____

60. A Poison Control Center may suggest the use of syrup of ipecac to _____ .

61. Poison control centers provide information on _____ _____ .

62. The telephone number to call in your community to obtain emergency medical services is _____ _____ .

63. The 911 telephone system must be used *only* for _____ .

Multiple Choice

Write the letter of the correct answer in the blank provided. There is only *one* correct answer.

_____ 1. A primary survey includes checking the patient for:
   A. An open airway and circulation.
   B. Breathing and circulation.
   C. A hemorrhage and circulation.
   D. An open airway, breathing, and circulation.

_____ 2. The most common signal of a heart attack is:
   A. Shortness of breath.
   B. A sharp, stabbing pain in the chest.
   C. Uncomfortable pressure, squeezing, fullness or pain in the center of the chest.
   D. Sharp chest pain radiating to the neck and left arm.

_____ 3. The ratio of compressions to breaths for one-rescuer CPR is:
   A. 5:1.
   B. 5:2.
   C. 15:1.
   D. 15:2.

_____ 4. The ratio of compressions to breaths for two-rescuer CPR is:
   A. 5:1.
   B. 5:2.
   c. 15:1.
   d. 15:2.

_____ 5. The rate of compressions for one-rescuer CPR performed on an adult is:
   A. 80 per minute.
   B. 100 per minute.
   C. 80 to 100 per minute.
   D. 15 per minute

_____ 6. The rate of compressions for two-rescuer CPR performed on an adult is:
   A. 80 per minute.
   B. 100 per minute.
   C. 80 to 100 per minute.
   D. 15 per minute

_____ 7. The rate of compression for CPR performed on an infant is:
   A. 80 per minute.
   B. 100 per minute.
   C. 80 to 100 per minute.
   D. 15 per minute.

_____ 8. The rate of compressions for CPR performed on a child is:
   A. 80 per minute.
   B. 100 per minute.
   C. 80 to 100 per minute.
   D. 15 per minute.

_____ 9. When performing the Heimlich maneuver on a choking victim, place the thumb side of your fist against the victim's:
   A. Abdomen slightly below the umbilicus.
   B. Abdomen slightly above the umbilicus.
   C. Sternum above the xiphoid process.
   D. Sternum above the rib cage.

_____ 10. When performing the Heimlich maneuver, use a:
   A. Quick upward thrust.
   B. Quick downward thrust.
   C. Slow upward thrust.
   D. Slow downward thrust.

_____ 11. Chest thrusts for a choking victim are to be used only when the victim is:
   A. Lying down.
   B. Sitting in a chair.
   C. Extremely thin.
   D. Markedly obese or in the later stages of pregnancy.

_____ 12. For a choking infant, perform _____ to relieve the obstruction.
   A. Back blows.
   B. Abdominal thrusts.
   C. Chest thrusts.
   D. Back blows and chest thrusts.

_____ 13. Which of the following are some of the signs of shock?
   (1) Slow strong pulse.
   (2) Rapid weak pulse.
   (3) Increased respirations.
   (4) Decreased respirations.
   (5) Lowered blood pressure.
   (6) Elevated blood pressure.

   A. 1, 4, and 5
   B. 1, 3, and 6
   C. 2, 4, and 5
   D. 2, 3, and 5

_____ 14. The first method to use to control severe bleeding in a patient is:
   A. Elevation.
   B. Direct pressure.
   C. The pressure point method.
   D. Application of a pressure bandage.

_____ 15. Compression on the _____ artery may be used to control superficial wounds of the forehead or the frontal part of the scalp.
   A. Temporal
   B. Facial
   C. Carotid
   D. Subclavian

16. Downward compression with the fingers on the _____ artery may be used to control bleeding in the arm and upper shoulder regions.
    A. Brachial
    B. Subclavian
    C. Temporal
    D. Radial

17. Compression of the _____ artery with the heel of the hand may be used to control bleeding from the leg.
    A. Femoral
    B. Radial
    C. Subclavian
    D. Brachial

18. _____ should be applied to first-degree (superficial) burns to help relieve pain and to prevent the formation of blisters.
    A. Butter
    B. Powder
    C. Cold water or cold compresses
    D. An antiseptic

19. _____ burns involve deeper layers of the epidermis, are painful, and usually form blisters.
    A. First-degree (superficial)
    B. Second-degree (partial thickness)
    C. Third-degree (full-thickness)
    D. Second- and third-degree

20. Sunburn is an example of a _____ burn.
    A. First-degree (superficial)
    B. Second-degree (partial thickness)
    C. Third-degree (full-thickness)
    D. Second- and third-degree

21. For burns on the face or eyes caused by a chemical, flush the victim's face and eyes with a gentle flow of cool water for at least _____ minutes.
    A. 5
    B. 10
    C. 15
    D. 20

22. After receiving an injection of penicillin in the office, a patient goes into an anaphylactic reaction. To help this patient breathe easier, position him or her in a _____ position.
    A. Sitting
    B. Supine
    C. Prone
    D. Lying down

23. When a patient in your clinic has a convulsion:
    (1) Move items near the patient that may cause harm.
    (2) Loosen constricting clothing.
    (3) Restrain the patient's movements.
    (4) Ensure an open airway.
    (5) Allow the patient to rest or sleep after the convulsion has subsided.

    a. (1), (2), (3), and (4)
    b. (1), (2), (4), and (5)
    c. (1), (3), (4), and (5)
    d. (2), (3), (4), and (5)

24. Epistaxis is the medical term for:
    A. Stroke
    B. Severe bleeding.
    C. Nosebleed.
    D. Vomiting blood.

25. A patient who has fainted should be placed in a _____ position.
    A. Sitting
    B. Supine position with the head lowered slightly
    C. Supine position with the head elevated slightly
    D. Semi-Fowler's

26. Indications that there is an elevation of intracranial pressure in a patient who has had a head injury include:
    (1) An increase in blood pressure.
    (2) A decrease in blood pressure.
    (3) Pupils dilating.
    (4) Pupils constricting.
    (5) A decrease in the state of consciousness.

    a. (1), (3), and (5)
    b. (2), (3), and (5)
    c. (1), (4), and (5)
    d. (2), (4), and (5)

_____ 27. Which of the following are signs and symptoms of an insulin reaction?
   (1) Perspiration, pallor, cold and damp skin
   (2) Tremors, restlessness, fatigue, faint feeling, confusion
   (3) Extreme hunger and possibly nausea
   (4) Flushed and dry skin, and dry tongue
   (5) Sweet or fruity odor to the breath

   a.   (1), (2), and (5)
   b.   (2), (3), and (4)
   c.   (3), (4), and (5)
   d.   (1), (2), and (3)

_____ 28. Syrup of ipecac may be used for victims of:
   A.   Fainting.
   B.   Nausea and vomiting.
   C.   Poisoning.
   D.   Anaphylactic shock.

Labeling

1. Label the following pressure points used to control severe bleeding (Figure 17-1).

a. _____

b. _____

c. _____

d. _____

e. _____

f. _____

g. _____

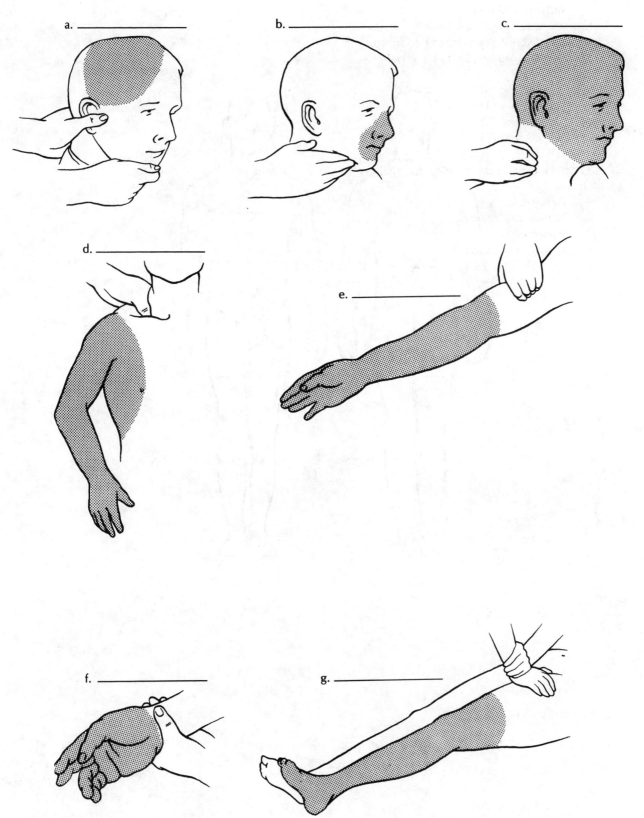

2. The percentage of total body surface involved usually determines the severity of a burn. The body surface is divided into areas by the rule of nine. Label the following diagrams according to the rule of nine indicating the percentage of the body surface involved (Figure 17-2).

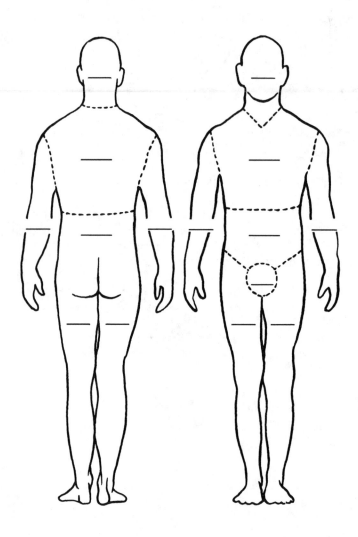

PERFORMANCE TEST

In a skills laboratory, with simulations of emergency situations, the medical assistant student is to demonstrate skill in performing the following procedures without reference to source materials. Time limits for the performance of each procedure are to be assigned by the instructor. The student will need a person to play the role of the patient.

1. Demonstrate the proper first aid treatment to be administered to patients who have experienced all the emergency situations given in this unit.
2. Demonstrate how to and locate the seven pressure points to be used when controlling severe bleeding.
3. Demonstrate on the manikin (if available) the correct method of administering CPR to an unconscious patient.

The student is expected to perform these skills with 100% accuracy.

PERFORMANCE CHECKLIST

Medical assistant students are to design their own step-by-step procedures and performance checklists for the performance test.

ANSWERS
Fill-In

1. The immediate and temporary care given the victim of an accident or sudden illness until the services of a physician can be obtained. It is the help that you can provide in emergencies until trained medical emergency personnel or a physician takes over.
2. a. Life is threatened.
   b. Situations develop that endanger a person's physical and/or psychological well-being.
   c. Pain and suffering occur.
3. a. Remain calm, reassure the patient, be empathetic, and do not panic. Act in an orderly, organized manner.
   b. Survey the situation to determine the nature of the emergency. A primary survey includes the ABCs for all emergencies; that is, check the patient for an open airway, for breathing and for circulation. A secondary survey is to examine the total body to determine what is wrong.
   c. Take immediate steps to remedy the situation.
   d. Seek medical help if needed and be able to describe the nature of the patient's condition.

4. Cardiopulmonary resuscitation, a combination of artificial respiration and artificial circulation
5. Life support
6. a. An effective respiration and pulse are restored to the victim.
   b. You are completely exhausted and cannot continue CPR.
   c. Care of the victim is turned over to medical or other properly trained personnel.
   d. The victim is pronounced dead.
7. a. A—airway opened
   b. B—breathing restored
   c. C—circulation restored
8. a. Uncomfortable pressure, squeezing, fullness or pain in the center of the chest behind the breastbone, which may spread to the shoulder, neck, jaw, or arms (the pain may not be severe)
   b. Sweating
   c. Nausea, and maybe vomiting
   d. Shortness of breath *or*
   e. A feeling of weakness
   f. Apprehension
9. 15:2; 80 to 100 times per minute
10. 5:1; 80 to 100 times per minute
11. ½ to 1; 100
12. 1 to 1½; 80 to 100
13. using a modified jaw thrust, keeping the victim's head in a fixed, neutral position
14. Heimlich; subdiaphragmatic abdominal thrusts
15. A state of collapse or a depressed condition of the circulatory system, occurring when the vital organs of the body are deprived of circulating blood flow necessary to sustain their normal cellular activity. It is a physiological reaction of the body to severe injury or insult.
16. a. Traumatic shock
    b. Hemorrhagic or hypovolemic shock
    c. Cardiogenic shock
    d. Septic shock
    e. Neurogenic shock
17. a. The pulse is weak, rapid, and irregular.
    b. Respirations increase in rate and are shallow.
    c. BP is lowered—less than 90 mm Hg systolic.
    d. The skin is markedly pale and may feel cold to the touch and moist with perspiration.
    e. The lips, nailbeds, tips of the fingers, and lobes of the ears may be bluish (cyanosis).
    f. The face may appear pinched and without expression.
    g. The eyes may be fixed into a stare and often lose their characteristic luster.
    h. The pupils may be dilated, especially in the late stages.

i. Occasionally, the patient may be unusually anxious, restless, or excited.

j. When conscious, the patient appears quite disinterested in the surroundings and complains little of pain, although he or she may be groaning.

k. Later the patient may become apathetic and unresponsive. Eyes are sunken with a vacant expression.

l. If untreated, the patient eventually loses consciousness. Vital signs drop, and death may occur.

18. a. Improve circulation of blood; control bleeding when necessary.

b. Ensure an open airway and an adequate supply of oxygen.

c. Maintain normal body temperature and keep the patient at rest.

d. Obtain medical assistance as and when required.

19. Lying flat

20. Oxygen (4 to 8 L) and epinephrine (1 to 3 ml of 1:1000 IU)

21. Arterial; venous; capillary

22. a. Control the bleeding immediately.

b. Protect the wound from contamination and infection (as is feasible).

c. Treat for shock.

d. Obtain medical attention.

23. a. Direct pressure

b. Elevation

c. Pressure bandage

d. Pressure points

24. a. Temporal artery

b. Facial artery

c. Carotid artery

d. Subclavian artery

e. Brachial artery

f. Femoral artery

g. Radial artery

25. MedicAlert

26. Outer layers; without

27. Are; do

28. Painless; do

29. 40

30. a. Relieve pain.

b. Prevent the formation of blisters.

31. a. Treat the person for shock.

b. Prevent infection.

c. Relieve pain.

32. Running water

33. Do not break

34. Should not

35. Heart and lung

36. The involuntary spasms or contractions of muscles caused by an abnormal stimulus to the brain or by changes in the chemical balance in the body

37. Protect the patient from causing harm to the body during the convulsion.

38. Nosebleed

39. Fainting

40. Have the patient in a sitting position, and pinch the lower portion of the nose between the thumb and index finger for 5 to 10 minutes.

41. Apply ice packs to the nasal and facial areas. Place a moistened gauze pad gently into the bleeding nostril, leaving one end of the gauze outside so that it can be removed easily, then pinch the nose between the thumb and index finger for 10 minutes. If this does not control the bleeding, medical attention should be obtained.

42. A partial or complete loss of consciousness of limited duration caused by a decreased amount of blood to the brain

43. Flat with the head lowered slightly

44. Lower the patient's head between the legs.

45. Instill a few drops of sterile oil into the ear canal.

46. Supine; Raise the head and shoulder (together).

47. Should not

48. Aspiration of any blood or mucus that may be present

49. Have the individual breathe into a paper bag held tightly over the mouth and nose for 10 minutes or more to replace the carbon dioxide that has been given off during hyperventilation. Remove the victim from the surroundings and provide reassurance to the victim.

50.

Insulin Reaction (Hypoglycemia)	Diabetic Coma (Hyperglycemia)
Onset	
Sudden	Gradual
Skin	
Perspiration, pallor cold and damp skin	Flushed warm, and dry skin, dry tongue
Behavior	
Tremors, restlessness, fatigue, faint feeling, headache, confusion, or strange behavior. May seem dazed or slow to respond. May appear irritable or grumpy.	Weakness, drowsiness, lethargy

Insulin Reaction (Hypoglycemia)	Diabetic Coma (Hyperglycemia)

Gastrointestinal tract

Extreme hunger, nausea	Thirst, nausea, and vomiting

Vision

Double vision	Eyeball tension low

Respiration

Shallow	Difficulty in breathing or air hunger

Pulse

Rapid or normal	Rapid, weak

Speech

Slurred	

Breath

No acetone smell	Sweet or fruity odor; smell of acetone

Level of Consciousness

May have loss of consciousness	Apparent confusion and disorientation. Coma if unattended

Blood glucose

Low (40-70 mg/100 ml)	High (over 200 mg/100 ml)

Urine Test

Sugar—absent, or a trace at most	Sugar—positive in high amounts
Acetone—negative	Acetone—positive

51. Give the patient some form of simple sugar, such as hard candy, sugar, or sweetened orange juice.
52. There is *no adequate first aid treatment* for hyperglycemia or diabetic coma. *Immediate medical treatment is necessary.*
53. a. Abrasions
    b. Avulsion
    c. Incisions
    d. Lacerations
    e. Puncture wounds
54. Should not
55. Tetanus

56. a. To induce vomiting, *except* when the person has swallowed corrosive or petroleum products, when the person is unconscious, when the person is convulsing, or if the substances ingested could absorb rapidly (for example, camphor; strychnine) or causes seizures or comas (for example, cyclic antidepressants).
    b. To prevent absorption of the poison.
    c. To maintain an open airway, breathing, and vital functions.
    d. To obtain medical attention without delay.
57. The type of poison ingested
58. Answers vary with the student's location
59. a. Is unconscious or in a coma
    b. Is having a convulsion
    c. Has ingested a petroleum product, for example, kerosene, lighter fluid, gasoline
    d. Has ingested a corrosive substance, for example, strong acids or alkalis
60. Induce vomiting.
61. The appropriate first aid and clinical management to use for cases of suspected or known poisoning. Some centers also offer specialized poisoning treatment and consultant services, professional training, and poisoning prevention education for consumers. Many centers are staffed by clinical pharmacists 24 hours a day, every day of the year.
62. Answer varies for each community.
63. Emergency situations when you need help quickly

Multiple Choice

1. D
2. C
3. D
4. A
5. C
6. C
7. B
8. C
9. B
10. A
11. D
12. D
13. D
14. B
15. A
16. B
17. A
18. C
19. B
20. A
21. C
22. A

23. B
24. C
25. B

26. A
27. D
28. C

Labeling

1. a. Temporal
   b. Facial
   c. Carotid
   d. Subclavian

   e. Brachial
   f. Radial-ulnar
   g. Femoral

2.

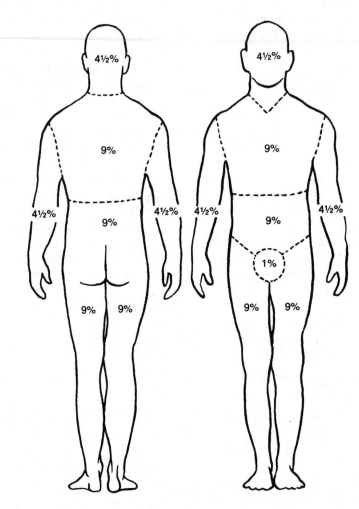

Answer to Figure 17-2

Unit 18

Anatomy and Physiology

In the blanks provided, write the answers that best complete the sentences:

1. _____ is the study of body structures and their location.

2. Cells are _____ _____ .

3. _____ are combinations of similar cells.

4. _____ are collections of tissues working together to perform a particular function.

5. A _____ consists of organs that work together to provide a major body function.

6. _____ is the study of the functions of the body.

7. Name the eleven major systems that compose the human body.

   a. _____
   b. _____
   c. _____
   d. _____
   e. _____
   f. _____
   g. _____
   h. _____
   i. _____
   j. _____
   k. _____

8. The _____ plane separates the front and back of the body.

9. The _____ plane divides the upper and lower body.

10. The _____ plane divides the body into right and left sides.

11. List the five cavities in the human body.

    a. _____
    b. _____
    c. _____
    d. _____
    e. _____

12. An imaginary line passing vertically and a line passing horizontally through the umbilicus divides the abdomen into the _____ and _____ .

13. _____ is the tendency of a cell or the whole organism to maintain a state of balance.

14. Describe the four main shapes of bones:

    a. _____
    b. _____
    c. _____
    d. _____

15. The _____ skeleton includes the 80 bones of the head and trunk. The _____ skeleton includes the 126 bones of the pelvis, shoulders, arms, and legs. There are normally _____ bones in the human body.

16. _____ attach bones to other bones in joints.

17. _____ join bones to muscles.

18. The bones of the trunk are the _____ , _____ , _____ , _____ , _____ , and _____ .

19. The backbone of the adult consists of vertebrae (number of bones) _____ .

20. The vertebrae are divided into groups as follows: the top 7 are called the _____ , the next 12 are called the _____ , or _____ , and the next 5 the _____ vertebrae.

21. The _____ between the vertebrae permit a variety of spinal motions and ease the jolts during walking or falling.

22. The _____ , or breastbone, a flat, blade-like bone, forms the front boundary of the upper part of the trunk.

23. The _____ is the lower part of the main bony framework of the body. It is formed by two large, flat irregular bones that spread outward at the top and narrow down at the lower edges in front.

24. Each side of the pelvis has a large hollow or socket below the flaring portion to receive the upper end of the thighbone, the _____ which fits into this socket, the acetabulum, forming the hip joint.

25. Above and in front of the rib cage and extending outward on either side, at right angles to the sternum (breastbone), are two long bones known as the _____ , or collarbones.

26. The shoulder blades are called the _____ bones.

27. The single long bone of the upper arm is called the _____ .

28. The two long bones of the forearm are the _____ and _____ .

29. Eight small, irregular _____ bones form the wrist.

30. The _____ is the longest and strongest bone in the body.

31. There are two long bones in the leg. The larger of the two is the _____ . The long, slender bone toward the outer side of the leg is called _____ .

32. The kneecap is called the _____ .

33. The ends of long bones contain red bone marrow. _____ , and _____ are produced there.

34. The formation and development of blood cells is called _____ .

35. Explain the functions of the more than 600 muscles in the human body.

a. _____

b. _____

c. _____

d. _____

e. _____

f. _____

36. The primary function of cardiac muscle is for _____ .

37. Two components of the circulatory system are the _____ and the _____ .

38. The cardiovascular system (CVS) consists of the _____ .

39. The lymphatic system consists of _____ .

40. The amount of blood in the body of an adult varies with _____.

41. The color of blood varies from bright to dark red, depending on the amount of _____ or _____ present in the red cells.

42. The liquid part of blood is known as the _____; it is light yellow in color, transparent, and almost entirely water.

43. _____ is blood plasma from which the fibrinogen and all clotting elements, the platelets and the red and white cells have been removed by permitting the blood to stand until it clots.

44. The three kinds of cells or corpuscles in the blood are _____, _____, and _____.

45. The RBCs (erythrocytes) are the most numerous and get their color from an iron compound called _____.

46. The RBCs are made in_____, are released into the blood stream, and live for about 4 months.

47. WBCs (leukocytes), some of which are formed in _____ and some of which are formed in _____, are larger than the RBCs but fewer in number.

48. Platelets, also called thrombocytes, are important in the process of_____. They are formed in _____.

49. The blood is carried through the body in a network of tubes of various sizes called _____, _____, and _____.

50. The upper chambers in the heart are called _____, and the lower chambers are called _____.

51. The lymphatic system is important as a rich source of _____, which serve as _____ _____, and it is involved in the overall function of the _____ system, which plays a critical role in protecting the body against disease.

52. The functions of the nervous system are to _____, _____, and _____ to maintain a steady state in the body (homeostasis).

53. The nervous system is divided into two major divisions: the _____ and the _____.

54. The central nervous system (CNS) is made up of the _____ and the _____.

55. The brain weighs about _____ pounds (1.4 kg) in the adult and reaches its full growth at about the _____ year.

56. The brain is covered by three membranes called _____.

57. The outer portion, or cortex of the brain is called the _____.

58. The _____ is the largest part of the brain. It contains the control centers for the five special senses of _____, _____, _____, and _____. It also controls speaking, learning, thinking, and remembering.

59. The back part of the brain is known as the _____. It controls the coordination of muscular activities.

60. The peripheral nervous system (PNS) consists of _____ and _____.

61. The two divisions of the autonomic nervous system are the:

a. _____

b. _____

62. The functions of the digestive system called the gastrointestinal system, include the

_____, _____, and

_____ of water and nutrients, and the

_____ of waste products that were not absorbed.

63. Name the main organs of the digestive system which form a tube often referred to as the alimentary canal of the gastrointestinal tract.

a. _____

b. _____

c. _____

d. _____

e. _____

f. _____

g. _____

h. _____

64. List the accessory organs that aid in the process of digestion.

a. _____

b. _____

c. _____

d. _____

e. _____

f. _____

65. The greatest amount of digestion and absorption of food takes place in the _____ .

66. The divisions of the small intestine are the

_____, _____, and

_____ .

67. The _____ is a major site for reabsorption of essential fluids and salts.

68. The _____ is the largest gland in the body.

69. The liver is a major storage area for sugar in the form of _____ , a ready fuel-energy source for muscle activity.

70. Some of the bile is stored in the _____ , where it is concentrated.

71. The pancreas is situated behind the

_____ .

72. Describe the three functions of the respiratory system.

a. _____

b. _____

c. _____

73. The organs of respiration are the _____ ,

_____ , _____ ,

_____ , _____ , and

_____ .

74. The _____ are the divisions of the trachea that enter the right and left lungs and divide into many branches that grow smaller and thinner-walled until they end in the air sacs, the

_____ .

75. A thin membrane, called the _____ , covers each lung and also lines the chest cavity.

76. The organs of the urinary system include the

_____ , _____ ,

_____ , and _____ .

77. Describe the two primary functions of the urinary system.

a. _____

b. _____

78. The basic structural unit of the urinary system is

the _____ .

79. The kidneys help maintain the state of homeostasis in the internal environment by _____ _____ .

80. The kidneys remove from the blood those salts, poisons, proteins, wastes, and water that are eliminated from the body as _____ .

81. The urine is carried away from the kidneys by two tubes called the _____ . The _____ are about 10 inches (25 cm) long and contract to move the urine down into the _____ .

82. The _____ is the narrow passageway from the bladder that ends in the outer opening through which urine is voided.

83. The male reproductive system consists of the

_____ , _____ ,

_____ , _____ ,

_____ , _____ ,

_____ , and _____ .

84. The two main functions of the testes are:

_____

_____

85. The female reproductive system contains the

_____ , which are two almond shaped glands that lie near the back wall of the pelvic cavity and produce the female sex cells known as

_____ .

86. The ovaries also secrete two important hormones: _____ and _____ .

87. There are two uterine tubes, also known as the

_____ .

88. The ovum passes into the fallopian tube and, if it is not fertilized within _____ hours it disintegrates and does not survive.

89. An impregnated ovum passes down into the uterus and becomes attached to the uterine wall. This is called _____ .

90. The _____ is a hollow, pear-shaped organ that is muscular and capable of great expansion. The lower part tapers to a narrow neck, the

_____ , which extends into the vagina.

91. Fertilization takes place in the _____ when a male sperm cell penetrates the ovum.

92. The _____ is the canal that lies between the bladder and the rectum. It surrounds the lower end of the uterus and opens into the vulva on the outside of the body.

93. The vulva, the external female genitals (Figure 18-15B), consists of the _____ ,

_____ and _____ .

94. If fertilization does not occur, a portion of the lining of the uterus is discarded as a bloody discharge, a process called _____ .

95. The glands involved in the endocrine system are

the _____ , _____ ,

_____ , _____ ,

_____ , _____ ,

_____ , _____ ,

_____ and _____ . The

secretions from these glands are released directly into the bloodstream and are called _____ .

96. Hormones direct many body processes including

_____ , _____ , and

_____ . Hormones regulate the body's reaction to stress and maintain the internal environment (homeostasis).

97. The _____ gland (the hypophysis) is often referred to as the "master gland" because the hormones that it produces regulate the secretion of other glands.

98. The _____ gland is located in the neck below the voice box. It regulates the metabolic activity of the individual.

99. There are two _____ glands, which are located above the kidneys.

100. The _____ secretes the hormone insulin.

101. During pregnancy the placenta serves as a temporary endocrine body. It produces _____

_____ , _____ ,

and _____ .

102. The testes secrete the male hormone

_____ ,

103. The ear is the organ of hearing and is divided into _____ , _____ ,

and _____ ear.

104. The _____ or _____ is a thin membrane that separates the external ear canal from the cavity of the middle ear.

105. The _____ is the thin, transparent mucous membrane that lines the lids and covers the anterior surface of the eyeball.

106. The eyeball is divided into two chambers separated by the _____ .

107. The outer layer of the eyeball is the _____ or the white of the eye. It is a touch-sensitive layer and is transparent over the front of the eyeball. The transparent section is called the

_____ .

108. The pigmented section over the front of the eyeball is called the _____ . The iris has an opening in the center, the _____

_____ .

109. The inner surface of the eyeball is the _____

_____ . The _____ contains the nerve fibers of the optic nerve and cells sensitive to light.

110. The ability to see objects at different distances is known as _____ and is accomplished when the curves of the surface of the lens are changed. Rays of light are bent as they enter the eye through the lens to make them focus on the

_____ .

111. In addition to hearing and sight we have three other special senses, _____ ,

_____ , and _____

112. The integumentary system is composed of the _____ and accessory structures. Accessory structures of the system include the

_____ , _____ ,

_____ , and _____ .

113. The skin stores energy and vitamins and produces Vitamin _____ from sunlight.

114. The _____ is the largest organ in the body.

115. The _____ , or cuticle, is the outermost layer of the skin and is composed of a surface of dead cells with an underlying layer of living cells.

116. The _____ , or corium, is called the "true" skin. The _____ contains the blood vessels and nerves.

117. The innermost layer of the skin is called the

_____ layer. Fatty (adipose) tissue of the _____ layer cushions and insulates the body's organs.

118. The three types of glands in the skin are the

_____ glands (sebaceous), _____ glands (sudoriferous), and _____ glands of the ear canal.

Multiple Choice

Write the letter of the correct answer in the blank provided. There is only *one* correct answer.

_____ 1. The femur, humerus, radius, and tibia are examples of _____ bones.
  A. Long
  B. Short
  C. Flat
  D. Irregular

_____ 2. There are _____ cervical vertebrae.
  A. 5
  B. 7
  C. 12
  D. 4

_____ 3. The breastbone is called the:
  A. Scapula.
  B. Sacrum.
  C. Sternum.
  D. Sphenoid.

_____ 4. The _____ is the longest and strongest bone in the body.
  A. Tibia
  B. Humerus
  C. Fibula
  D. Femur

_____ 5. The _____ is the collarbone.
  A. Clavicle
  B. Scapula
  C. Cranium
  D. Sternum

_____ 6. Thrombocytes is another name for:
  A. RBCs.
  B. WBC.
  C. Platelets.
  D. Leukocytes.

_____ 7. The liver produces:
  A. Bile.
  B. Insulin.
  C. Hydrochloric acid.
  D. Amylase.

_____ 8. The brain and spinal cord are part of the:
  A. Peripheral nervous system.
  B. Sympathetic nervous system.
  C. Central nervous system.
  D. Parasympathetic nervous system.

_____ 9. The _____ plane divides the body into right and left sides.
  A. Coronal
  B. Transverse
  C. Thoracic
  D. Sagittal

_____ 10. The kidneys are located in the _____ cavity.
  A. Thoracic
  B. Abdominal
  C. Pelvic
  D. Peritoneal

_____ 11. Muscles are needed to aid in movement and to protect the internal organs.
  A. True
  B. False

_____ 12. The _____ carry oxygen to the body cells.
  A. Platelets
  B. RBCs
  C. WBCs
  D. Lymphocytes

_____ 13. _____ anemia is due to disease of the bone marrow or destruction of the bone marrow by certain agents, especially chemicals.
  A. Pernicious
  B. Iron-deficient
  C. Sickle-cell
  D. Aplastic

_____ 14. The _____ carry blood away from the heart.
  A. Lymphatics
  B. Veins
  C. Capillaries
  D. Arteries

_____ 15. If the coronary arteries become severely narrowed insufficient blood reaches the:
  A. Carotid arteries.
  B. Chest cavity.
  C. Heart muscle.
  D. Lungs.

16. The lymphatic system is a rich source of:
    A. Platelets.
    B. RBCs.
    C. Lymphocytes.
    D. Thrombocytes.

17. The peripheral nervous system consists of:
    A. 12 pairs of cranial nerves and 31 pairs of spinal nerves.
    B. The brain and spinal cord.
    C. 21 pairs of spinal nerves.
    D. 21 pairs of spinal nerves and 12 pairs of cranial nerves.

18. The liver and tongue can be considered as accessory organs of the digestive system.
    A. True
    B. False

19. The _____ is the largest gland in the body.
    A. Stomach
    B. Pancreas
    C. Gallbladder
    D. Liver

20. Food passes from the mouth to the stomach through the:
    A. Trachea.
    B. Esophagus.
    C. Larynx.
    D. Duodenum.

21. The greatest amount of digestion and absorption of food takes place in the:
    A. Stomach.
    B. Small intestine.
    C. Large intestine.
    D. Colon.

22. Urine passes from the kidneys to the urinary bladder through the:
    A. Urethra.
    B. Ureters.
    C. Uterine tubes.
    D. Nephron units.

23. The process of ovulation occurs in the:
    A. Uterus.
    B. Ovarian tube.
    C. Ovary.
    D. Fallopian tube.

24. Sperm are produced in the:
    A. Ovary.
    B. Prostate gland.
    C. Testes.
    D. Seminal vesicles.

25. The hormone epinephrine is produced by the _____ gland. This hormone helps to increase heart rate during stressful times.
    A. Pituitary.
    B. Thyroid.
    C. Parathyroid
    D. Adrenal

26. The main male sex hormone is called:
    A. Estrogen.
    B. Progesterone.
    C. Cortisone.
    D. Testosterone.

27. Another name for the eardrum is the:
    A. Tympanic membrane.
    B. Oval window.
    C. Eustachian tube.
    D. Malleus.

28. The _____ of the eye varies in size with the amount of light admitted, contracting to shut out bright light and enlarging in dim light.
    A. Lens
    B. Pupil
    C. Iris
    D. Cornea

29. Another name for sweat glands is _____ glands.
    A. Sebaceous
    B. Sudoriferous
    C. Endocrine
    D. Ceruminous

30. _____ is the most common type of skin cancer.
    A. Basal cell carcinoma
    B. Squamous cell carcinoma
    C. Melanoma
    D. Hemangioma

Labeling

The labeling and the diagramming exercises were taken from Gerdin, Judith: *Student workbook for health careers today*, (1991, Mosby-Year Book).

Body Planes

Label the diagram of the body planes (Figure 18-1, *a to c*) using the following terms:

Transverse   Coronal   Sagittal

Body Cavities

Label the diagram of the body cavities (Figure 18-2) using the following terms. Shade the cavities that are considered to be located in the dorsal section of the body. In the spaces provided, list at least two body organs or parts found in each cavity.

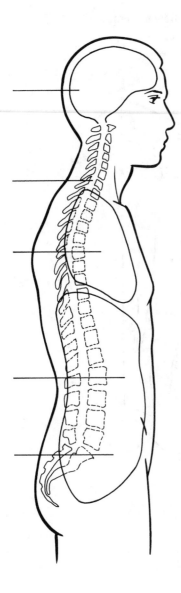

Cranial cavity   Thoracic cavity
Spinal cavity   Abdominal cavity
Pelvic cavity

Body Cavity   Organs located in the cavity

1. _____   _____

2. _____   _____

3. _____   _____

4. _____   _____

5. _____   _____

Anterior Skeleton Bone Identification

Label the diagram of the anterior skeletal system (Figure 18-3) using the following terms:

Metacarpals	Sternum	Clavicle	Carpals
Patella	Phalanges	Ulna	Metatarsals
Humerus	Mandible	Cranium	Cervical vertebrae
Fibula	Maxilla	Tibia	Ischium
Tarsals	Vertebral column	Radius	Costal
Femur	Pubis	Ilium	

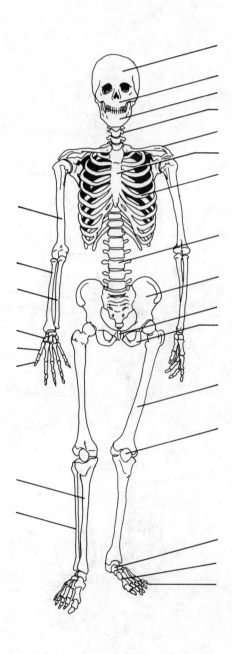

Posterior Skeleton Bone Identification

Label the diagram of the posterior skeletal system (Figure 18-4) using the following terms:

Calcaneus	Thoracic vertebrae	Scapula	Lumbar vertebrae
Sacrum	Femur	Metatarsals	Tarsals
Ilium	Cervical vertebrae	Coccyx	Carpals
Cranium	Phalanges	Tibia	Radius
Metacarpals	Humerus	Fibula	Ulna

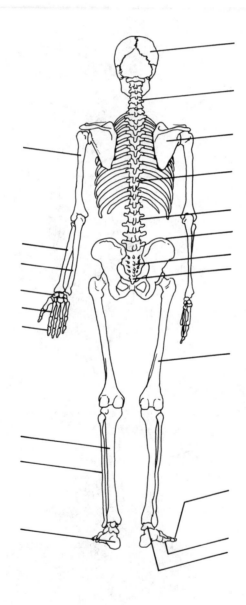

Anterior Muscle System

Label the diagram of the anterior muscular system (Figure 18-5) using the following terms:

Masseter	Rectus femoris	Vastus lateralis	Sartourius
Biceps brachii	Seratus anterior	Sternocleidomastoid	Quadriceps femoris
Pectoralis major	External oblique	Vastus medialis	Rectus abdominis
Flexor carpi	Deltoid	Trapezius	Tibialis anterior

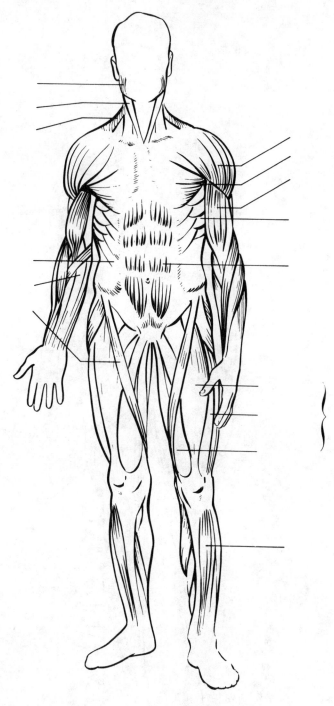

Posterior Muscle System

Label the diagram of the posterior muscular system (Figure 18-6) using the following terms:

Semitendinosus   Extensor carpiulinaris   Infraspinatus fascia   Biceps femoris
Gluteus medius   Extensor carpi radialis   Extensor digitorium   Latissimus dorsi
Gracilis   Soleus   communis   Rhomboideus
Gastrocnemius   Triceps   Trapezius   Gluteus maximus

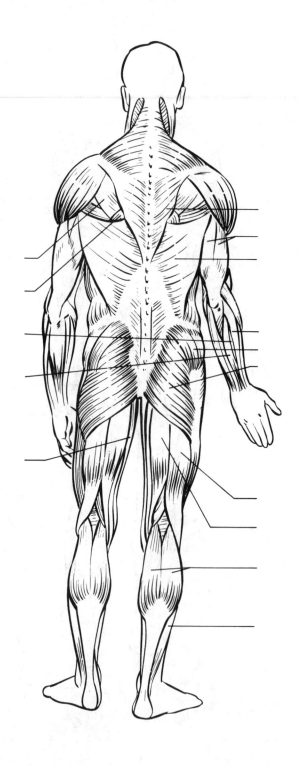

The Heart

Label the diagram of the heart (Figure 18-7) using the following terms:

Superior vena cava	Septum	Aorta	Bicuspid valve (mitral)
Right ventricle	Pulmonary valve	Inferior vena cava	Left atrium
Tricuspid valve	Left ventricle	Pulmonary artery	Aortic valve
Pulmonary vein	Right atrium		

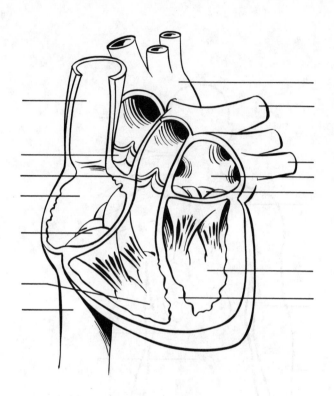

Arteries

Label the diagram (Figure 18-8) to show the location of the following arteries. Put an asterisk (*) next to the eight locations that might be used to measure a pulse rate.

Brachial	Temporal	Anterior tibial	Popliteal
Subclavian	Carotid (external)	Abdominal aorta	Radial
Dorsalis Pedis	Femoral	Renal	Posterior tibial

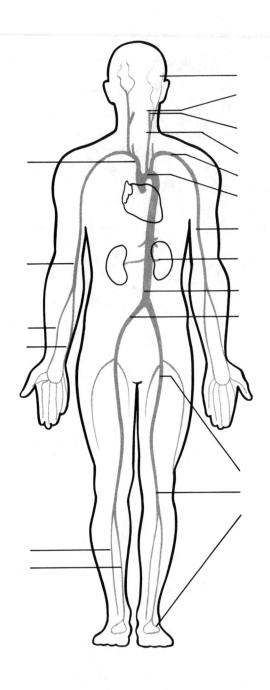

Pressure Points

Label Figure 18-9 to indicate the pressure points that may be used to stop bleeding using the following terms:

Femoral artery
Popliteal artery

Pedal artery
Brachial artery

Radial artery
Posterior tibial artery

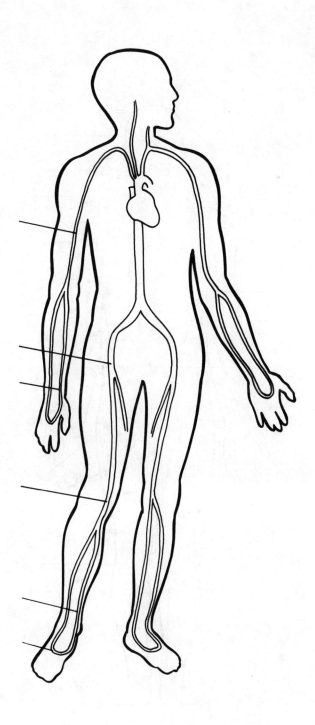

Veins

Label the diagram (Figure 18-10) to show the location of the following veins:

Subclavian
Radial
Anterior tibial
Common iliac

Temporal
Superior vena cava
Innominate
Axillary

Jugular (external)
Median
Median cubital
Great saphenous

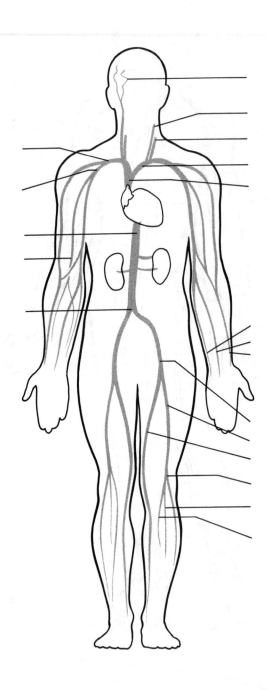

The Brain

Label the diagram of the brain (Figure 18-11) using the following terms. In the spaces provided, list the main function of each part of the brain.

Midbrain　　　　　　　Medulla　　　　　　　Spinal cord
Frontal lobe　　　　　　Cerebrum　　　　　　　Pons
Temporal lobe　　　　　Parietal lobe　　　　　Cerebellum
Occipital lobe

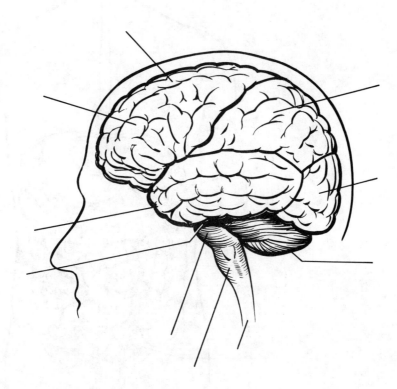

The Digestive System

Label the diagram of the digestive system (Figure 18-12) using the following terms. Place an asterisk next to the three accessory organs of the digestive system. In the spaces provided, describe the function of each of the organs of the system.

Pancreas
Small intestine
Appendix
Descending colon
Parotid gland
Sublingual gland
Esophagus
Mouth
Ascending colon
Liver
Submandibular gland
Gallbladder
Anus
Transverse colon
Stomach
Rectum

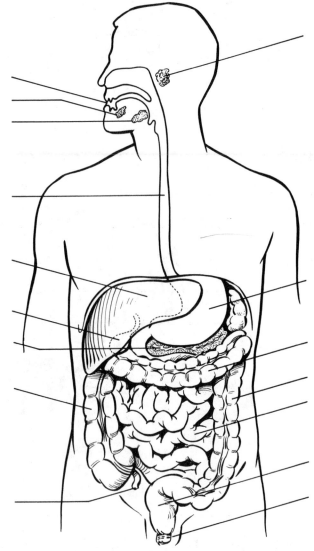

Organ Function Chart Fill-In

	Organ	Function
1.	Mouth	
2.	Esophagus	
3.	Stomach	
4.	Small intestine	
5.	Appendix	
6.	Ascending colon	
7.	Transverse colon	

The Respiratory System

Label the diagram of the respiratory system (Figure 18-13) using the following terms. List the main function of each of the parts of the system in the spaces provided.

Oral cavity
Bronchiole
Nasal cavity
Larynx
Epitlogtis

Diaphragm
Right lung
Alveoli
Bronchus

Left lung
Sinus
Trachea
Pharynx

Respiratory System Part Function Chart Fill-In

System Part	Main Function
1. Oral cavity	
2. Nasal cavity	
3. Sinus	
4. Larynx	
5. Pharynx	
6. Trachea	
7. Epiglottis	
8. Bronchus	
9. Bronchiole	
10. Alveoli	
11. Left lung	number of lobes -
12. Right lung	number of lobes -

Figure 18-13

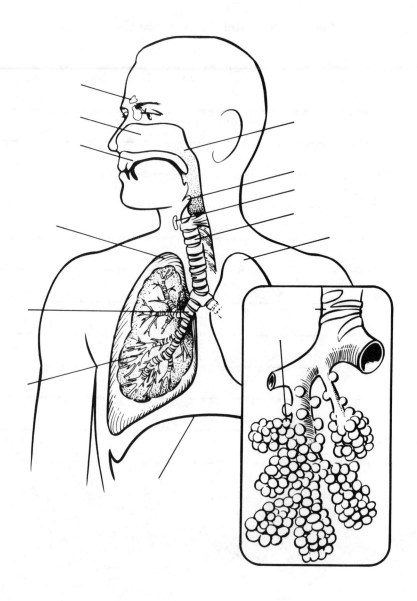

The Urinary System

Label the diagram of the urinary system (Figure 18-14) with the following terms. In the spaces provided, list the main function of each of the parts of the system.

Ureter   Bladder   Urethra
Urinary meatus   Kidney

Urinary System Function Chart Fill-In

<u>System Part</u>   <u>Main Function</u>

1. Kidney   _____

2. Ureter   _____

3. Bladder   _____

4. Urethra   _____

5. Urinary meatus _____

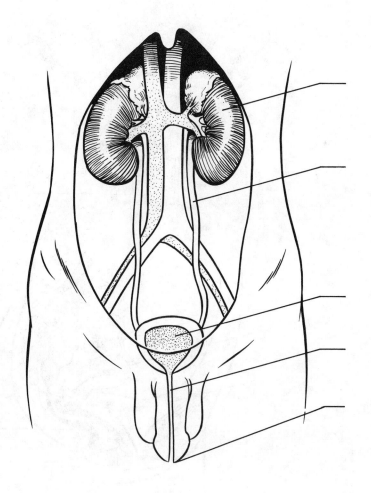

Female Reproductive System

Label the diagrams of the female reproductive system (Figures 18-15 a-b) using the following terms. In the spaces provided, list the main function of the listed parts.

Uterus (2)   Cervix   Vagina (2)
Ovary (2)   Urinary bladder   Fallopian tube
Rectum

Female Reproductive Part Function Chart Fill-In

Reproductive Part	Main Function
1. Ovary	
2. Uterus	
3. Vagina	
4. Cervix	
5. Fallopian tube	

A

B

Male Reproductive System

Label the diagram of the male reproductive system (Figure 18-16) using the following terms. In the spaces provided, list the main function of the listed parts.

Prostate gland	Urethra	Rectum	Testis
Urinary meatus	Penis	Cowper's gland	Ejaculatory duct
Urinary bladder	Scrotum	Vas deferens	Glans penis
Epididymis	Seminal vesicle		

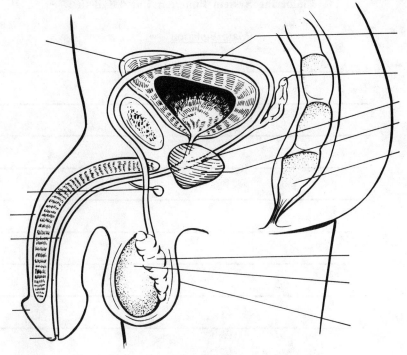

Male Reproductive Part Function Chart Fill-In

Reproductive Part   Main Function

1. Cowper's gland _____

2. Penis _____

3. Urethra _____

4. Glans penis _____

5. Urinary meatus _____

6. Vas deferens _____

7. Seminal vesicle _____

8. Ejaculatory gland _____

9. Prostrate gland _____

10. Epididymis _____

11. Testis _____

12. Scrotum _____

The Endocrine System

Label the diagram of the endocrine system (Figure 18-17) using the following terms. In the spaces provided, list the main function of each of the glands of the system.

Adrenal	Thymus	Ovary (female)
Testes (male)	Pituitary	Pancreas
Parathyroid	Pineal body	Thyroid

Endocrine System Function Chart Fill-In

	System Part	Main Function
1.	Pituitary	_____
2.	Pineal body	_____
3.	Thyroid	_____
4.	Parathyroid	_____
5.	Thymus	_____
6.	Pancreas	_____
7.	Adrenal	_____
8.	Ovary	_____
9.	Testes	_____

Figure 18-17

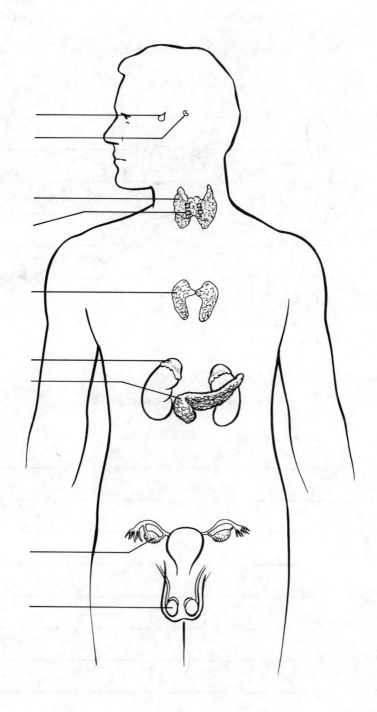

The Ear

Label the diagram of the ear (Figure 18-18) using the following terms. In the spaces provided, list the main function of each part of the year.

Malleus   Oval window   Incus
pinna   Stapes   Tympanic membrane
Auditory canal   Cochlea   Vestibule
Semicircular canal

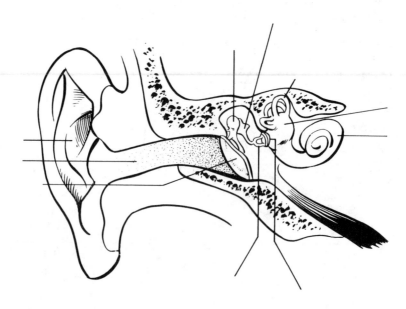

Ear Part Function Chart Fill-In

Ear Part	Main Function
1. Pinna	
2. Auditory canal	
3. Tympanic membrane	
4. Malleus	
5. Incus	
6. Stapes	
7. Semicircular canal	
8. Cochlea	
9. Vestibule	
10. Oval window	

The Eye

Label the diagram of the eye (Figure 18-19) using the following terms. In the spaces provided, list the main function of each part of the eye.

Ciliary muscle   Conjunctiva   Lens   Optic nerve
Suspensory ligaments   Iris   Pupil   Cornea
Retina   Choroid coat   Posterior chamber Sclera
Anterior chamber

Eye Part Function Chart Fill-In

Eye Part   Main Function

1. Conjunctiva   _____

2. Ciliary muscle   _____

3. Iris   _____

4. Anterior chamber   _____

5. Pupil   _____

6. Cornea   _____

7. Lens   _____

8. Suspensory ligaments _____

9. Sclera   _____

10. Choroid coat   _____

11. Retina   _____

12. Optic nerve   _____

13. Posterior chamber   _____

ANSWERS
Fill-in

1. Anatomy
2. The smallest unit/structures capable of reproducing and maintaining life. They compose all living things.
3. Tissues
4. Organs
5. Body system
6. Physiology
7. a. Skeletal
    b. Muscular
    c. Circulatory (cardiovascular and lymphatic)
    d. Nervous
    e. Digestive
    f. Respiratory
    g. Urinary
    h. Reproductive
    i. Endocrine
    j. Sensory
    k. Integumentary
8. Coronal
9. Transverse
10. Sagittal
11. a. Thoracic
    b. Abdominal
    c. Pelvic
    d. Cranial
    e. Spinal
12. Right and left upper quadrants; the right and left lower quadrants.
13. Homeostasis
14. a. Long bones. These bones are longer than wide. Examples of long bones are the femur, humerus, radius, ulna, tibia, and fibula.
    b. Short bones. These bones have similar width and length. Examples of short bones include the tarsals, metatarsals, carpals, and metacarpals.
    c. Flat bones. These bones have two layers with space in between. Examples include the cranium, ribs, scapula, and sternum.
    d. Irregular bones. These are bones that do not fit into the other categories. Examples include the vertebrae, mandible, patella, ilium, and the ossicles in the ear.
15. Axial; appendicular; 206
16. Ligaments
17. Tendons
18. Vertebrae, sternum, ribs, scapulae, clavicles, and pelvis
19. 26
20. Cervical; thoracic; dorsal; lumbar
21. Intervertebral disks
22. Sternum
23. Pelvis
24. Femur
25. Clavicles
26. Scapulae
27. Humerus
28. Radius; ulna
29. Carpal
30. Femur
31. Tibia. fibula
32. Patella
33. RBCs, some types of WBCs and platelets
34. Hematopoiesis
35. a. Aid in movement
    b. Provide and maintain posture
    c. Protect internal organs
    d. Provide movement of blood, flood, and waste products through the body
    e. Open and close body openings
    f. Produce heat
36. Contraction of the heart
37. Cardiovascular system; lymphatic system
38. Heart and blood vessels
39. Lymphatic vessels, lymph nodes, lymph, and specialized lymphatic organs such as the spleen and thymus
40. Weight
41. Oxygen or carbon dioxide
42. Blood plasma
43. Blood serum
44. RBCs, and WBCs, and platelets
45. Hemoglobin
46. The red marrow of the bones
47. Red bone marrow; lymph nodes; spleen
48. Blood clot formation. red bone marrow
49. Arteries, veins, and capillaries
50. Atria; ventricles
51. Lymphocytes (a type of WBC); as a protection against infection; immune
52. Sense, interpret, and respond to internal and external environmental changes
53. Central nervous system; peripheral nervous system
54. Brain; spinal cord
55. 3; 20th
56. Meninges
57. Cerebrum
58. Cerebrum, sight, hearing, touch, smell, and taste
59. Cerebellum
60. 12 pairs of cranial nerves; 31 pairs of spinal nerves; brain; spinal cord
61. a. Sympathetic system
    b. Parasympathetic system

62. Ingestion, digestion, absorption; elimination
63. a. Mouth
    b. Oropharynx
    c. Esophagus
    d. Stomach
    e. Small intestine: duodenum, jejunum, and ileum
    f. Large intestine: cecum, colon (ascending, transverse, descending, and sigmoid colon)
    g. Rectum
    h. Anal canal and anus
64. a. Salivary glands: parotid, submandibular, sublingual
    b. Tongue
    c. Teeth
    d. Liver
    e. Gallbladder
    f. Pancreas
65. Small intestine.
66. Duodenum, jejunum, and ileum
67. Colon
68. Liver
69. Glycogen
70. Gallbladder
71. Stomach
72. a. The exchange of gases between the blood and the lungs
    b. The exchange of air between the lungs and the ambient air.
    c. The maintenance of oxygen-carbon dioxide balance in the blood
73. Nose, pharynx, larynx, trachea, bronchi, and lungs
74. Bronchi; alveoli
75. Pleura
76. Two kidneys, two ureters, one bladder, and one urethra
77. a. To regulate the chemical composition of body fluids
    b. To remove body wastes by filtering blood
78. Kidney
79. Selectively excreting or reabsorbing various substances according to the needs of the body
80. Urine
81. Ureters. ureters; bladder
82. Urethra
83. Testes, epididymis, cowper's gland, vas deferens, prostate gland, urethra, penis, two seminal vesicles, and one ejaculatory duct
84. To make male reproductive cells called spermatozoa (sperm) and to secrete testosterone, the principal male hormone.
85. Ovaries; ova (eggs)
86. Estrogen; progesterone
87. Fallopian tubes

88. 24-36
89. Implantation
90. Uterus, cervix
91. Distal third of either fallopian tube
92. Vagina
93. Labia, clitoris, and hymen
94. Menstruation
95. Pineal, pituitary, thyroid, parathyroids, thymus, pancreas, adrenals, ovaries, testes, and the placenta during pregnancy. hormones
96. Growth, metabolism, and reproductive functions
97. Pituitary
98. Thyroid
99. Adrenal
100. Pancreas
101. Chorionic gonadotropins, estrogens, and progesterone
102. Testosterone
103. External, middle, and inner
104. Eardrum or tympanic membrane
105. Conjunctiva
106. Lens
107. Sclera, cornea
108. Iris. pupil
109. Retina. Retina
110. Accommodation, retina
111. Taste, smell, and touch
112. Skin; hair, nails, specialized glands, and nerves.
113. D
114. Skin
115. Epidermis
116. Dermis; dermis
117. Subcutaneous
118. Oil, sweat, and ceruminous

Multiple Choice

1. A
2. B
3. C
4. D
5. A
6. C
7. A
8. C
9. D
10. B
11. A
12. B
13. D
14. D
15. C
16. C
17. A

18. A
19. D
20. B
21. B
22. B
23. C
24. C
25. D
26. D
27. A
28. B
29. B
30. A

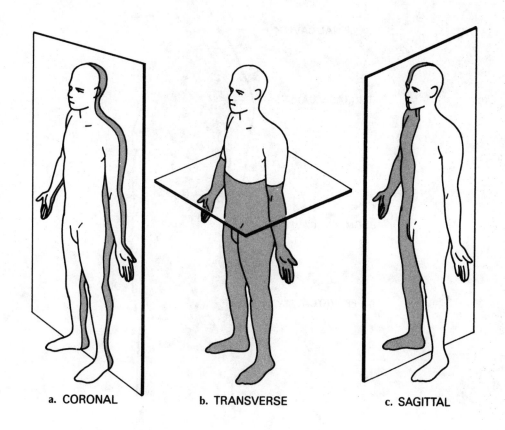

a. CORONAL   b. TRANSVERSE   c. SAGITTAL

Answer to Figure 18-1, *a to c*

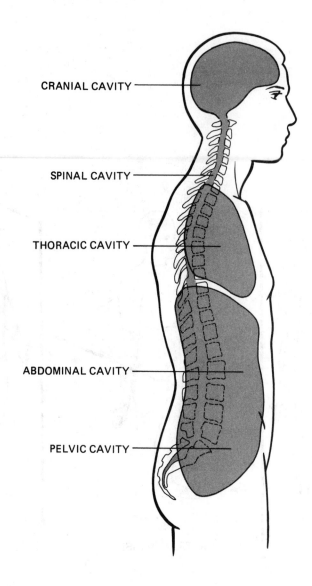

CRANIAL CAVITY

SPINAL CAVITY

THORACIC CAVITY

ABDOMINAL CAVITY

PELVIC CAVITY

Answer to Figure 18-2

Body Cavity	**Organs located in the Cavity (at least two)**
1. Thoracic cavity	Lungs, heart, esophagus, trachea, major blood vessels
2. Abdominal cavity	Stomach, gallbladder, pancreas, intestines, liver, spleen, adrenal glands, kidneys
3. Pelvic cavity	Reproductive organs, bladder, rectum
4. Cranial cavity	Brain, ventricles, glands
5. Spinal cavity	Spinal cord, nerves

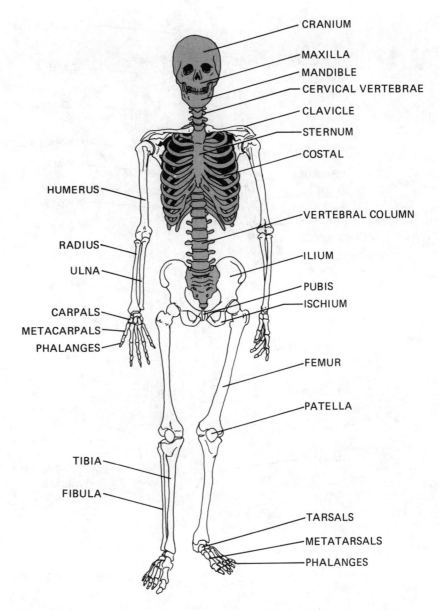

Answer to Figure 18-3

Posterior Skeleton Bone Identification

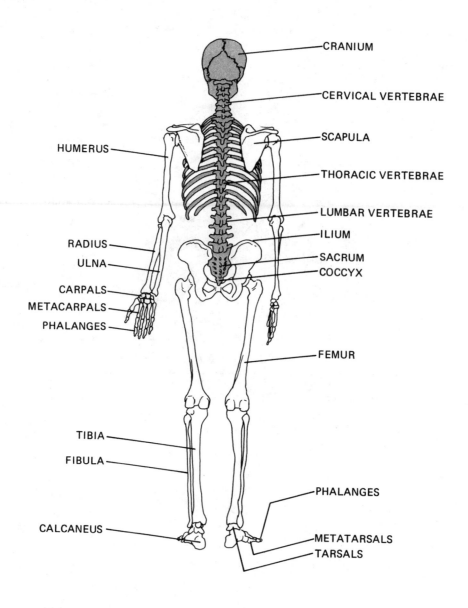

CRANIUM

CERVICAL VERTEBRAE

SCAPULA

HUMERUS

THORACIC VERTEBRAE

LUMBAR VERTEBRAE

RADIUS

ILIUM

ULNA

SACRUM

COCCYX

CARPALS

METACARPALS

PHALANGES

FEMUR

TIBIA

FIBULA

PHALANGES

CALCANEUS

METATARSALS

TARSALS

Answer to Figure 18-4

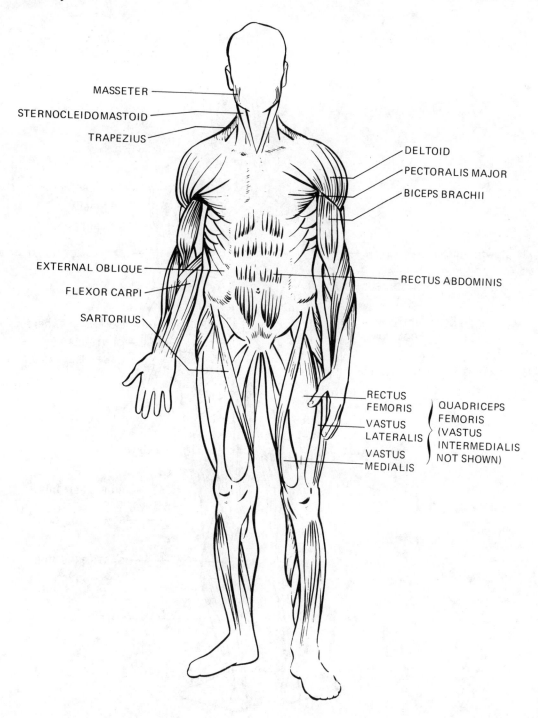

MASSETER

STERNOCLEIDOMASTOID

TRAPEZIUS

DELTOID

PECTORALIS MAJOR

BICEPS BRACHII

EXTERNAL OBLIQUE

FLEXOR CARPI

SARTORIUS

RECTUS ABDOMINIS

RECTUS FEMORIS

VASTUS LATERALIS

VASTUS MEDIALIS

QUADRICEPS FEMORIS (VASTUS INTERMEDIALIS NOT SHOWN)

Answer to Figure 18-5

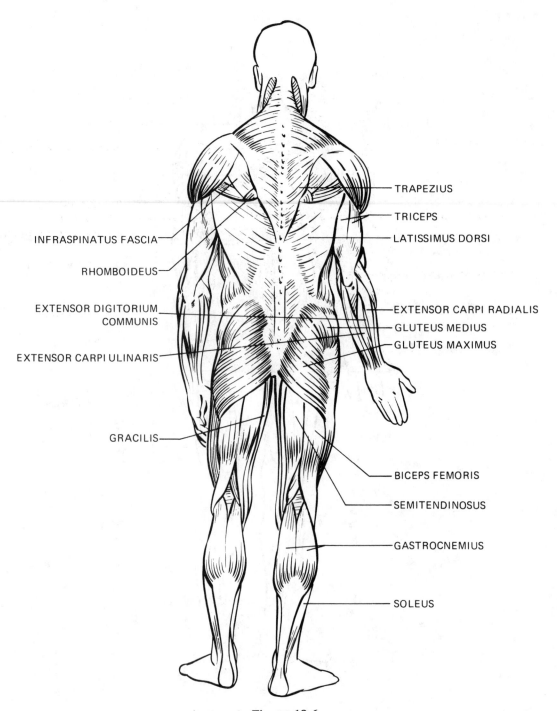

TRAPEZIUS

TRICEPS

LATISSIMUS DORSI

INFRASPINATUS FASCIA

RHOMBOIDEUS

EXTENSOR DIGITORIUM COMMUNIS

EXTENSOR CARPI RADIALIS

GLUTEUS MEDIUS

GLUTEUS MAXIMUS

EXTENSOR CARPI ULINARIS

GRACILIS

BICEPS FEMORIS

SEMITENDINOSUS

GASTROCNEMIUS

SOLEUS

Answer to Figure 18-6

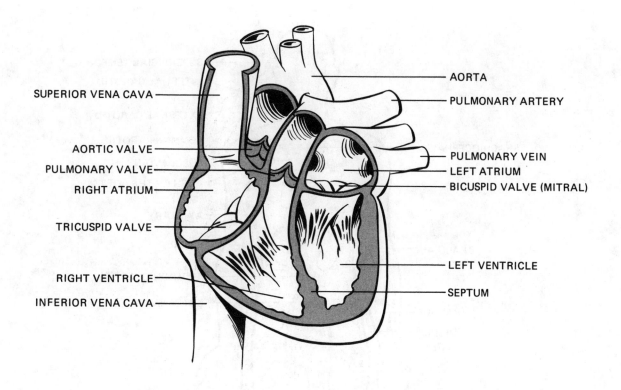

SUPERIOR VENA CAVA

AORTIC VALVE

PULMONARY VALVE

RIGHT ATRIUM

TRICUSPID VALVE

RIGHT VENTRICLE

INFERIOR VENA CAVA

AORTA

PULMONARY ARTERY

PULMONARY VEIN

LEFT ATRIUM

BICUSPID VALVE (MITRAL)

LEFT VENTRICLE

SEPTUM

Answer to Figure 18-7

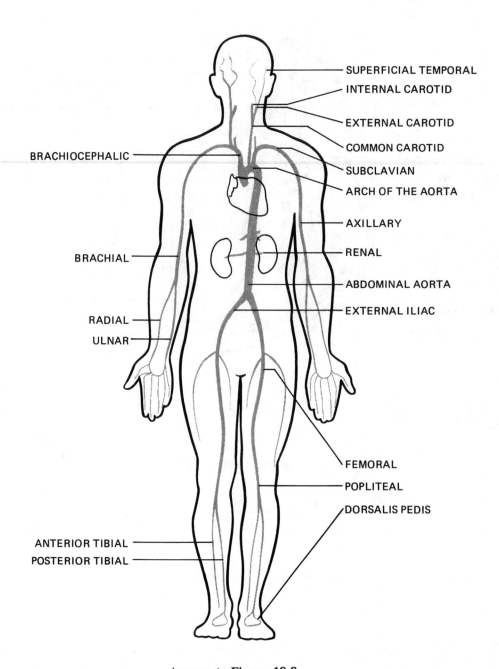

SUPERFICIAL TEMPORAL

INTERNAL CAROTID

EXTERNAL CAROTID

COMMON CAROTID

BRACHIOCEPHALIC

SUBCLAVIAN

ARCH OF THE AORTA

AXILLARY

BRACHIAL

RENAL

ABDOMINAL AORTA

EXTERNAL ILIAC

RADIAL

ULNAR

FEMORAL

POPLITEAL

DORSALIS PEDIS

ANTERIOR TIBIAL

POSTERIOR TIBIAL

Answer to Figure 18-8

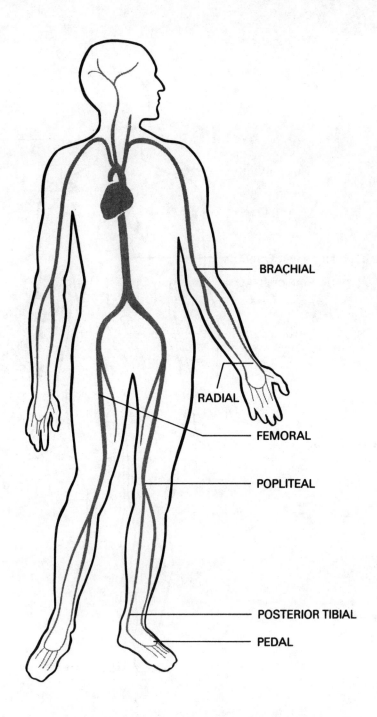

BRACHIAL

RADIAL

FEMORAL

POPLITEAL

POSTERIOR TIBIAL

PEDAL

Answer to Figure 18-9

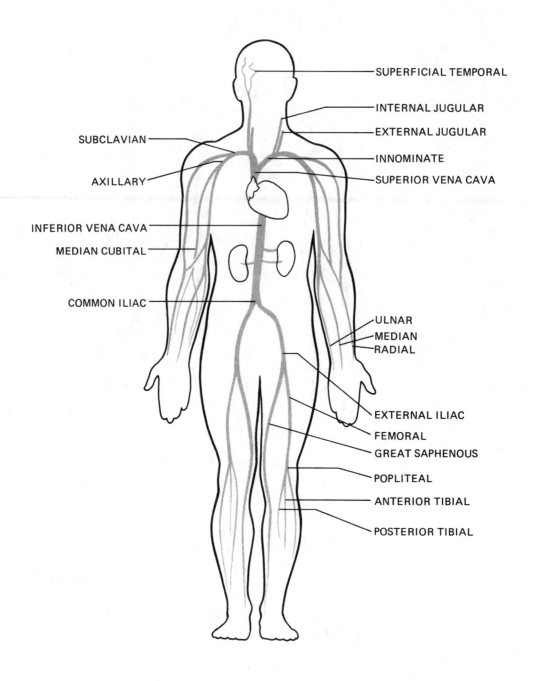

SUPERFICIAL TEMPORAL

INTERNAL JUGULAR

EXTERNAL JUGULAR

SUBCLAVIAN

INNOMINATE

AXILLARY

SUPERIOR VENA CAVA

INFERIOR VENA CAVA

MEDIAN CUBITAL

COMMON ILIAC

ULNAR
MEDIAN
RADIAL

EXTERNAL ILIAC

FEMORAL

GREAT SAPHENOUS

POPLITEAL

ANTERIOR TIBIAL

POSTERIOR TIBIAL

Answer to Figure 18-10

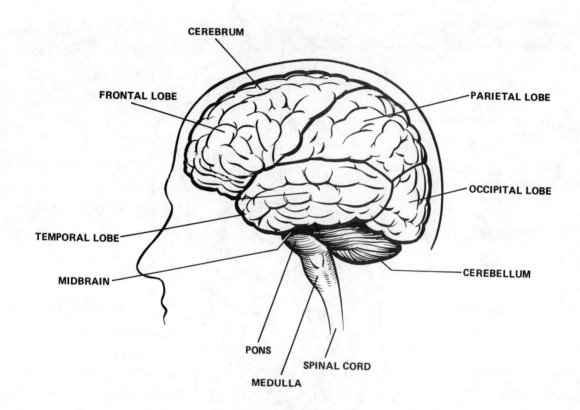

Answer To Figure 18-11

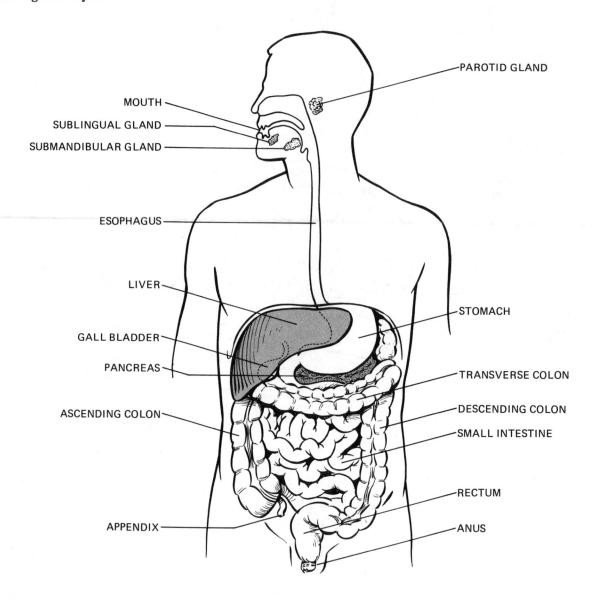

PAROTID GLAND

MOUTH

SUBLINGUAL GLAND

SUBMANDIBULAR GLAND

ESOPHAGUS

LIVER

GALL BLADDER

PANCREAS

ASCENDING COLON

APPENDIX

STOMACH

TRANSVERSE COLON

DESCENDING COLON

SMALL INTESTINE

RECTUM

ANUS

Answer to Figure 18-12

Organ Function Chart Fill-In

	Organ	**Function**
1.	Mouth	Chew food, taste food, begin digestion of starches
2.	Esophagus	Carry food from mouth to stomach by peristalsis
3.	Stomach	Physical and chemical digestion
4.	Small intestine	Absorption of food, digestion
5.	Appendix	Unknown
6.	Ascending colon	Transport of food through body; absorption of water, vitamins, electrolytes, and bile salts back into bloodstream; production of vitamin K
7.	Transverse colon	Same as ascending colon

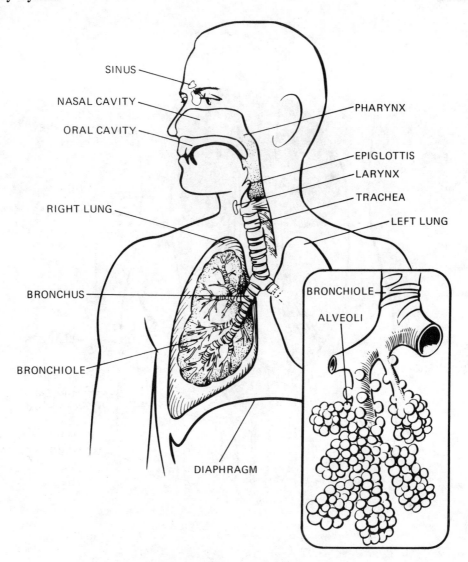

Answer to Figure 18-13

Respiratory System Part Function Chart Fill-In

System Part	Main Function
1. Oral cavity	Alternate entry for air when the nasal passage is blocked
2. Nasal cavity	Entry for air into body, filter of foreign particles, warms and moistens air
3. Sinus	Regulates temperature of air
4. Larynx	Voice box, makes sound as air passes through
5. Pharynx	Throat, funneling the air to the trachea, passage for food and air
6. Trachea	Windpipe, keeps airway open to lungs
7. Epiglottis	Prevents food and liquid from entering bronchi and lungs
8. Bronchus	Passage for air to the lungs
9. Bronchiole	Funnels air to the alveoli in the lungs
10. Alveoli	Area of gas exchange by diffusion
11. Left lung	Number of lobes = 2
12. Right lung	Number of lobes = 3

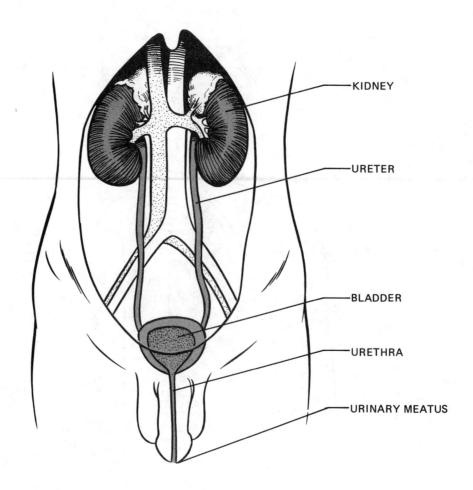

- KIDNEY
- URETER
- BLADDER
- URETHRA
- URINARY MEATUS

Answer to Figure 18-14

Urinary System Function Chart Fill-In

System part	Main Function
1. Kidney	Filters the blood to remove wastes from the blood
2. Ureter	Moves urine from kidneys to bladder by peristaltic action
3. Bladder	Holds urine until it is excreted
4. Urethra	Moves urine from bladder to outside of body
5. Urinary meatus	Opening through which urine leaves body

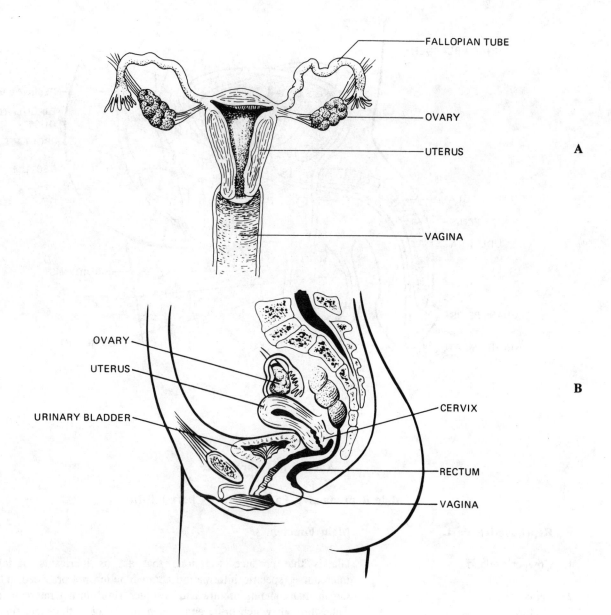

Answer to Figure 18-15

Female Reproductive Part Function Chart Fill-In

	Reproductive part	Main function
1.	Ovary	Produces eggs and hormones (estrogen and progesterone) that regulate the menstrual cycle and help maintain pregnancy
2.	Uterus	Muscular structure that holds the fetus during pregnancy
3.	Vagina	Muscular tube that extends from the cervix to the exterior of the body and is the site of sexual intercourse and passageway for delivery of the baby
4.	Cervix	Neck of the uterus that thins and opens for delivery of the baby
5.	Fallopian tubes	Transport the mature ovum from the ovary to the uterus

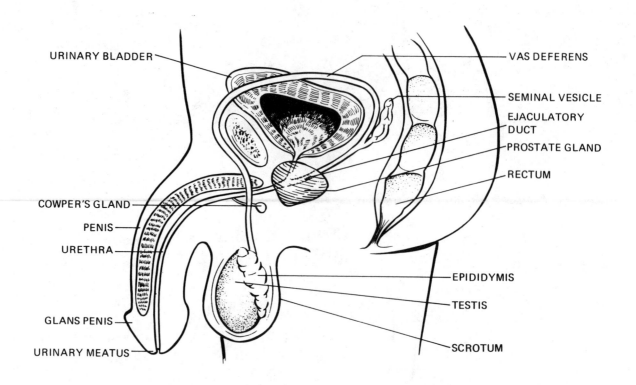

Answer to Figure 18-16

Male Reproductive Part Function Chart Fill-In

Reproductive Part	Main Function
1. Cowper's gland	Glands that produce secretions that act as lubricants during sexual intercourse (specific information about function not provided in textbook)
2. Penis	Organ that contains urethra and becomes rigid during intercourse
3. Urethra	Tube through which urine and semen pass (not at the same time) to exit the male reproductive system
4. Glans penis	Blunt structure at end of penis that functions as part of the erectile organ for intercourse
5. Urinary meatus	Opening end of penis through which urine and semen pass
6. Vas deferens	Tubes that transport semen into the ejaculatory duct
7. Seminal vesicle	Adds fluid to increase the volume and nourish the sperm
8. Ejaculatory duct	Contains semen during addition of fluids before ejaculation
9. Prostate gland	Secretes a fluid that protects the sperm
10. Epididymis	Tube on the surface of each testis that stores the sperm while the mature
11. Testis	Glands that reproduce the sperm and testosterone
12. Scrotum	Sac that contains the testis glands below the level of the abdomen to allow the sperm a necessary lower temperature for development (specific information not provided in textbook)

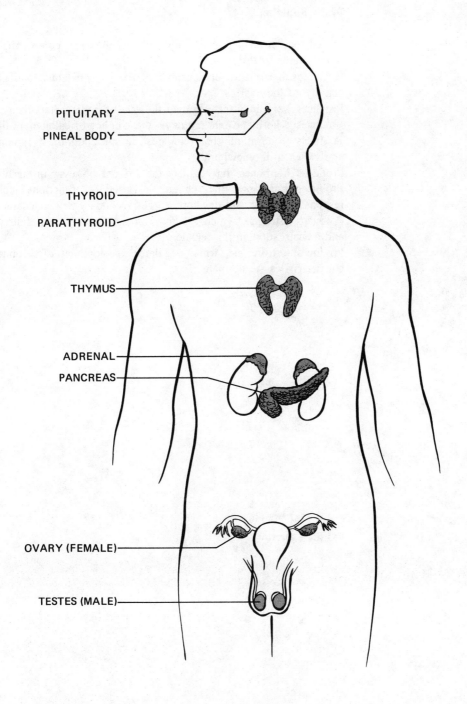

PITUITARY

PINEAL BODY

THYROID

PARATHYROID

THYMUS

ADRENAL

PANCREAS

OVARY (FEMALE)

TESTES (MALE)

Answer to Figure 18-17

Endocrine System Function Chart Fill-In

System Part	Main Function
1. Pituitary	Called the "master" gland, produces hormones that control the actions of other glands of the system
2. Pineal body	Regulates the release of hormone of the hypothalamus and perhaps the activity of the ovaries
3. Thyroid	Produces hormones that regulate the rate of body metabolism
4. Parathyroid	Produces a hormone that regulates the amount of calcium in the blood
5. Thymus	Produces a hormone that regulates the production of lymphocytes or antibodies in the newborn
6. Pancreas	Produces hormones that regulate the amount of sugar in the blood
7. Adrenal	Produces hormones that regulate a variety of functions including the response to stress and development of secondary sexual characteristics
8. Ovary	Produces estrogen, which regulates breast development, hair placement, and menstruation in the female
9. Testes	Produces testosterone, which regulates development of secondary sexual characteristics in the male

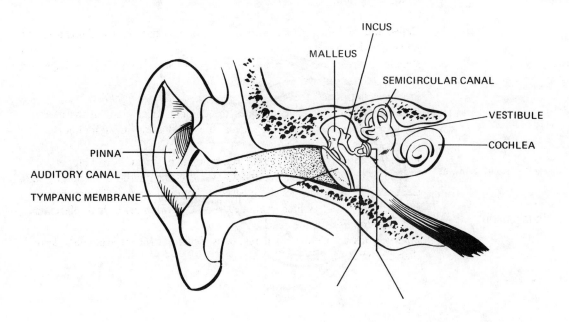

Answer to Figure 18-18

Ear Part Function Chart Fill-In

Ear Part	Main Function
1. Pinna	Collects and funnels sounds into the ear
2. Auditory canal	Collects and transmits sounds to eardrum
3. Tympanic membrane	Vibrates to transmit sound to the bones of the ear
4. Malleus	One of the three bones of the ear that mechanically transmit the sound vibrations to the inner ear
5. Incus	One of the three bones of the ear that mechanically transmit the sound vibrations to the inner ear
6. Stapes	One of the three bones of the ear that mechanically transmit the sound vibrations to the inner ear
7. Semicircular canal	Sense of balance when body is in motion
8. Cochlea	Converts the mechanical vibrations of the ear to neural impulses
9. Vestibule	Maintains static or resting equilibrium or balance
10. Oval window	Point of contact of the bones of the ear and the cochlea

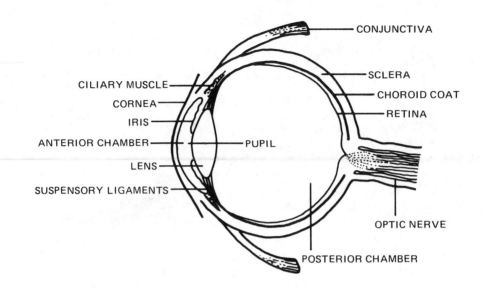

CONJUNCTIVA

SCLERA

CHOROID COAT

RETINA

CILIARY MUSCLE

CORNEA

IRIS

ANTERIOR CHAMBER

PUPIL

LENS

SUSPENSORY LIGAMENTS

OPTIC NERVE

POSTERIOR CHAMBER

Answer to Figure 18-19

Eye Part Function Chart Fill-In

Eye Part	Main Function
1. Conjunctiva	Mucous membrane that protects and lubricates the eyelids and part of the eye
2. Ciliary muscles	Muscles that move the eye
3. Iris	Muscles around the pupil that control the amount of light coming into and out of the eye
4. Anterior chamber	The space between the cornea and lens that is filled with aqueous humor
5. Pupil	Opening through which light passes into the eye
6. Cornea	Focuses images
7. Lens	Focuses and directs incoming light on the retina
8. Suspensory ligaments	Ligaments that are attached to and move the lens
9. Sclera	Supports and gives structure to the eye
10. Choroid coat	Inner layer of the eye that contains the blood supply for the eye
11. Retina	Contains specialized cells that are sensitive to light and create impulses that are sensed by the optic nerve
12. Optic nerve	One of the cranial nerves that carries messages from the eye to the brain
13. Posterior chamber	The eyeball is filled with a fluid called vitreous humor that gives firmness and shape to the eye

Unit 19

Nutrition

SUGGESTED ACTIVITIES

1. Record all food and drink intake for 7 days. List each food and drink under one of the five headings from the food guide pyramid (Figure 19-1). For example, if you had cereal,, milk, and sugar for breakfast, record the cereal under the bread group, the milk under the milk group, and the sugar under the fats, oils, and sweets group. Determine if you had the recommended amount of servings, too many, or not enough from each group to maintain a healthy weight for you.

    In 1 week, give your food chart to one of your classmates for review and evaluation. Meet with your reviewer to go over the findings. Discuss the strengths and weaknesses of your diet, and any changes needed to improve your diet.

2. Using Form A apply the dietary guidelines to your diet.

3. Using Form B, create a sample day of food intake for yourself.

4. Complete Form C and discuss your findings in class.

5. Bring to class a label from one of your favorite foods. Analyze the label, Discuss the percentage of protein, fat, carbohydrate, sugar, sodium (salt), and fiber in the food. Is the food a good choice?

6. Do a research paper on the eating disorders anorexia nervosa, and bulimia nervosa. Discuss the definition, related causes, how societal pressures may influence these conditions, and the methods used for managing each.

    Discuss the role of education in preventing and reducing the risk of developing one of these disorders.

Figure 19-1

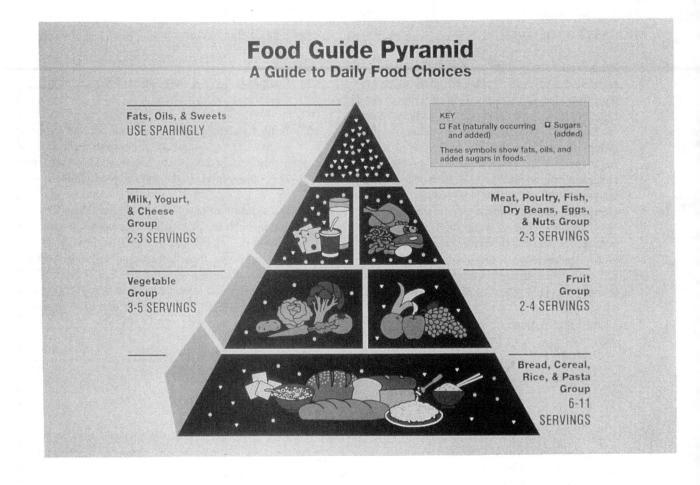

Food Guide Pyramid
A Guide to Daily Food Choices

Fats, Oils, & Sweets
USE SPARINGLY

KEY
☐ Fat (naturally occurring and added) ▽ Sugars (added)
These symbols show fats, oils, and added sugars in foods.

Milk, Yogurt, & Cheese Group
2-3 SERVINGS

Meat, Poultry, Fish, Dry Beans, Eggs, & Nuts Group
2-3 SERVINGS

Vegetable Group
3-5 SERVINGS

Fruit Group
2-4 SERVINGS

Bread, Cereal, Rice, & Pasta Group
6-11 SERVINGS

FORM A

Guidelines	Personal Evaluation	Improvements Needed
1. Eat a variety of foods.		
2. Maintain a healthy weight.		
3. Choose a diet low in fat, saturated fat, and cholesterol.		
4. Choose a diet with plenty of vegetables, fruits, and grain products.		
5. Use sugars only in moderation.		
6. Use salt and sodium only in moderation.		
7. If you drink alcoholic beverages, do so in moderation.		

Create a sample day of food intake for yourself according to the Food Guide Pyramid. List foods that you know you will eat, not merely foods you know you should eat.

Meal/Snack   Foods   Why?

FORM C

I. Which foods listed have the highest fat content?

1. Apple, peach, or banana
2. Triscuits, wheat thins, or saltines (all crackers)
3. Potato chips, pretzels, or peanuts
4. Bagel, English muffin, or bran muffin
5. Turkey salami, ham, or roast beef
6. Sour cream, cream cheese, or mayonnaise
7. Palm oil, corn oil, or canola oil
8. Jam, apple butter, or jelly
9. Ketchup, salsa, or mustard

II. Do you usually eat foods high in fiber content?

III. Do you salt your foods when cooking and/or before eating them?

IV. Do you frequently eat processed foods?

V. Do you eat at least two servings of calcium-rich food per day?

VI. Do you eat fruits and vegetables rich in beta-carotene?

VII. What do you consider "good" foods?

VIII. What do you consider "bad" foods?"

IX. How do you feel after you have eaten a "good" food?

X. How do you feel after you have eaten a "bad" food?

XI. If you gain weight, how do you feel about yourself?

XII. If you lose weight, how do you feel about yourself?

XIII. At what weight would you feel the best? Is it a realistic weight?

XIV. How do you feel about your present weight?

Fill-In

In the blanks provided, write the answers that best complete the sentences:

1. A substance derived from food that provides the body with nourishment is called a _____ _____.

2. The mechanical and chemical breakdown of food into substances small enough to be absorbed and used by body cells to maintain life is called _____.

3. _____, _____, and _____ are examples of uniform definitions, which describe a food's nutrition content.

4. The six main classifications of nutrients required by the body to maintain health are _____ _____, _____, _____, _____, _____, and _____.

5. _____ are often thought of as the building blocks of our body. They are found in every living cell.

6. Proteins are composed of chains of approximately 20 _____, nine of which are called essential _____.

7. To function and survive, the body needs the _____ essential amino acids. These are obtained from foods referred to as _____ _____.

8. The best food sources of complete proteins are _____, _____, _____, _____, and _____.

9. Foods that do not contain all of the essential amino acids are called _____. Examples of these foods include _____ _____.

10. Combining various sources of incomplete protein foods supplies an adequate amount of the amino acids needed for _____. An example of this is eating _____.

11. Describe the main functions of protein in the body.
    a. _____
    b. _____
    c. _____
    d. _____
    e. _____

12. Nutritionists recommend that_____ percent of the daily caloric requirement be derived from protein sources.

13. Excess protein, like excess calories from any source, is stored as _____.

14. It is suggested that fat intake be restricted to no more than _____ percent of a person's daily caloric requirement.

15. An area of concern is that about _____ percent of the fat in foods is "hidden" fat, often not visible to the eye.

16. Some sources of hidden saturated fats are _____, _____, _____, _____, _____, and _____.

17. Examples of tropical oils which are saturated fats are _____, _____, and _____.

18. Explain the functions of fat in the body.
    a. _____

b. _____

c. _____

d. _____

e. _____

f. _____

g. _____

h. _____

i. _____

19. Saturated fat comes from _____,

_____ , _____ ,

_____ , _____ ,

_____ , and _____ .

20. _____ fats can increase the level of cholesterol in the blood.

21. An excessive amount of cholesterol in the blood is associated with an increased risk for _____ disease.

22. No more than _____ percent of a person's daily caloric intake should come from saturated fats.

23. The two types of unsaturated fats are _____ and _____ fats.

24. _____ fats include vegetable oils and fish oils (Omega-3 fatty acids).

25. Cholesterol is an important component for a healthy body because it is essential for _____

_____

_____

_____ .

26. Cholesterol is found in food that comes from _____ sources.

27. There is no cholesterol in foods from _____ _____ sources.

28. It is thought that _____ fats found in animal fats and other sources contribute to the formation of cholesterol in the body thereby increasing the body's normal supply.

29. Cholesterol is transported to and from the body cells by compounds called _____ .

30. The _____ are commonly referred to as the "good guys" or the "good cholesterol."

31. The _____ are commonly referred to as the "bad guys" or the "bad cholesterol."

32. The _____ -density lipoproteins are the major carriers of cholesterol in the bloodstream. They contain 60 to 70 percent of the serum cholesterol.

33. The higher the level of _____ in the bloodstream, the lower the risk for cardiovascular disease.

34. The low-density lipoproteins (LDLs) carry cholesterol to _____ .

35. High-density lipoproteins (HDLs) carry cholesterol _____ .

36. Apeson's daily intake of cholesterol should be limited to _____ mg or less.

37. The chief sources of carbohydrates are _____ _____ .

38. Carbohydrates provide the main source of _____ _____ for all body functions. They are also necessary for _____ .

39. Identify the sources of simple sugars.

a. _____

b. _____

40. It is recommended that less than _____ percent of a person's total caloric requirement be obtained from the refined sugars.

41. Name some sources of complex carbohydrates or starches.

    a. _____

    b. _____

    c. _____

    d. _____

42. Ideally, complex carbohydrates should account for _____ to _____ percent of a person's daily caloric requirement.

43. Most people should decrease their intake of _____ _____ sugars and increase their intake of _____ sugars and starches.

44. Calories are the amount of _____ that can be derived from protein, fat, and carbohydrate in food.

45. One gram of protein provides _____ calories.

46. One gram of carbohydrate provides _____ calories.

47. One gram of fat provides _____ calories.

48. When taking in more calories than the body requires for its energy needs, the excess calories are converted and stored as _____.

49. Write the formula for determining the percentage of calories in a food supplied from fat.

    a. _____

    b. _____

50. Daily caloric requirements vary and depend on:

    a. _____

    b. _____

    c. _____

    d. _____

    e. _____

    f. _____

    g. _____

51. _____ is a term used to denote calories obtained from a food source that provides energy but very little other nutritional value.

52. The fat-soluble vitamins are vitamins _____ , _____ , _____ , and _____ .

53. The water-soluble vitamins are vitamins _____ , and _____ .

54. Minerals are inorganic substances that make up nearly 5% of the body. The macrominerals or major minerals which the body needs in greater amounts each day include _____ , _____ , _____ , _____ , _____ , _____ , and _____ .

55. Minerals are needed for a variety of body functions including _____

    _____

    _____

    _____ .

56. The best way to get the necessary minerals is by _____ .

57. The average adult contains _____ quarts of water with 40% of that water in the body cells, 83% in the blood, 75% in the brain and muscle tissue, and 22% in bone tissue.

58. The functions of water in the body are _____

    _____

    _____

    _____

    _____

    _____ .

59. Water is lost from our body daily through the processes of _____, _____, _____, and _____.

60. It is recommended that a person drink at least _____ cups of water daily since some water is supplied by foods, such as fruits and vegetables, as well as other beverages.

61. The main sources of dietary fiber come from _____, _____, and _____. Dietary fiber is not found in _____.

62. Explain the functions of dietary fiber.

   a. _____
   b. _____
   c. _____
   d. _____
   e. _____
   f. _____
   g. _____
   h. _____
   i. _____
   j. _____
   k. _____

63. The National Cancer Institute recommends an intake of _____ grams of fiber per day.

64. The best way to get an adequate amount of fiber in the diet is by _____.

65. The keys to healthful eating are _____, _____, and _____.

66. List the seven dietary guidelines for Americans.

   a. _____
   b. _____
   c. _____
   d. _____

   e. _____
   f. _____
   g. _____

67. Many foods are good sources of several nutrients. For example, vegetables and fruits provide _____. Breads and cereals supply _____; whole-grain foods are also good sources of _____. Milk provides _____. Meat, poultry, and fish provide _____.

68. To eat a nutritious diet, a person must select _____.

69. The many nutrients the body needs can be obtained by choosing different foods from these five groups daily: _____, _____, _____, _____, and _____.

70. Describe the steps necessary to decrease caloric intake.

   a. _____
   b. _____
   c. _____
   d. _____
   e. _____
   f. _____

71. Sugars and many foods that contain them in large amounts supply calories, but are limited in _____.

72. List the foods recommended on a clear diet.

   a. _____
   b. _____
   c. _____
   d. _____
   e. _____

73. List the foods recommended on a mechanical or dental soft diet.

a. _____

b. _____

c. _____

d. _____

e. _____

f. _____

g. _____

74. Foods recommended on a high-fiber diet include all foods with increased emphasis on _____ _____ .

75. A low residue, also called a low-fiber diet, is recommended for patients with _____ _____ .

76. A low-fat diet is generally recommended for a patient who has _____ ,

_____ , or _____ . It is also highly recommended for everyone to reduce the risk of _____ .

77. A diet with varied amounts of sodium/salt is used for patients with _____ ,

_____ , _____ , and

_____ .

78. A moderately restricted sodium diet would include _____ to _____ mg of sodium per day.

79. State the recommendations for a peptic ulcer diet.

a. _____

b. _____

c. _____

Multiple Choice

Write the letter of the correct answer in the blank provided. There is only *one* correct answer.

_____ 1. Dietary habits can:
A. Promote health.
B. Reduce our risk and prevent certain diseases.
C. Increase our risk for certain diseases.
D. A and B.
E. A, B, and C.

_____ 2. _____ are often thought of as the building blocks of the body.
A. Proteins
B. Fats
C. Carbohydrates
D. Vitamins
E. Minerals

_____ 3. To function adequately, the body requires _____ essential amino acids that must be obtained from the food that a person eats.
A. 5
B. 7
C. 9
D. 11
E. 15

_____ 4. Nutritionists recommend that _____ percent of a person's daily caloric requirement be obtained from foods that are good sources of protein.
A. 5 to 10
B. 12 to 15
C. 15 to 20
D. 16 to 20
E. 50 to 58

_____ 5. Fats are *not* needed in the average diet.
A. True
B. False

_____ 6. Approximately _____ percent of the average person's body weight is fat.
A. 25
B. 35
C. 20
D. 15
E. 10

334

_____ 7. Nutritionists recommend that dietary fat be reduced so that it is only_____ percent of a person's daily calorie intake needed to maintain a healthy weight.
   A. 5 to 10
   B. 12 to 15
   C. 25
   D. 30
   E. 58

_____ 8. Sources of hidden fats in foods are found in:
   A. Snack foods.
   B. Meat.
   C. Crackers.
   D. A and B.
   E. A and C.

_____ 9. Saturated fats are found in:
   A. Corn oil.
   B. Coconut oil.
   C. Palm kernel oil.
   D. A and B.
   E. B and C.

_____ 10. Saturated fats can increase the level of cholesterol in the blood.
   A. True
   B. False

_____ 11. Red meat, butter, eggs, and dairy products are good sources of:
   A. Polyunsaturated fats.
   B. Saturated fats.
   C. Monounsaturated fats.
   D. Fiber.
   E. Unsaturated fats.

_____ 12. No more than _____ percent of a person's daily calorie intake should come from saturated fats.
   A. 30
   B. 20
   C. 10
   D. 40
   E. 50

_____ 13. _____ fats are the more beneficial unsaturated fats because they lower levels of cholesterol and LDLs.
   A. Monounsaturated
   B. Polyunsaturated
   C. Lipid
   D. Polyunsaturated fatty
   E. Saturated

_____ 14. The body produces all of the cholesterol that it needs; therefore it is not necessary for a person to eat foods containing cholesterol.
   A. True
   B. False

_____ 15. A good source of cholesterol in foods comes from:
   A. Plant sources.
   B. Animal sources.
   C. Plant and animal sources.
   D. Starchy vegetables.
   E. Foods high in sugar content.

_____ 16. Increased levels of serum cholesterol are associated with an increased risk for:
   A. Diabetes.
   B. Anemia.
   C. Heart disease.
   D. Kidney disease.
   E. Liver disease.

_____ 17. When choosing foods it is very important to look at the saturated fat content in addition to the amount of cholesterol if any, because the body turns saturated fat into cholesterol.
   A. True
   B. False

_____ 18. The _____ lipoproteins are commonly referred to as the "good guys" or "good cholesterol."
   A. Very low density
   B. Very, very low density
   C. Low Density
   D. High density
   E. Very high density

19. The _____ lipoproteins are commonly referred to as the "bad guys" or "bad cholesterol."
   A. Very low density
   B. Very, very low density
   C. Low Density
   D. High density
   E. Very high density

20. The higher the level of _____ lipoproteins in the blood, the lower the risk for cardiovascular disease.
   A. Very low density
   B. Very, very low density
   C. Low Density
   D. High density
   E. Very high density

21. Dieticians recommend that a daily intake of cholesterol be limited to _____ mg or less.
   A. 100
   B. 200
   C. 250
   D. 150
   E. 300

22. The _____ carry cholesterol to blood vessels where it is deposited.
   A. VLDLs
   B. VVLDs
   C. LDLs
   D. HDLs
   E. VHDLs

23. Naturally occurring sugars are found in:
   A. White sugar.
   B. Brown sugar.
   C. Honey.
   D. Syrup.
   E. Fruits and vegetables.

24. Ideally, complex carbohydrates should account for _____ percent of the daily calorie intake needed to maintain a healthy weight.
   A. 10 to 20
   B. 20 to 30
   C. 30 to 40
   D. 40 to 50
   E. 50 to 60

25. One gram of protein provides the body with _____ calories.
   A. 4
   B. 5
   C. 9
   D. 30
   E. 40

26. One gram of fat provides the body with _____ calories.
   A. 4
   B. 5
   C. 9
   D. 30
   E. 40

27. One gram of carbohydrate in food provides the body with _____ calories.
   A. 4
   B. 5
   C. 9
   D. 30
   E. 40

28. Calories obtained from _____ are called empty calories because they are low in nutritional value.
   A. Red meat
   B. Eggs
   C. Carrots
   D. Alcohol
   E. Fatty foods

29. The fatsoluble vitamins are vitamins:
   A. B and C.
   B. A, D, E, and K.
   C. A, B, C, and D.
   D. E and K.
   E. D, E, and B.

30. The watersoluble vitamins are:
   A. A, D, E, and K.
   B. B and C.
   C. E and K.
   D. D, E, and B.
   E. A, B, C, and D.

31. The macrominerals include:
   A. Calcium.
   B. Iron.
   C. Sodium.
   D. A and C.
   E. A, B, and C.

32. Water is a vital _____ needed for life and survival.
    A. Protein
    B. Mineral
    C. Carbohydrate
    D. Nutrient
    E. Vitamin

33. There is water in such foods as chicken, cookies, and cheese.
    A. True
    B. False

34. The main source of dietary fiber come from:
    A. Grain products.
    B. Fruits and vegetables.
    C. Meats.
    D. A and B.
    E. A, B, and C.

35. Soluble fiber is thought to help in reducing blood cholesterol levels.
    A. True
    B. False

36. High-fiber diets are thought to increase the risk for colon cancer.
    A. True
    B. False

37. The National Cancer Institute recommends an intake of _____ grams of dietary fiber per day.
    A. 10 to 20
    B. 20 to 30
    C. 30 to 40
    D. 5 to 10
    E. 15 to 20

38. A good source of dietary fiber is found in:
    A. Steak.
    B. Eggs.
    C. Oatmeal.
    D. Cheese.
    E. Pies and cakes.

39. Any food that supplies calories and nutrients can be part of a nutritious diet.
    A. True
    B. False

40. Many women and young girls need to eat more calcium-rich foods, such as milk and milk products, to get the calcium they need for healthy bones throughout life.
    A. True
    B. False

41. Recent research suggests that people can weigh a little more as they grow older without added risk to health.
    A. True
    B. False

42. Sugars are eaten in many forms including:
    A. White table sugar (sucrose).
    B. Glucose.
    C. Honey.
    D. A and B.
    E. A, B, and C.

43. Sugars and starches are found in:
    A. Meats.
    B. Milk.
    C. Fruits.
    D. A, B, and C.
    E. B and C.

44. Fresh and plain frozen vegetables contain more sodium than canned vegetables.
    A. True
    B. False

45. Heavy drinkers are often overnourished because alcohol helps the body absorb nutrients.
    A. True
    B. False

46. A person on a clear liquid diet could have:
    A. Creamed soups.
    B. Milk and milkshakes.
    C. Plain flavored gelatin.
    D. A and B.
    E. A, B, and C.

47. A person with a peptic ulcer should probably avoid:
    A. Cauliflower.
    B. Onions.
    C. Caffeine-containing foods.
    D. B and C.
    E. A, B, and C.

1. Nutrient
2. Digestion
3. "Light," "low fat," "high fiber"
4. Proteins, fats, carbohydrates, vitamins, minerals, and water.
5. Proteins
6. Amino acids; amino acids
7. Nine; complete proteins
8. Meat, milk, cheese, eggs, and fish
9. Incomplete protein foods. legumes (dry beans and peas, soybean curd, tofu), grains, nuts, and seeds
10. Protein synthesis; peanut butter on wheat bread
11. a. Promotes growth, repair, and maintenance of musculoskeletal and other body tissues
    b. Serves as a framework for bones, muscles, blood, hair, and fingernails
    c. Helps to regulate some body processes by serving as a component of hormones and enzymes
    d. Helps to maintain the acid-base balance in the body
    e. Serves as a source of energy (4 calories for every gram of protein consumed)
12. 12 to 15
13. fat
14. 30
15. 60
16. Snack foods, cookies, crackers, nondairy whipped toppings, nondairy creamers, and cereals.
17. Palm, coconut, can palm kernel oils.
18. Fats:
    a. Provide a concentrated source of energy; (Every gram of fat provides 9 calories.)
    b. Help satisfy appetite
    c. Help in making food taste good
    d. Store the fatsoluble vitamins
    e. Aid in transporting the fatsoluble vitamins (A, D, E, and K)
    f. Help to keep skin healthy
    g. used for tissue building, but most of the fat is stored for future energy needs
    h. Provide stamina
    i. Provide insulation for the body against low temperatures
19. Animal sources such as meats, lard, eggs, and dairy products, and plant fats from coconut oil, palm oil, and palm kernel oil.
20. Saturated
21. Cardiovascular
22. 10
23. Polyunsaturated, monounsaturated
24. Polyunsaturated
25. The functioning of body systems, such as the nervous system, for the formation of cell membranes, and for the formation of many hormones including the sex hormones, and other body substances, such as bile salts and nerve fibers
26. Animal
27. Plant
28. Saturated
29. Lipoproteins
30. HDLs
31. LDLs
32. Low
33. HDLs
34. Blood vessels where it is deposited
35. Away from the arteries and back to the liver for processing and removal, thereby helping to decrease the risk for heart disease
36. 300
37. The sugars (simple carbohydrates) and the starches (complex carbohydrates)
38. Energy; the metabolism of other nutrients
39. a. Refined sugars such as white sugar, brown sugar, honey, and syrup.
    b. Naturally occurring sugars as found in fruits and vegetables
40. 10 percent
41. a. Vegetables such as broccoli, cabbage, cauliflower, carrots, yams, potatoes
    b. Fruits such as citrus fruits and yellow fruits
    c. Grains such as wheat rice, oats, corn, breads, and pastas
    d. Cereals
42. 50 to 60
43. Refined; naturally occurring
44. Energy
45. 4
46. 4
47. 9
48. Body fat. 3500
49. a. Grams of fat x 9 = "fat" calories
    b. $\frac{\text{Fat calories}}{\text{Total calories}}$ x 100 = Percentage of calories from fat
50. a. Age: Generally young people need more calories than older people.
    b. Sex: Generally men need more calories than women.
    c. Body frame: The larger the body frame, the more calories are needed to maintain the weight.
    d. Weight: Heavier people need more calories than lighter people to maintain their weight.

e. Percentage of body fat: Women have more body fat (average 19 percent to 24 percent) than men (average 12 percent to 17 percent).

f. Activity level: The more active people are the more calories they burn and need to maintain body weight

g. Basal metabolic rate: The basal metabolic rate is the amount of energy (calories) needed when the body is at rest to maintain basic body activities, such as temperature, respiration, circulation, muscle tone, and peristalsis. This is a special test performed with the person at rest in a comfortable environment 14 to 18 hours after the last meal was eaten.

51. Empty calorie
52. Vitamins A, D, E, and K
53. Vitamins B and C
54. Calcium, phosphorus, magnesium, sodium, potassium, chlorine, and sulfur.
55. The building of teeth and bones, and the regulation of a number of body processes, including muscle contraction, transmission of messages over the nerves, blood clotting, and protein and RBC formation.
56. Eating a variety of foods in a balanced diet
57. 40 to 50
58. Every cell in the body needs water. It serves as a medium for all chemical reactions in the body. In addition, water:
    • Regulates the body temperature
    • Carries oxygen and nutrients to all cells
    • Removes wastes from all cells
    • Lubricates the joints
    • Protects tissues and organs
    • Prevents dehydration
    • Replaces sweat losses during and after exercising or exposure to heat or elevated temperatures.
59. Urination, respiration, defecation, and through the skin whether perspiring or not
60. Six to eight
61. Grain products, fruits, and vegetables. Animal products, such as milk and meats
62. a. Fiber promotes increased chewing, which is good for the teeth.
    b. Food sources of fiber are lower in fat than animal food sources and most people need to decrease their intake of fat.
    c. Fiber food sources increase a person's intake of vitamins.
    d. Fiber food sources have fewer additives than processed foods.

e. Insoluble fiber promotes normal elimination by providing bulk for stool formation and thus hastening the passage of the stool through the colon.

f. Insoluble fiber helps to satisfy appetite by creating a feeling of fullness. This also helps in weight control.

g. Fiber in the diet also helps to control weight because the foods have fewer calories than other foods sources.

h. Soluble fibers may play a role in reducing the level of cholesterol in the blood.

i. Soluble fiber is thought to slow down the release of carbohydrates from the source of those carbohydrates. It holds onto the sugar and releases it slower so that the benefits of the sugar can be derived for a longer period of time.

j. Fiber is thought to protect against heart disease, gallbladder disease, hiatal hernia, varicose veins, appendicitis, diabetes, breast and colon cancer, constipation, and diverticulosis because of some of the preceding functions.

k. Food sources rich in fiber are usually less expensive than foods from other sources.

63. 20 to 30
64. Eating a variety of foods that contain dietary fiber
65. Moderation, balance, and variety
66. a. Eat a variety of foods.
    b. Maintain healthy weight.
    c. Choose a diet low in fat, saturated fat, and cholesterol.
    d. Choose a diet with plenty of vegetables, fruits, and grain products.
    e. Use sugars only in moderation.
    f. Use salt and sodium only in moderation.
    g. If you drink alcoholic beverages, do so in moderation.
67. Vitamins A and C, folic acid, minerals, and fiber
    B vitamins, iron, and protein
    Fiber
    Protein, B vitamins, vitamins A and D, calcium, and phosphorus
    Protein, B vitamins, iron, and zinc
68. A variety of foods
69. Vegetables, fruits, grain products, milk and milk products, and meats and meat alternatives
70. a. Eat less fat and fatty foods.
    b. Eat more fruits, vegetables, and breads and cereals—without fats and sugars added in preparation and at the table.
    c. Eat fewer sugars and sweets.
    d. Drink little or no alcoholic beverages.
    e. Eat smaller portions.

f. Limit second helpings.

71. Nutrients

72. a. Clear soups such as broth or bouillon
     b. Clear coffee, tea, or carbonated beverages (as allowed and tolerated)
     c. Clear fruit juices, such as apple or cranberry
     d. Plain, flavored, gelatin and popsicles
     e. Hard, clear candies

73. a. Chopped or ground meats and vegetables
     b. Soups
     c. All liquids
     d. Casseroles
     e. Canned fruits
     f. Well-cooked vegetables
     g. Tender meats such as baked chicken or turkey

74. Fiber-rich foods which include vegetable, fruits, especially raw fruits and vegetables, legumes, whole-grain breads, and cereals. (See Table 19-8 and 19-9 in the textbook.)

75. Indigestion, diarrhea, colitis, ileitis, as well as for patients who have had a colostomy and for those having radiation therapy

76. Liver, gallbladder, or pancreatic disease. heart disease and cancer of the colon, prostate, and breast, and obesity.

77. High blood pressure, congestive heart failure, fluid retention, renal disease, and cirrhosis.

78. 2000 to 1000

79. a. Eat small to moderate servings at mealtime to avoid gastric distention.
     b. Avoid caffeine-containing foods (coffee, tea, colas, chocolate), decaffeinated coffee, all alcohol, and black or red pepper. These foods are known to increase gastric acid secretion.
     c. Some individuals must avoid gas-producing foods, which have a tendency to cause distress. Examples include carbonated beverages, onions, brussel sprouts, cauliflower, and cabbage.

13. A
14. A
15. B
16. C
17. A
18. D
19. C
20. D
21. E
22. C
23. E
24. E
25. A
26. C
27. A
28. D
29. B
30. B
31. D
32. D
33. A
34. D
35. A
36. B
37. B
38. C
39. A
40. A
41. A
42. E
43. E
44. B
45. B
46. C
47. E

Multiple Choice

1. E
2. A
3. C
4. B
5. B
6. D
7. D
8. E
9. E
10. A
11. B
12. C